LIVING AFTER MENTAL ILLNESS:
Innovations in Services

LIVING AFTER MENTAL ILLNESS

INNOVATIONS IN SERVICES

Edited by CHARLES PATMORE

CROOM HELM
London • New York • Sydney

© 1987 Charles Patmore
Croom Helm Ltd, Provident House, Burrell Row,
Beckenham, Kent, BR3 1AT

Croom Helm Australia, 44-50 Waterloo Road,
North Ryde, 2113, New South Wales

Published in the USA by
Croom Helm
in association with Methuen, Inc.
29 West 35th Street
New York, NY 10001

British Library Cataloguing in Publication Data

Living after mental illness : innovations in
  services.
  1. Mentally ill — Rehabilitation — Great
  Britain
  I. Patmore, Charles
  362.2'0425'0941   RC439.5
  ISBN 0-7099-4081-5
  ISBN 0-7099-4085-8 Pbk

Library of Congress Cataloging-in-Publication Data

Living after mental illness.

  "Published in the USA by Croom Helm in Associaton
with Methuen, Inc." — T.p. verso.
  Bibliography: p.
  Includes index.
  1. Mental health services. 2. Mentally ill—
Rehabilitation. 3. Mentally ill—Employment.
I. Patmore, Charles. [DNLM: 1. Community Mental
Health Services—Great Britain. 2. Mental Disorders—
rehabilitation. WM 29 FA1 L7]
RA790.L59 1987   362.2'0425   87-13668
ISBN 0-7099-4081-5
ISBN 0-7099-4085-8 (pbk.)

Printed and bound in Great Britain by Mackays of Chatham Ltd, Kent

CONTENTS

ACKNOWLEDGEMENTS

Thanks are due to MIND (National Association
for Mental Health) for the opportunity to produce
this book. It grew out of National MIND training
courses which I organised during the period 1980 to
1986. These offered unusual opportunity to
investigate this subject and to meet the people
whose contributions make up this book. Five of the
chapters originate in fact from tape transcripts
of sessions on these courses. In particular,
organising MIND's 1984 Annual Conference,
'Life after mental illness? Opportunities in an
age of unemployment', offered a special focus for
researching the work with which this book is
concerned.

Special gratitude is due to Melanie Langton who,
together with Barbara Poole in the Training
Department at MIND, contributed so much hard and
accurate work in typing the manuscript.

Charles Patmore   1987

ABOUT THE CONTRIBUTORS

Christine Barrowclough and Nicholas Tarrier are clinical psychologists with Salford Health Authority, engaged in evaluating the impact of different clinical services for people recovering from schizophrenia and their families.

Carol Williams set up Alternatives, a West London project for people who had been unemployed for a long time. Currently she is Senior Training Officer at Lambeth Employment Training Scheme.

Nigel Jones was formerly Manager of Hammersmith Social Services' Erconwald Street Mental Health Project. Currently he is Principal Officer for Mental Health with Hammersmith Social Services.

Christine Embleton is the present Manager of Erconwald Street Mental Health Project.

Jan Marsden is Group Therapist in Charge at Harpurhey Centre, Manchester.

Teresa Leo set up and ran an independent Citizens Advice Bureau at Tooting Bec Hospital.

Richard Grover is Trust Secretary at the Peter Bedford Trust, Islington, London.

Judy Scott is Work Development Officer at Kensington and Chelsea Mental Health Association.

Corinne Brewer formerly worked as a Disablement Resettlement Officer and as an organiser at Portugal Prints, a Westminster Association for Mental Health employment project. Currently she is a Training Officer with National MIND.

Jane Richardson is a mental health social worker who worked at Fountain House in New York under an exchange arrangement. Currently she works for Toc H in Buckinghamshire, as a Development Officer with self-help groups for people recovering from mental illness.

Mike Twomey works for the Manpower Services Commission with a responsibility for the management and development of the Sheltered Placement Scheme.

Andrew Milroy is Manager of the North Derbyshire
Mental Health Services Project, based at
Chesterfield.

Rick Hennelly is Social Worker at the North
Derbyshire Mental Health Services Project.

Gillian Lomas was formerly Co-Director of the
Community Psychiatry Research Unit in Hackney,
attached to St.Bartholomews Hospital Medical
College. Currently she works for the Sainsbury
Trust.

Charles Patmore is Senior Research Officer with
Good Practices in Mental Health, London. He was
previously a Training Officer with National MIND
and compiled this book through contacts made
while designing MIND courses for people working
in community-based mental health services.

INTRODUCTION

Particularly now that jobs are so hard to get,
mental health workers must focus on
opportunities and resources in their clients'
everyday lives

Recovery from mental illness means becoming able to
fulfill tasks which contribute towards your own
well-being or the well-being of others. It means
being able to manage your own life and have some
practicable vision of your future towards which you
can plan and take action. It means sufficient
supports, rewards and consolations in your everyday
life to endure commonplace adversity or misfortune.
It means assuming social roles and a way of life
which define you in your own eyes and those of
others as a 'well' person.

All this requires opportunities for appropriate
roles, tasks and relationships. But lack of these
is a major problem for many people recovering from
mental illness in today's high unemployment
society. For decades mental health workers relied
on their clients moving on to jobs. A job could
offer a ready means for making a start again and
for redressing some of the losses of relationships
and social identity which can result from a mental
breakdown. It could offer a positive focus for
everyday living, could open roles and networks in
mainstream society, and, through money, could bring
choices of leisure and housing and pursuit of major
personal goals.

Because employment was so widely available
until the mid-seventies, mental health workers paid

relatively little attention to other opportunities in mainstream life which help a person to re-establish themselves after a breakdown. Instead, segregated workshops or long-term day centres were the main futures on offer to the relatively small proportion of people who were unable to move on to jobs. Rehabilitation programmes only rarely worked directly with opportunities for an individual outside the walls of hospital or day unit.

Today, though, very many people remain unemployed after mental illness. Some face a virtual void outside hospital or day centre. Traditional approaches to rehabilitation and aftercare leave them in the lurch. Particularly affected are people who have lost their social networks or whole way of life as a result of mental illness. Without special help they risk exclusion from the sort of roles, relationships and material resources which nourish recovery. They risk being trapped in unemployment and consequent long-term poverty and social isolation, lacking routes back into mainstream social networks and facing a vacuum of practicable hopes and goals.

This book enables mental health workers to share ideas on helping people who get stuck in this situation. It is a series of contributions from different workers. Each explores some particular angle on enhancing opportunities after mental illness or helping a person build on those resources they still possess. They cover a wide range of responses. For instance, some concern using family contacts or community leisure activities as a base for meeting people and participating in mainstream social circles. Others focus on improving someone's chances of getting employment under today's conditions. Others, still, concern housing, self-help groups, work opportunities outside formal employment and some innovative responses to long-term poverty. Besides variety, contributions have been selected for being practicable within limited resources. Many could be utilised in some form or other by a single worker. All follow a common theme of helping recovery take root outside the four walls of hospital or mental health centre buildings through working directly on opportunities and resources in an individual's everyday life.

The first contribution comes from Christine Barrowclough and Nicholas Tarrier in Chapter Two. They are clinical psychologists with the Salford Community Mental Health Project. They have been developing and evaluating an innovative nine month intervention programme for people who are returning to live with their families after a hospital admission for schizophrenia. Their programme aims to assist through each stage of the recovery process, from initial return to a worried family to longer term issues outside the home, like roles and goals for the future. One emphasis is using families' positive potential for support, long-term relationships and shared resources, while working to ease negative, stressful aspects of family life. Another is the use of mainstream community settings like voluntary work or adult education, rather than segregated psychiatric day units, as opportunities which enable people to function socially outside the home and develop an identity in 'well' society.

Mainstream social settings like adult education classes and community centres are the focus of the second contribution, Chapter Three. Carol Williams set up 'Alternatives', a West London project for people who had been unemployed long-term and were seeking alternatives to loneliness and lack of activity and focus in life. Many of her clients had, in fact, moved on from psychiatric facilities to empty lives and thence sought out this project. She describes an approach she used for helping people, who were often socially inhibited, withdrawn and fearful, to develop a routine of leisure or educational activities which took them outside their homes.

Chapters Four, Five, Six and Seven are concerned with models for mental health day services which can offer ready bridges to mainstream opportunities and make it easy for staff to incorporate the sort of roles described in this book. In Chapter Five Hammersmith's Erconwald Street Mental Health Project is described by two of its managers, Nigel Jones and Christine Embleton. Funded as a Social Services day centre, this service places special emphasis on redressing the loss of valued roles, identities and relationships which can be such a serious consequence of mental illness. A prime aim is to enable users to develop opportunities and social connections outside the building rather than solely inside it. It has developed a distinctive 'Core and Cluster' model, which has stood the test of time. Details are supplied on its resources and their deployment so that comparison with other models is possible. Chapter Six discusses common pitfalls facing day services which seek a more outward-looking

orientation. In Chapter Seven Jan Marsden, Group
Therapist at Harpurhey Centre, Manchester,
describes how a day centre can build links to
voluntary work and adult education opportunities in
particular.
All steps to a fuller life cost some money.
However little, this may still represent a serious
problem for someone living long-term on
Supplementary Benefit and lacking any savings or
reserves. Chapter Eight, 'Strategies to Counter
Poverty', discusses various responses to the
serious social restrictions imposed by long-term
poverty. One approach is to check welfare benefits
to ensure that full entitlement is claimed.
Research has shown that users of psychiatric
services quite often fail to claim proper
entitlement. In Chapter Nine Teresa Leo, formerly a
CAB worker at Tooting Bec Hospital, describes how
mental health workers can seek to maximise their
clients' incomes through welfare benefits advocacy.
Another response to poverty is to set up amenity or
benevolent funds which make direct grants to
claimants, within DHSS regulations. Such grants can
appreciably broaden social opportunities,
particularly for people who are likely to depend on
Supplementary Benefit for the rest of their lives.
It is possible to finance such funds legitimately
through commercial activities to which
beneficiaries contribute their labour. Chapter
Eight includes a summary of the DHSS regulations
governing this little used opportunity . In Chapter
Ten Richard Grover, Trust Secretary at the Peter
Bedford Trust, describes a workscheme which
finances such a fund. This scheme also shows how
meaningful work can be provided for almost anyone
who seeks it, without centralised resources or
restrictive costs.
In Chapter Eleven Judy Scott, Work Development
Officer at Kensington and Chelsea Mental Health
Association, describes a scheme for training
people who have suffered mental illness in high
earning skills in home and office services, which
they can utilise on a self-employed basis. A small
umbrella agency organises advertising and
distributes orders. It also liaises with local DHSS
concerning work while on Benefit, for instance
concerning amenity grants or the substantial part-
time earnings permitted on certain Benefits. For
some people this scheme opens opportunities to escape
poverty by legitimately augmenting their Benefit
long-term. For others it offers a chance to

gradually test their earning power while on the safety net of Benefit, then move off to self-support through self-employment.

This leads on to enhancing people's prospects for open employment. In Chapter Twelve Corinne Brewer, a former Disablement Resettlement Officer, discusses simple, practical ways in which a mental health worker can help a client towards effective job-search, liaise with specialist employment services, and provide support during job-seeking. In Chapter Thirteen Jane Richardson, Development Officer for Toc H in Buckinghamshire, describes the Transitional Employment approach which she witnessed while working at Fountain House in New York. The Fountain House Transitional Employment Programme enhances former psychiatric patients' employment prospects through arranging temporary jobs in mainstream businesses. Besides wages, this offers recent work experience and references from ordinary employers. Employers join this scheme because Fountain House takes over recruitment and training for these jobs and guarantees immediate replacement whenever a job-holder is absent. Prior to Transitional Employment, Fountain House offers rehabilitation and training programmes which can be focussed directly towards such firm job opportunities.

Another way into an ordinary workplace is the Manpower Services Commission's Sheltered Placement scheme, which can accommodate people with significant disabilities. Mike Twomey, an MSC official involved in developing the scheme, describes it in Chapter Fourteen. The scheme enables people who are registered disabled to take up a job in an ordinary workplace and at an ordinary wage, thanks to a subsidy from the MSC which compensates for assessed shortfall in output. It is expectations of a worker's output which are sheltered in Sheltered Placements. Otherwise this arrangement makes 'sheltered' employment a means for integration with an ordinary workforce and vastly broadens the types of work available.

In Chapter Fifteen Andrew Milroy and Rick Hennelly describe the North Derbyshire Mental Health Services Project, based at Chesterfield. This innovative service addresses everyday opportunities on a number of fronts. One aim is to enable people recovering from mental illness to offer each other friendship and support through an informal friendship network within their own communities, a special issue in this partly rural catchment. A prominent feature of the Project is a range of self-managing groups, which combine elements of social clubs and self-help groups, and offer people recovering from mental illness a long-term resource network which is both informal, local and under their own control.

In Chapter Sixteen Gillian Lomas, who was formerly Co-Director of Hackney's Community Psychiatry Research Unit, discusses how well-chosen rehousing can sometimes act as the lynchpin of a person's support system. She reviews how a home can sometimes meet a range of a person's social needs, in addition to providing a roof over their head. She argues for special efforts to help each individual get a housing arrangement which suits their preferred style of life and offers a real base for growth and development.

Each of these chapters explores ways in which services for the treatment of mental illness can lead on to opportunities for mental health in everyday life. Central to the whole book is the contention that this is a crucial need for many people who suffer mental illness. Accordingly Chapter One, 'Services Which Lead Somewhere', discusses reasons why opportunities after mental illness need such attention. It outlines the rationale for this book's emphasis on work, family contacts, friends and access to activities and institutions in mainstream society.

Chapter One

SERVICES WHICH LEAD SOMEWHERE

Charles Patmore

One small-scale survey neatly illustrates problems
which can face people recovering from mental
illness in today's high unemployment society. In
1982 Anne Birch followed up a sample of 25 people
who left three admission wards in a Manchester
hospital during an eight week study period. Her
findings are presented in her book 'What Chance
Have We Got? Occupation and employment after mental
illness: patients' views' (1). First she
interviewed patients who were due to be discharged
while they were still in hospital. She then
interviewed them again during their third month out
of hospital. Interviews focussed on how a person
was spending their time, how this was affecting
their morale, and their hopes in terms of work or
occupation. Predominantly these were people who
had stayed in hospital only a short while. Over
half had spent under three weeks in hospital. Only
five had stayed over two months, the longest stay
being for seven months. Many described their
problem as depression.

By the second interview Anne Birch found them
mainly, "unemployed, bored, and more or less stuck
at home. The interviewees spoke of having nothing
to do, feeling their lives were being wasted and
having no future plans. They spoke of being lonely
and missing the company of workmates .... Most of

1

these people faced some degree of financial
hardship or worried about being financially
dependent on husband or else the state."
    Of these twenty-five people, when she
interviewed them during their third month out of
hospital:

> "Only eight of the people I saw at home had
> the support of part or full-time day care.
> Three people had indeed been fortunate enough
> to return to work. Fourteen people were
> spending most of the time during those initial
> weeks out of hospital just sitting around at
> home, bored, with very little to do. Twelve
> of those had returned to exactly the same
> situation, ie.lack of activity, that they had
> left behind when they were admitted to
> hospital."(1)

    Of the fourteen ex-patients without jobs or
day care there were six who expressed interest in
voluntary work, adult education classes, community
centres or other ways they might make their lives
more active. All of them, though, were still at a
planning stage and made comments on difficulties
they faced concerning confidence or simply finding
out about relevant opportunities. No help with
this was available for them from mental health
workers. As for the rest, Anne Birch writes:

> "Otherwise the general outlook was sad,
> nothing to look forward to. Two people said,
> only half jokingly, that they might be dead by
> then, six feet under. These three quotations
> sum up the general feeling.
>
> 'No plan, it's the same thing every day - no
> future at all. I haven't a clue (what will
> happen in six months).'
>
> 'Dunno - might win the pools - something to
> look forward to.'
>
> 'Can't look forward to anything different, can
> I.'"(1)

    This survey emphasises how little attention
mental health workers give to the void which
nowadays faces many of their clients after
hospital. —Hospital-based staff took relatively
little interest in situations facing patients after

discharge. Social workers and community nurses were thin on the ground, with less than half of this sample receiving a follow-up visit by the time of the second interview. When available, they tended to help with a strictly limited range of issues. Employment, work or use of time got least attention of all.

"Seventeen people had not discussed any of these issues although most had discussed domestic problems such as housing, family or social security. So according to the patients almost half of them had no expectations of receiving support towards using 'work' time when they left hospital."(1)

Anne Birch points to aspects of occupation besides advice on employment where her survey subjects could have also benefitted from assistance. There is the whole question of access to mainstream leisure and social activities, which sometimes represent important resources for mental health. But finding such activities and making a start with them may be no simple matter for someone recovering from mental illness. Concerning those interviewees who did voice ideas about using their time, Anne Birch comments:

"There are, in fact, in a city the size of Manchester, many hundreds of clubs and organisations which could be a source of interest and activity. The problem is how does someone get in touch with these on leaving hospital.

Jack was fortunate in that the hospital put him in touch with a volunteer bureau. Even so he had not heard anything from them in the three months since he had been out of hospital.... So far Pete did not even know how to get in touch with a volunteer agency.

Susan did not know where to go initially, but she had developed enough inner strength to go and enquire at the local community centre. Louise was aware of the local community centre activities but did not think they would suit her. How else could she find out where to go? Christine was relying on a friend to give her moral courage to go along to the local adult education centre. What would happen to

3

someone who did not have such a friend? What
would have happened to Janet if her fear of
stigma had persisted in preventing her from
looking for alternative activities?

All these questions add up to one: who helps
ex-psychiatric patients make use of their
unemployed time? Most had to spend most of
their time sitting at home with little to do.
Whom could they turn to to change this
situation? It seems that there is a genuine
gap in local provision ... I felt that these
people needed some very specific help and
encouragement to find out what was available
in their own local area."(1)

Such non-attention towards issues of
occupation after mental illness has been noted in
other, wider ranging surveys of mental health
services. For instance, Mike Floyd conducted a
study of employment problems facing people
recovering from schizophrenia. To obtain a
representative sample he followed up patients
leaving three large psychiatric hospitals and three
District General Hospital psychiatric units. He
comments:

"At present social workers appear to regard
their responsibility for clients as being
largely confined to their domestic problems
and situations. Few were observed to take a
very active part in helping our subjects in
dealing with their employment problems, while
psychiatrists and nurses - and more
surprisingly occupational therapists - were
even less likely to be concerned with this
aspect of their patients' lives."(2)

Explanation is needed how such an important
aspect of the recovery process comes to be so
neglected by mental health services. Anne Birch
asks:

"In what ways did hospital help them towards
coping once they were back at home? Their
stories show that greatest emphasis is placed
on medical, domestic and emotional matters.
It seems from the interviews that little
professional space is given towards preparing
them for the difficulties they will face in
the field of open employment. Also it seems

4

that they receive little preparation towards
finding alternative activities to fill in
their time once they are back at home and
unemployed. I found it strange that so much
professional time and financial resources are
spent on the individual whilst s/he is in
hospital. Once out of hospital one can only
really comment on the lack of resources than
the quality of them. The interviewees
appeared to receive a minimum of aftercare,
and employment or other occupational advice
featured only slightly in this."

THE YEARS OF FULL EMPLOYMENT

One reason is that for very many years
employment was so readily available that even
people with appreciable disadvantages like periods
of mental illness could get jobs quite easily.
Mental health workers became used to so many of
their clients moving on to jobs that they rarely
felt pressed to attend to issues of occupation for
those who did not. Mental health services looked
towards a sharp divergence of possible futures for
their users. Either people left for jobs or to
care for families, as productive members of
mainstream society. Or prolonged day care,
sheltered work or extended hospital residence would
be available, if someone's difficulties were so
serious as to preclude employment even during those
twenty-five years up to the mid-seventies when jobs
were very accessible. The latter response usually
involved services which segregated people away from
the community like conventional day centres,
sheltered workshops, hospital industrial units or
the large hospitals themselves. There were units
which would defer discharge as a rule until
patients had jobs to go to. One DHSS circular from
the early 'seventies conveys, perhaps, the thinking
behind aftercare services in those days. The new
Local Authority psychiatric day centres should
provide, it said, "relatively short term
rehabilitation for those likely to return to open
employment or domestic duties, and long-term,
perhaps permanent, work or occupation for those
whose chances of return to employment are poor."
(3) Since those words were written there has been
a huge numerical increase in "those whose chance of
return to employment are poor". They now include
people of much greater coping ability, people who
might formerly have got jobs relatively easily.

There is little, though, which relates to them in
the basic structure on which today's services are
based, the model enunciated in 1975 by 'Better
Services for the Mentally Ill'.(4)
    Research on changing access to employment
illustrates the influence of employment
opportunity. One unusual study suggests there are
critical levels of local job-competition at which
open employment becomes very difficult for people
leaving psychiatric hospital. Roger Morgan and
Adrian Cheadle studied how fluctuations in local
unemployment affected successful job-getting by
patients from a Regional psychiatric rehabilitation
hospital in the West Midlands during the years 1964
to 1973.(5)
    This hospital had placed 426 patients in open
employment over the period. People eligible for
job placement included many who had suffered
serious problems. Median length of stay for the
sample was three years. The hospital was strongly
oriented to helping patients move on to jobs.
There was, the authors write:

    "a powerful if unwritten policy to make
    subsequent employment a necessary condition of
    discharge. Although one can live in the
    Welfare State without having to work to
    support oneself, various social and other
    pressures appear to make it a demoralising and
    anti-therapeutic experience which disabled
    people ought to avoid if possible. There was
    no accessible sheltered employment in the
    Region in 1961 and there is still very little
    in 1974. For these reasons the hospital has
    striven consistently throughout the period to
    place its patients in open employment, as the
    only satisfactory way of resettling them.
    Given this consistent aim, any observed
    fluctuations in the extent to which it was
    achieved may be due to variations in the
    number of job opportunities or in the quality
    of the patients seeking them."

Variations in average level of patients'
functioning were assessed from test records of
measures of mental state, social withdrawal and
work performance. These were set against
fluctuations in local employment to see which was
the better predictor of number of job placements
for each quarter during the ten year period.

6

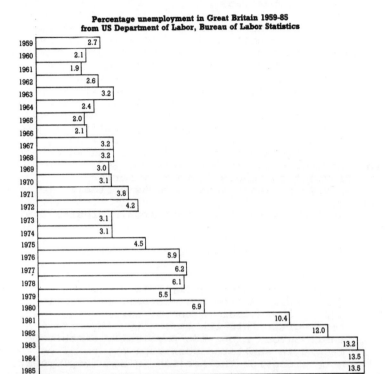

Figure 1.1

The number of jobs available locally and the number of other unemployed people competing for them emerged as the reason why during some quarters far more people moved out of hospital to a job than during others. Within the low levels of unemployment occurring during this period even quite small fluctuations had sizeable effects for people close to critical margins of employability, like former psychiatric patients. The authors comment:

"Placement was relatively easy when the unemployment rate was below 2%. Placements were halved when the rate was between 2% and 5%. It was further reduced when the rate was above 5%. The shape of our graph curve suggests that placement would be practically impossible in the presence of a rate of about

7

6% or higher".(5)

For mental health workers' purposes, it is obviously your local unemployment rate which is relevant, not the national average figure. But the two large, sudden increases in average national unemployment do, roughly speaking, delineate the three levels of declining job availability which have just been mentioned. The 1974 OPEC oil price rise ended a long period of low-unemployment and easy access to jobs for psychiatric patients. From 1975 to 1979 came a phase of medium difficulty in Morgan and Cheadle's terms. In 1979 the advent of the Thatcher government rapidly doubled unemployment to levels where many former psychiatric patients face enormous obstacles to employment.

Another perspective comes from Professor David Goldberg:

"My own training as a psychiatrist was heavily influenced by social psychiatrists such as R K Freudenberg, Douglas Bennett and John Wing who, in an age of nearly full employment, brilliantly showed how mentally ill people could regain their sense of self-worth - and reintegrate into the community - by offering their labour alongside physically disabled people in sheltered workshops or, as often as not, alongside the healthy in open employment.

When the time came for me to play a part in setting up a new psychiatric service in Manchester, we were able to open rehabilitation facilities based on the model I had learned from my teachers. In the first few years all went fairly well, despite the fact that unemployment in South Manchester ten years ago was considerably higher than it had been in London in the 1960s. In 1973 we surveyed the 103 patients who had passed through the rehabilitation workshop in the previous year, and found to our great disappointment that two-thirds of them were not employed three months after leaving us but were at home doing next to nothing, most of them still experiencing symptoms. Nonetheless, we had placed 11% in sheltered workshops, and 22% in open employment. We did this by using 'job-finding groups' and by giving patients TV feedback of their work

8

performance in the workshop: the range of
tasks we offered reflected the kind of light
industrial work available in local factories;
staff from the Manchester Business School
interviewed our patients as though they were
having real job selection interviews, and gave
them helpful feedback. By means of these
strategies we were able to get many
schizophrenic patients into jobs at a time
when able-bodied men were being turned back to
the dole queue.

Six years later Tom Carnwarth repeated the
survey for me and found that patients were now
spending longer in the workshop, so that only
half as many people passed through in the
course of a year. This time however almost
90% were without jobs of any kind after their
discharge, and none had found employment when
Tom followed them up two years later.
Furthermore, the patients who did go back to
work tended to have jobs that were being held
open for them. The function of our workshop
had changed in a very significant way. We
were no long helping patients to acquire work
skills and thus to ascend Donald Early's
'occupational ladder': we were now merely
preserving work habits in those who had a job
to go back to."(6)

Further illustration might be these figures
for job placement from a psychiatric day centre in
Harrow, cited in a study of the effects of
unemployment on Social Services facilities. Though
Harrow's unemployment rate was only 6.4% in January
1985, attrition of job prospects and increase in
length of stay are evident.

Clients Discharged from Day Centre to New Jobs
in Open Employment in Harrow

1973   14 clients, average stay 10 weeks
1981   10 clients, average stay 16 weeks
1982   10 clients, average stay 17.5 weeks
1983   7 clients, average stay 28.5 weeks
1984   None to date

(From Susan Balloch and Chris Hume 'Caring for
Unemployed People')(7)

Of course many people missed out on a system

which looked so much to employment as a locus for
opportunities after illness - women with heavy
family commitments, for instance, people
approaching retirement age or people with markedly
fluctuating abilities which exclude them from
conventional employment. There were many people
even then, as David Goldberg points out, who ended
up at home doing nothing. But for very many people
these plentiful jobs did offer a ready route to
opportunities which support recovery. It was a
straightforward and convenient route, too, from the
point of view of mental health services. It was
practicable for remote, large catchment psychiatric
hospitals. It meant that their building-bound
rehabilitation programmes could successfully
resettle people without too much difficult distant
work on their users' home opportunities. It
offered newer, community-located rehabilitation
services a model for operating which did not
require too painful a break from the building-bound
practices of the traditional psychiatric hospital.
So accessible was employment up to the
mid-seventies that in many services mental health
workers did not even see the need to help clients
over job-seeking.

Important stepping-stones from hospital to job
in this conventional system of services are day
hospitals and, for people with longer-term needs,
day centres. Eight of Anne Birch's interviewees
attended a hospital day unit which had a fairly
typical social therapy and craft-work orientation.
Some of them emphasised how much meeting other
people there helped them, how attending gave a
job-like structure to day and week and how it
boosted their morale and social confidence. But
this day centre did no more than the hospital, the
CPNs or social workers to help users towards work,
leisure activities or social networks which could
offer a longer-term focus for their lives after
leaving the centre. It supported people, made them
feel better and more confident. But it did not
lead anywhere. This matches the findings of the
National Day Care Project back in 1976 which
surveyed many psychiatric day units across Britain.
It found that users named improved confidence and
good relationships within the centre as their main
gains, but rarely mentioned changes in their lives
outside it (8). Anne Birch comments: "So far very
few schemes nationally have helped the
ex-psychiatric patient to find ways of making use
of existing community resources. Day care may

provide a stepping-stone between hospital and home but eventually the individual faces unemployment alone."
    Anne Birch's survey presents mental health services as consistently failing to open access to opportunities which can support the crucial latter stages of recovery when a person moves away from mental health services and seeks to resume an ordinary life. Small and informal as is this survey, it may well represent a fairly typical national picture. The services studied were certainly no worse than average, probably better in fact. Unemployment in Manchester is only slightly above national average. If anything, the survey understates some aspects of the problem. The people Anne Birch interviewed were indeed depressed and demoralised at their lack of occupation, their isolation and their lack of money. Nevertheless her sample seems low on the people who suffer most of all from professionals' inability to work across the transition from hospital or day centre to an ordinary life. These are people who have little or nothing to return to in the way of social connections or supports, unlike many of Anne Birch's interviewees who were currently married, had pleasant homes and families living nearby and had been away in hospital only briefly. A sample drawn from a service catering for sufferers from recurrent psychotic illnesses might present a much bleaker picture. The social disruptions caused by serious mental illness or extended hospitalisation can result in some people losing their friends, spouse, home and even their entire family connections, not to mention their job. They may face a truly awful vacuum on leaving hospital, without openings to any identity, role, relationships or sustenance other than as an ex-psychiatric patient.

WHY OPPORTUNITIES AFTER MENTAL ILLNESS MATTER

    There is an important truism about why opportunities after mental illness matter. This is that recovery means regaining functioning - being able to gradually take on tasks you could not manage when ill, being able to relate to people afresh, being able to take initiatives. Also, an important natural stage in recovery is to venture again into mainstream society, away from professional carers and immediate family and affirm the identity of a 'well' person through resuming

11

old acquaintances or meeting new people. This obviously cannot occur without the necessary opportunities. There need to be opportunities for work, for mixing with people, for gradually taking productive or responsible roles, or for making mainstream social contacts. A research study by Alan Breier and John Strauss followed for a year the experiences of 20 people recovering from a psychotic episode (9). It focussed on the types of social contact and opportunity for relationships which they found helpful at different stages. The authors found recovery involved two phases, a 'convalescent' phase followed by a 'rebuilding' phase. Patients reported needing different types of help, relationships and social opportunities during the two different phases. During the 'rebuilding' phases they felt more active, started planning for the future and sought roles and contacts in mainstream society. Looked at in terms of these concepts, British mental health services are quite well attuned to the needs of the 'convalescent' phase. But, currently, it is rare that they open opportunities appropriate to the needs of the 'rebuilding' phase.

A further reason why attention to this stage is crucial is the need to renew a system of informal supports for anyone recovering from mental illness. Sustained recovery requires access to the sort of informal personal support systems which all of us need to feed our interest or engagement in life, sustain our morale and keep us going during periods of adversity. For all human beings our mental health depends in part on the positive, rewarding elements in our everyday lives and our sources of consolation when facing difficulties. We vary considerably as individuals as to how we derive such supports. Common sources include close, loving relationships, family roles, jobs, friends or, for some people, an identity in local community or neighbourhood. Sometimes hobbies or sports make a contribution, sometimes religious or political commitments. Some people gain an underlying strength from pursuit of long-term goals or a certain vision of their future. Most of us change our support systems many times in our lives. But we always need supports in some form or other. With weak supports we are much more likely to break down in the face of crisis or serious adversity. We will find it harder, too, to persevere with difficult undertakings. Support systems do not guarantee against mental illness or its recurrence.

But they make breakdown in the face of adversity less likely and considerably assist recovery. That informal support systems help sustain mental health seems plain common sense. But it has now been charted by a growing body of careful, scientific research into social factors which affect risk of mental ill-health. A well-known, pioneering study was George Brown's research on depression among women in Camberwell (10). This demonstrated how women who had either close, confiding marital relationships or jobs which took them out of the home were much less likely to develop depression if they suffered a serious set-back in life than women who lacked such supports or outlets. So it is plainly important that someone who is recovering from mental illness can develop or rebuild a network of personal supports. Mental health work is not complete without this.

MENTAL ILLNESS AND LOSS OF SOCIAL CONNECTIONS

Such issues require particular attention on account of the tragic, vicious circle process whereby mental illness can destroy or seriously damage a person's social opportunities and support systems. Some people are fortunate enough to emerge from a breakdown with their connections unbroken. They may have secure housing, supportive spouses, or jobs held open by sympathetic employers - three of Anne Birch's interviewees, for instance, had jobs to return to. But others may suffer terrible dislocation and social disruption, especially where a psychotic illness is concerned. They may lose their jobs when hospitalised. Their marriages may break up or they may become alienated from family or friends in the turmoil surrounding a breakdown. They may lose their homes and even their personal possessions. Time spent in hospital deepens the separation between a person and anything remaining from their previous way of life. Often such consequences to a psychotic episode can be a much greater problem than the episode itself. They can create a vacuum in which it is extremely difficult for a person to help themselves. This is how some people become forever trapped in limbo following mental illness, isolated, unemployed, stuck in demoralising housing and lacking any realistic opportunities for establishing themselves again. One recent US research study illustrates

how mental illness risks destroying a person's
social connections. A team at New York University
Medical Centre studied how schizophrenia can affect
an individual's social network (11). They compared
the social networks of people who had suffered more
than one episode of schizophrenia with those of
people undergoing their first attack of the
illness. They conclude that much of the loss of
relationships and social opportunities, which
affect many people who suffer from schizophrenia,
is the result of the disruption which a person's
first breakdown causes to their social world. It
is not a pre-illness trait or a natural inclination
for people who suffer from schizophrenia. With
appropriate help, they argue, such network collapse
might be substantially prevented.

This study interviewed people who had
recently been admitted to hospital for a
schizophrenic breakdown. Fifteen people were
selected, aged 18 to 45 years old, who were
suffering their first breakdown. A matched group
of fifteen other people were selected, all of whom
had suffered at least one previous admission for
schizophrenia over the last year. Each person was
interviewed in depth about their social world.

People who had suffered previous
schizophrenic breakdowns tended to currently know
far fewer people than those suffering their initial
illness. While only one of the former group lacked
any social contacts, their networks typically
comprised less than a third of the number of people
with whom the first admission group had contact.
Their number of actual contacts each week was
around half that of the latter. In particular the
multiple admission group had lost relationships
with people outside their families. On average
they had only a third as many friends and social
acquaintances as the first admission group and a
fifth of the number of formal relationships with
people like doctors, employers or teachers.

Family links were a proportionally larger
component of the social networks of people who had
suffered previous breakdowns. But these, too, had
shrunk, only not as much as non-family connections.
A full third of the previous admission group had no
contact with any family member, while none of the
first admission group lacked such contacts.

Social networks subsequent to schizophrenia
tended to include notably fewer important or close
relationships. One third of the interviewees in
the multiple admission group did not have a very

14

good friend, a very close contact, or a very
important person in their lives. They rated a
significantly smaller proportion of their
relationships as 'very important' or 'very close'
than did people suffering their first illness.
    The authors of this research emphasise that
such loss of social contacts does not reflect lack
of social interest either before or after first
breakdown. Neither group showed a history of
isolation during adolescence. There were signs how
the multiple admission group were trying to develop
new relationships to replace the network they had
lost. Their non-family relationships tended to be
more recent, despite their being on average older
than the first admission group.
    Thus these serious social losses seem
largely secondary consequences of schizophrenic
breakdown. The authors point to first breakdown and
hospitalisation as a crisis point when a person
risks dramatic loss of relationships. They urge
that professionals intervene to forestall this:

> "If it is true that much of the network change
> undergone by schizophrenics occurs after the
> first break, then it is occurring at a time
> when the patient had presumably come under
> professional care. It means that a sensitized
> professional may have the opportunity to alter
> this picture .... In part, this may be
> accomplished by educating the family and
> friends of schizophrenic patients. Educating
> old network members may make them more willing
> to accept the patient back into the network,
> and help them to be more tolerant of his
> deficits. In addition, developing strategies
> to relieve the family and friends of the
> concomitant stress of illness, such as
> providing a variety of backup services to the
> patient and his linkages, may facilitate the
> maintenance of the patient's network....
>
> Active intervention on both an individual and
> a network level at the time of the first
> psychotic episode is essential in order to
> avoid network collapse and resultant social
> isolation."

> (Lipton, Cohen, Fischer & Katz
> 'Schizophrenia: a network crisis')(11)

Mental health services are often severely

limited in their responses to this problem of
network collapse and social vacuum after mental
illness. For decades they relied on employment as
a bridge to post-illness opportunities and building
a new social network. Rehabilitation services
concentrated on assisting a person's social skills,
confidence and coping ability to the point where
they would be able to hold down a job and use this
as the basis for a new support system. Another
established service response to the problem is the
group home. Originally mainly oriented to former
long-stay in-patients, shared housing has become
extended to many others, as jobs have become
scarcer, as an opportunity for a new network and
support system.

WORK AND MENTAL HEALTH

        Heavy reliance on such single, simple
responses has hindered the development of more
complex, flexible ways of helping people rebuild
networks and informal supports. But the focus on
employment is very understandable when one
considers the extraordinary number of positive
consequences which can flow from the single step of
getting a job. Employment can contribute immediate
elements of a support system through daily social
contacts, a structure to your day and week, an
identity as a healthy, contributing person in
mainstream society, and, of course, money. It can
make longer term contributions, too, like the
choices of housing, leisure and social life, which
wages can make possible, friendships made at work,
or the opportunity to pursue long-term personal
goals, where again money is often crucial. Of
course not every job offers all of these things.
There are some jobs which offer but few of them.
There are jobs, too, which are oppressive,
degrading and harmful rather than supportive -
conflicts with workmates are, in fact, the cause of
some people's breakdowns. But much more frequently
employment offers a remarkable short-cut to meeting
a cluster of major needs for someone recovering
from mental illness. For a person who has suffered
serious social losses from an episode of illness, a
job can offer a unique opportunity to regain
ground. A former patient put it like this at MIND's
1984 Annual Conference, 'Life after mental illness?
Opportunities in an age of unemployment':

        "I suffered severe depression and received

treatment for three years, both as an
in-patient and as an out-patient. I
subsequently got a job. I strongly feel I owe
my recovery to finding employment ... No
matter what the original cause of the
breakdown, the sufferer almost always loses
their job because of the illness. The prime
cause of your breakdown may be losing your
partner. It usually follows then that you
also lose your home, your friends and very
often even your relatives. Then when you're
staggering under this burden, your employer
decides he no longer wants you and this last
blow is often what finally topples you. If
only you can return to a job that's held open
for you as quickly as is possible following
your initial treatment, you can build again
but with even your job gone, you then stand
very little chance of being able to fight back
... A simple job, short hours with the option
to increase these hours as the patient
improves, staggered hours to allow for various
difficulties the patient may face on returning
to work, no pressurised deadlines to meet and
a congenial working atmosphere will almost
certainly result in recovery. Mixing with
'well' people will almost certainly have a
good effect and a salary will give the patient
back his or her dignity which is all important
and perhaps even more important his or her
confidence will begin to return."

Discussion of employment's many benefits
often prompts comparison between the difficulties
of people who face unemployment following mental
illness and those of other unemployed people.
Recent research on unemployment in the general
community has established significant hazards to
anyone's mental health from having nothing to do.
Studies of large samples of unemployed people show
that a sizeable minority develop significant mental
health difficulties, as measured by their scores on
tests like the General Health Questionnaire (GHQ),
which can assess a respondent's risk of a clinical
level of mental ill-health. A particularly clear
demonstration of the consequences of unemployment
comes from a study which followed large numbers of
individuals first from school or jobs into
unemployment, then back to getting a job or a place
on a workscheme. GHQ scores worsen as a person
becomes unemployed, then sharply improve when they

get a job (12). Other research has charted how
unemployed people tend to become separated from
society, abandoning ventures outside their home or
retreating into invalidism.
Such studies underline how undermining
unemployment can be for anyone's mental health.
There are in fact plenty of points of contact
between the experiences of unemployed ex-patients
and those of other unemployed people. But it is
crucial to note the points of difference. Some
research studies comment how profoundly reactions
to unemployment are patterned by the situation
facing an individual. Reactions are patterned by
influences like whether the person retains a social
network when unemployed, whether they have a sense
of 'breadwinner' obligations and family
responsibility, whether they have socially valued
roles outside employment, the meaning they attach
to joblessness and so on. Thus people leaving
psychiatric treatment will react to unemployment in
ways that are influenced by the extra problems they
may face.
As mentioned, this includes the problem of
network collapse. Some people recovering from
mental illness may have recently lost in a space of
months practically everything they have built up in
their lives - friends, career, even home and
family. Without a credible initial foothold for
restarting their lives, like that which a job can
sometimes give, they may be overcome by feelings of
devastation and despair. Many people, furthermore,
will have suffered a series of hurtful failures or
blows to their confidence or self-esteem in the
events leading up to their breakdown. They may be
urgently needing some activity or area of life
where they can show to themselves and others that
their illness has passed, that they can be useful
or competent again. To many people, their families
and the wider community keeping a job is an overt
sign that a person is now 'well' and staying
'well'. Another way in which a job fosters a 'well'
identity is through giving daily social contacts
with workmates in mainstream society. Quite often,
in today's high unemployment society, when people
do manage to replace networks lost through mental
illness, their new network consists entirely of
other ex-patients met through a segregated world of
group homes, social clubs and mental health day
centres. Such a network may offer strong social
support. But it may make being an ex-patient your
dominant social identity. Yet another issue is

18

that with some forms of mental illness learning to cope in spite of residual symptoms is a crucial element in recovery. The structure and demands of a job can provide an excellent framework for this, keep one busy and distract from the symptoms which can rapidly overwhelm some people if they face stretches of empty time.

Such issues considered, the gap which often results from joblessness has special implications for people recovering from mental illness, besides its common negative effects on mental health. At a time when people particularly need occupation, social contacts, a positive social role and a sense of a future, unemployment can frustrate all these needs, bring hopelessness and heighten sense of deviance. Another former patient speaking at the 1984 MIND Conference made the distinction like this:

> "It is essential that I work. I am not saying that with work I will certainly stay healthy but without it I will very likely be ill again. Of course, I know there are millions of people who need jobs. I am sure everyone here knows the high incidence of depression amongst the unemployed. It is not just the poverty, which is bad enough, but the lack of status, of contact with workmates and the structure it gives to life. The difference though is between someone being hungry and someone who is starving. I am starving. Add to all the difficulties that go with being unemployed, the stigma of being mentally ill and an illness that feeds off isolation and lack of worth and I face going back to hospital again or worse."

WHAT ASSISTS RECOVERY?

There is one particularly compelling argument about the practical consequences of opportunities which meet such needs during recovery. It comes from a thesis recently advanced by Richard Warner, a British-trained psychiatrist and anthropologist who heads a community mental health programme in Colorado, USA.

Schizophrenia affects a similar proportion of the population across all societies and cultures studied. But there are wide variations in how readily sufferers recover from the illness in different societies. These large differences have

now been carefully established and are not just
confusions between researchers. Despite far poorer
mental health services, rural Third World societies
offer much better recovery prospects than
industrialised Western ones. In countries like
India, Nigeria or Mauritius duration of
schizophrenic illness is typically brief. Recovery
without any residual social impairment is far more
common and fewer sufferers experience recurrent
episodes of the illness. Warner quotes WHO figures
showing average Third World outcome figures to
offer more than twice as good a prospect as Western
societies that a schizophrenic episode will be
short-lasting and followed by a full recovery
without any residual social impairment for at least
the next two years. Comparatively rare in the
Third World are people suffering protracted
schizophrenic illnesses with pronounced and
permanent problems in social functioning.

Worst prospects for recovery exist in
industrialised societies like our own, particularly
when unemployment is high. Somewhat intermediate
figures come from the USSR, which is industrialised
but where jobs are easily available. Best
prospects are found in rural Third World locations.
Where Third World countries are industrialised and
urbanised, the picture shifts towards the poor
recovery figures of a Western society. Richard
Warner comments:

"The general conclusion is unavoidable.
Schizophrenia in the Third World has a course
and prognosis quite unlike the condition as we
recognise it in the West. The progressive
deterioration which Kraepelin considered
central to his definition of the disease is
rare in non-industrial societies, except
perhaps under the dehumanising restrictions of
a traditional asylum. The majority of the
Third World schizophrenics achieve a
favourable outcome. The more urbanised and
industrialised the setting, the more malignant
becomes the illness. Why should this be
so?"(13)

His principal explanation is that return to
valued social role can be crucial to good recovery
from schizophrenia. In rural Third World societies
such opportunities are relatively accessible to
people at all stages of recovery, thanks to the
host of minor work roles across a wide spectrum of

demand and difficulty which are involved in such
non-wage economies. In contrast, in a wage-earning
industrial society if you cannot perform well
enough to get and keep a full-time job, you have
few other opportunities for constructive roles or
activities. Furthermore if unemployment rises, so
do the ability levels required before one can get
access to a productive role. People with any sort
of difficulty then become excluded. Warner writes:

"... the low recovery rates in schizophrenia
during the Great Depression were possibly
related to labor-force dynamics. The
apparently superior outcome for schizophrenia
in the USSR may be a result of full employment
and an emphasis on work rehabilitation in that
country. The picture which has now been drawn
of schizophrenia in the Third World gives more
support to the notion that the work role may
be an important factor shaping the course of
schizophrenia.

In non-industrial societies that are not based
upon a wage economy, the term 'unemployment'
is meaningless... Underemployment and
landlessness may become common but
unemployment is rare. Unemployment, however,
may reach high levels in the urbanized and
industrial areas of the Third World. The
return of a psychotic to a productive role in
a non-industrial setting is not contingent
upon his actively seeking a job, impressing an
employer with his worth, or functioning at a
consistently adequate level. In a non-wage,
subsistence economy, psychotics may perform
any of those available tasks which match their
level of functioning at a given time.
Whatever constructive contributions they can
make are likely to be valued by the community,
and their level of disability will not be
considered absolute. Dr Adeoye Lambo, a
psychiatrist well known for developing a
village-based treatment and rehabilitation
programme in Nigeria, reports that social
attitudes in Nigerian rural communities permit
the majority of those with mental disorders to
find an appropriate level of functioning and
thus to avoid disability and deterioration.
In India, research workers for the WHO
follow-up study of schizophrenia encountered
difficulty in interviewing their cases as the

ex-patients were so busy - the men in the
fields and the women in domestic work. The
more complete use of labor in pre-industrial
societies may encourage high rates of recovery
from psychosis." (14)

As to what forms of work might particularly
assist recovery, Warner draws on John Wing's
assessment of the two environmental factors most
conducive to good recovery from schizophrenia. One
is freedom from consistently critical attitudes
from the people with whom one lives or, conversely,
from over-involved, anxious, over-protective
behaviour on their part. But the other factor
concerns opportunities to develop a successful work
role. It is that work should be available with
"stable expectations precisely geared to the level
of performance that the individual can actually
achieve". Richard Warner comments:

"Industrial society gives relatively little
leeway for adapting a job to the abilities of
the worker. High productivity requirements
and competitive performance ratings may be
particularly unsuitable for a rehabilitating
schizophrenic. In a peasant culture he or she
is more likely to find an appropriate role
among such tasks of subsistence farming as
livestock management, food and fuel gathering,
or child care.

Many clinicians in the West have noticed that
the demands of a full 40 hour week are overly
taxing for psychotic clients .... Workload
expectations are more readily adjusted to meet
the capacities of the marginally functional
individual in a village setting than in the
industrial labour market. There can be little
doubt that it is simpler for a schizophrenic
to return to a productive role in a
non-industrial community than in the
industrial world. The merits of tribal and
peasant labour systems are apparent: as in the
West during a period of labour shortage, it is
easier for family and community members to
reintegrate the sick person into the society,
and the psychotic is better able to retain his
or her self-esteem. The result may well be not
only better social functioning of the
psychotic person but also more complete
remission of the symptoms of the illness.

Other WHO data more clearly document an
association between occupation and outcome.
Farmers were more likely than patients of any
other occupation to experience the most benign
pattern of illness - full remission with no
relapses - and the unemployed were least
likely to experience such a mild course to the
psychosis."(13)

Easier return to socially valued occupational
roles is Richard Warner's major explanation for
better recovery from schizophrenia in the Third
World. He also emphasises the contribution of
generally tolerant, non-critical, non-stigmatising
attitudes on the part of family, extended family
and wider community to all but prolonged, violent,
or socially disruptive manifestations of mental
illness. While the latter may get harsh social
reactions, rural Third World societies are often
far more ready to accept, adapt to or ignore more
typical forms of psychotic behaviour, which in the
West would risk long-term loss of status within a
person's network, if not outright ostracism. Such
greater opportunity to retain social networks and
enter new ones adds to a person's sense of
belonging and chance for return to a socially
valued role. Where attitudes within families are
concerned:

"The emphasis on community involvement in the
treatment of mental illness in non-industrial
societies similarly tends to reduce family
tensions. Responsibility is shared broadly
and the patient often escapes blame and
criticism, allowing the family to be more
supportive. According to recent research, for
example, relatives of schizophrenics in
Chandigarh, north India, are much less likely
to be demanding or critical of their psychotic
family member than are the relatives of
schizophrenics in the industrial world. In
London, nearly a half of schizophrenics have
such emotionally stressful relatives; in
Rochester, New York, the proportion is
similar; but in north India, fewer than a
fifth of schizophrenic patients were found to
have critical and demanding relatives."(14)

Warner concludes:

23

"In the Western world, schizophrenics are generally poor, unemployed and isolated. Few observers would argue that the schizophrenic in the Western world is, in general, well integrated into society... In the Third World, by contrast, the psychotic is more likely to return to a useful working role and to retain his or her self esteem, a feeling of value to the community, and a sense of belonging. These are things which four billion dollars does not buy the schizophrenic in the United States or elsewhere in the Western world. Such differences may account, perhaps, for the superior outcome from schizophrenia in the developing world."(13)

WHAT NEEDS TO BE DONE?

This viewpoint suggests that services for people leaving hospital in Britain need to link to opportunities for activity, challenge and socially valued roles, at flexible levels of demand and stress, which can restore functioning and support recovery. We need services which enable someone recovering from mental illness to progress steadily, stage by stage, to whatever positive social roles he or she can manage at the time. We need services which make readily possible that re-entry to mainstream society which can be so difficult without a job. We need services which genuinely lead somewhere. They must neither abruptly halt assistance at some half-way point, like leaving hospital or leaving a hostel, nor channel people into a cul-de-sac, like some sheltered workshops or day centres which open no subsequent options to the person ready to go further.

How should British mental health workers respond? One strong element must be assisting ex-patients to get open employment. However high unemployment rises, there will always be some former patients who might get some of the jobs available. Today's intense competition for jobs requires systematic, focussed approaches to enhancing their employment prospects which go beyond conventional work preparation programmes. This might mean, for instance, schemes which arrange initial temporary employment to circumvent the disadvantage of broken work records and lack of references. Likewise for special access to training in skills in contemporary demand. It

24

might mean, too, special arrangements to support clients during the crucial early months in a job or where mental health workers hand over to generic employment services, whose programmes may be ill-suited for vulnerable individuals.

But today's job competition also requires recognition that many people will be unemployed for long periods of time. For them we need links to opportunities besides open employment which can offer social contact, occupation, self-esteem, a socially valued identity, and some sort of base for personal goals and hopes about the future. We need this for those many former patients who would have easily got and kept jobs at the levels of competition of six or seven years ago, but not today. We need this, also, for all those people whose low stress thresholds or fluctuating abilities will always exclude them from standard, full-time open employment. Very important, there are many women with heavy child care commitments which preclude a full-time job yet who may urgently need social supports. We must recognise, too, that today's blue collar employment patterns increasingly involve intermittent unemployment, even for people who are basically successful contenders in the labour market. So many ex-patients who do get jobs are likely to also risk subsequent spells of unemployment. They, too, will benefit from mental health services which seek to open other opportunities and resources in users' everyday lives. It is wrong to see a straight choice between either promoting employment or concentrating on options outside employment, as the issue is sometimes presented. Mental health services need a wide and flexible repertoire of responses so that for each individual their services can lead on to opportunities and resources which match that person's desires, needs, and current level of functioning and which are genuinely within their grasp.

One important theme must be seeking opportunities besides employment which offer participation in the mainstream social world. Another will be enabling people to build or rebuild social networks with friends and family. Another will be opportunities for the activity, challenge, structure, and self-esteem which comes from work. This will include opening work opportunities outside conventional employment, like work on a self-employed or voluntary basis, which can make work accessible to people who otherwise would never get a chance to work.

ONE SURVEY OF SERVICE USERS' VIEWS

Some signposts for action come from what service users themselves say. One recent American survey interviewed a couple of hundred long-term psychiatric service users living in 30 different 'board and care' homes in Los Angeles (15). They were interviewed about factors contributing to satisfaction or dissatisfaction with their lives. An individual's overall sense of satisfaction and well-being emerged as linked to ratings of satisfaction in eight specific areas of life. These were home situation, links with family, social relations and friendships, leisure activities, finances, sense of safety from crime, employment situation, and general health and access to health care.

Their satisfactions in these areas were compared with those of a mainstream community sample and three samples from other disadvantaged groups - unmarried parents, black people, and people picked for their low socio-economic status.

Employment was a central value for many residents of these hostels. Three-quarters of those who had jobs were at least 'mostly satisfied' in this area of life. But five times as many were unemployed and two thirds of these felt 'terrible', 'dissatisfied' or at best 'mixed' about lack of a job. The remaining third of those who were unemployed were satisfied with this state of affairs. Half of those who wished a job were currently looking for work. But the other half were not, though no less dissatisfied with unemployment. The authors comment: "This suggested that many of those who were not seeking work may have given up on finding a job, yet retained a desire for work. With increased opportunities, some might have bettered their life conditions through employment".(15)

Maintaining contact with their families was a distinctive concern among these hostel residents. A slight majority were satisfied with their relationships with their families. Satisfaction was rated greatest by those with most frequent contact with family. Ratings of dissatisfaction meant less contact than the resident wished. They seemed particularly vulnerable to estrangement from

family. A quarter had not seen any family member
in the past year. The large minority who expressed
dissatisfaction at low family contact marks this
out as one of three areas of life where the hostel
residents fared significantly worse than the
special control samples from other disadvantaged
groups, as well as the mainstream control group.

Another distinctive difference from the other
disadvantaged groups was the greater numbers of
residents who wanted more in the way of friends and
social relationships. This reflected their
isolation, with less than half visiting someone
outside their hostel on a regular basis. But 60%
did express satisfaction in this area of life. The
most common reason for satisfaction was that they
had one close friend, often a fellow resident. Two
thirds of residents reported such a close
friendship.

Two issues emerged as important to the sort of
home environment these hostels provided. Residents
who had a room to themselves or some other
opportunity for privacy were significantly happier.
The other was a surprise, shocking finding that a
good third of all residents had been robbed or
assaulted in the previous year, quite often within
these hostels. Fears about personal safety made
this the third most common source of
dissatisfaction and another distinctive difference
from any control group. Beware the common British
practice of giving vulnerable people hard-to-let
flats on rough, crime-ridden Council estates.

The most common dissatisfaction of all was
shortage of money. This put even unemployment into
second place. Two-thirds of residents felt 'mixed'
or worse about what were in fact extremely low
incomes. This includes a fifth who rated their
situation as 'terrible'. The hostel residents were
more dissatisfied about their incomes than any
control group in the study.

This survey enumerates common areas where
users of mental health services need help, like
social isolation, unemployment and poverty. In one
sense it is a bleak picture showing them as much
less satisfied than other citizens in most areas of
life. Indeed 44% of these board and care home
residents said they felt "mixed" or "mostly
dissatisfied" about their lives in general, a
rating which is usually given by only one person in
ten among the general population. But in another
sense this survey brings encouragement. It
establishes how some uncomplicated practical

remedies could achieve a greater sense of well-being and satisfaction for many long-term users of mental health service. 56% of the residents said they were "mostly satisfied" about their lives and a similar proportion gave this rating in every area of life aside from income, unemployment and personal safety. The reasons some residents experienced such satisfaction or well-being, where others did not, were straightforward reality factors, usually amenable to intervention given the will and the resources. For instance, many unemployed residents hungered after jobs; those who actually held them seemed generally satisfied as a result. Likewise establishing a single close friendship seemed for many people to redress the isolation to which residents were prone. It was opportunities to meet such basic needs - along with family contacts, privacy at home, adequate income, safety from crime, and so on - which influenced a person's overall self-rating of well-being and satisfaction. There are some clear pointers to how mental health workers should concentrate their energies.

This study is no broad, representative survey of the concerns and needs of people recovering from mental illness. Its data derive from a special sample of people with serious long-term problems at the least advantaged end of the American health care spectrum, the 'board and care' hostel. Two-thirds had received schizophrenia diagnoses. Less than half had ever married, and less then one in twenty were currently married. Furthermore, the study examines solely subjective feelings of satisfaction and dissatisfaction - there are, of course, many other important angles on opportunities which benefit people after mental illness. Nevertheless, this research does give useful confirmation of the importance of opportunities and resources in everyday life for the morale and sense of well-being of people who have suffered mental illness. It is clear encouragement for mental health workers to help individuals gain access to long-term resources for everyday life like a job, a nice home, a well-liked social club, or a higher level of welfare benefit. The eight areas this study found to correlate with overall sense of well-being, could offer a handy framework for assessing where help is needed: home, family links, friends, leisure, work, money, safety and physical health.

HOW CAN MENTAL HEALTH WORKERS RESPOND?

From various angles we have considered
needs for social connections, positive social
roles, meaningful occupation and material resources
like reasonable housing and income. Here is a
range of basic interventions which respond to these
needs:

* Systematically enhancing prospects for open
  employment through guidance on job-search,
  training and work experience, liaison with
  employers and support throughout the whole
  process of getting back to work.

* Developing special employment opportunities
  which accommodate the impaired or fluctuating
  abilities which exclude many sufferers from
  mental illness from conventional employment.
  Such opportunities should affirm as much as
  possible a valued, productive identity and
  membership of mainstream society.

* Opening opportunities for realistic, purposeful
  work for people who cannot get open or
  sheltered employment: part-time work within
  welfare benefit earnings limits, voluntary work
  to finance amenity or benevolent funds,
  voluntary work for other purposes. Tasks
  covering a spectrum of demand and challenge to
  make work available to everyone at all stages
  and degrees of recovery.

* Maximising income for clients on welfare
  benefits through checking benefit entitlements
  and enlisting specialist help in pressing full
  claims effectively.

* Access to grants or loans for emergencies or
  special purposes through amenity fund,
  benevolent fund or credit union style schemes.

* Helping restore or improve links with family
  and extended family as a long-term resource for
  relationships, social activities and access to
  other family members' resources and social
  networks.

* Encouraging renewal of contacts with friends
  and aquaintances or development of new social
  networks.

Services which lead somewhere

*   Facilitating access to leisure pursuits or
    community activities, particularly where these
    open roles in mainstream society or a chance
    to meet new people.

*   Clubs and self-help groups for people
    recovering from mental illness which offer
    opportunity to make or continue friendships in
    natural, informal settings which keep away from
    roles or images connected to mental illness.

*   Helping people get the sort of housing which
    meets their personal priorities.

This book consists of contributions by individuals
whose work represents one or another of the
responses just described. Between them they cover
at least one way of approaching each of these
responses. They are summarised in the Introduction.

A COUPLE OF CLARIFICATIONS

        These contributions have been selected as
resources for the everyday practice of mental
health workers. They can be used by mental health
teams, by community mental health centres, day
centres or District General Hospital psychiatric
units. Most of these responses can also be used on
a small scale, by a single worker with a single
client for instance. A consideration in the
selection of items for this book has been whether a
lone fieldworker might be able to use the idea, at
least in an abridged or truncated form.
        These approaches all represent demands on
the time of mental health workers. Often they are
roles which mental health workers must directly
perform themselves. Sometimes though they involve
liaison with other workers, like welfare benefit,
employment or housing specialists. But this
likewise makes demands on time. One reaction is to
perceive this as an impossibly large extra tier of
work for mental health workers, on top of their
more conventional commitments. But the resource
requirements of these approaches should not be
exaggerated.
        In the first place, by no means does
everyone need help concerning opportunities after
mental illness. Always some service users have
much more than others in terms of roles and
opportunities they can resume. It is possible to

30

prioritise people who suffer a conspicuous dearth of opportunities. Then there is the extent to which other tasks might be reduced or transformed if a rehabilitation service reorganised its work to make opportunities after recovery a focus. Such reorganisation often means the same staff members are in fact combining conventional day service and fieldwork functions. Resource costs must be assessed with this in mind. For instance Chapter Two concerns a programme of family and individual work by two psychologists. If this seems time-intensive, reflect how in the case-study cited it precluded need for formal day services and, perhaps, special housing too. Similarly, the Erconwald Street Mental Health Project described in Chapter Five is in fact financed as a Social Services day centre. But it also fulfils roles for its users which might otherwise require field social workers or community workers. The details supplied concerning its costs and workload suggest that it is in no way exorbitant in resource terms. This book advocates that substantial day service staff time be invested in helping individuals take up voluntary work, get jobs or MSC Sheltered Placements, or in developing social clubs, transitional employment schemes and so on. But this would be balanced by reduced use of formal day services.

NEW WINE AND OLD BOTTLES

A common problem with these approaches is not so much lack of resources as difficulty in using existing personnel and resources within conventional Health and Social Services structures, which have evolved from a different style of service. Innovations which would require relatively little time and money can face problems over which profession's time or which service's budget should be utilised. Many of the roles described in this book do not come within the conventional remit of any particular discipline among mental health professionals. They may involve blurring or breaking conventional role boundaries, like those between social work, occupational therapy or nursing disciplines or between 'fieldwork' and 'day care', if staff resources are to be redeployed effectively. Another complication to using existing staff resources in a commonsense fashion concerns catchment size and centralisation of service.

Services which lead somewhere

Certain approaches described here are most practicable and economic in services where staff are deployed round small local catchments, like 'patch' social work. This way a worker or a small team can specialise in local contacts and local opportunities in one community, can get to know community facilities, helpful citizens, organisations and employers. But the larger the catchment from which a team's clients are drawn, the more time-consuming and impracticable it is to become familiar with opportunities local to all clients. Another source of hindrance can be mechanisms for measuring service and assigning budgets which are inherited from segregated residential units.

Mental health workers need to anticipate such problems and, where necessary, campaign to up-date their service's structure to better suit this sort of work. As mentioned previously, for decades rehabilitation services operated a simple linear model whereby people moved through a sequence of services, which were focussed within buildings, on to a job as their social base and source of post-recovery opportunities. Today's organisational structures, staff roles, team sizes and catchments reflect, in part, what was economic or efficient within that rather over-simple, easy-to-plan system. They tend towards centralisation of service, since local networks are not a consideration for programmes focussed inside buildings. They tend towards staff playing the well-differentiated, specialised roles which are practicable within large teams serving such large catchments. It is to be expected that many structures bequeathed from this model prove awkward for different, more community-oriented roles. Gradual change to more appropriate service organisation and structure is all part of the steady transition from remote psychiatric institutions to services which can work close to their user's everyday realities, problems and opportunities in the community.

It is worth noting that some substantial re-organisation is required from many other helping services now that employment is no longer so available for their clients to move on to. Susan Balloch and Chris Hume's study, 'Caring for Unemployed People', reviews how pervasive is this problem (7). It discusses implications for services for mentally handicapped and physically handicapped people, ex-offenders and teenagers leaving 'care', as well as mental health services. Adaptations are needed from all these services.

APPROPRIATE HELP FOR DIFFERENT STAGES OF RECOVERY

There is another occasional misunderstanding about the approaches described here. This is that such emphasis on opportunities in everyday life dismisses or devalues skilled therapeutic work on emotional, psychological or medical aspects of a person's problems. Far from it. The directions described here complement appropriate use of psychotherapy, medication, behavioural therapies or plain rest and retreat. They do not replace them. They are for the latter stages of recovery when a person is getting over their illness or emotional problems and is wishing to re-start their life. These different aspects of mental health work need each other if either is to make optimal contribution to recovery from mental illness.

Only in services where 'treatment' roles are emphasised to an unbalanced extent or to the exclusion of other forms of help should the approaches advanced here be seen as a challenge or threat. It is true that there are some new community-based services which do overemphasise psychotherapies and downplay opportunities for occupation, social contact and decent housing. But most mental health services are not like this. For them the approaches advanced in this book should be seen as helpful, complementary resources. They need to be co-ordinated with more conventional mental health work. Often they need to be done by the same workers or in close liaison so that appropriate opportunities are available when a person is ready to take the next step, so that therapeutic or rehabilitation work can be oriented to current challenges a person is facing outside psychiatric environments. Very plainly some of these approaches require additional skills which are not currently included in any mental health profession's training. But they also need to be guided by good understanding of mental illness and its after-effects. So much of the issue is continuity of help. The services a person receives should span a variety of needs and stages of recovery, without the abrupt cut-off points or circumscribed professional roles which have been discussed earlier. So it is often important that the same workers combine formal therapeutic skills with the means to promote opportunities which support recovery.

NOTES

1. Anne Birch, 'What Chance Have We Got?
   Occupation and employment after mental illness
   - patients' views', Manchester MIND 1983,
   available from MIND Bookshop, 4th Floor, 24-32
   Stephenson Way, London NW1 2HD

2. Michael Floyd, Eva Gregory, Hugh Murray,
   Rosemary Welchman, 'Schizophrenia and
   Employment', Occasional Paper No.5, Tavistock
   Institute of Human Relations, 1983

3. Douglas Bennett, 'Day Treatment in England' in
   'Proceedings of Adult Psychiatric Day
   Treatment', Ed. Shippits & Kroll, University of
   Minnesota, 1977

4. 'Better Services for the Mentally Ill', HMSO
   1975

5. Roger Morgan and Adrian Cheadle 'Unemployment
   impedes resettlement', Social Psychiatry,
   Volume 10, 1975, pp. 63-67

6. David Goldberg, 'Rethinking Rehabilitation' in
   'Life after Mental Illness? Major papers from
   MIND's 1984 Annual Conference', MIND
   Publications 1985

7. Susan Balloch, Chris Hume, Brian Jones and
   Peter Westland, 'Caring for Unemployed People',
   Bedford Square Press, London, 1985

8. Carol Edwards and Jan Carter, 'Day services and
   the mentally ill', chapter in 'Community Care
   for the Mentally Disabled' Ed. Wing & Olsen,
   OUP, 1979

9. Alan Breier and John Strauss, 'The role of
   social relationships in recovery from psychotic
   disorders', American Journal of Psychiatry,
   Volume 141, 1984, pp. 949-955

10. George Brown and Tirril Harris, 'Social Origins
    of Depression', Tavistock, 1978

11. Frank Lipton, Carl Cohen, Elizabeth Fischer, Stephen Katz, 'Schizophrenia: a network crisis', <u>Schizophrenia Bulletin</u>, Volume 7, 1981, Issue No.1

12. M H Banks and P R Jackson, 'Unemployment and risk of minor psychiatric disorder in young people: cross-sectional and longitudinal evidence', <u>Psychological Medicine</u>, Volume 12, 1982, pp. 789-798

13. Richard Warner 'Recovery from schizophrenia in the third world', <u>Psychiatry</u>, Volume 46, 1983, pp. 197-211

14. Richard Warner '<u>Recovery from Schizophrenia</u>', Routledge & Kegan Paul, London, 1985

15. Anthony Lehman, Nancy Ward and Lawrence Linn, 'Chronic mental patients: the quality of life issue', <u>American Journal of Psychiatry</u>, Volume 139, 1982, pp. 1271-1275

Chapter Two

RECOVERY FROM MENTAL ILLNESS: FOLLOWING IT THROUGH
WITH A FAMILY

Christine Barrowclough and Nicholas Tarrier

Editorial Introduction

Christine Barrowclough and Nick Tarrier are
clinical psychologists working in the Salford
Health Authority. For the past four years
they have been developing and assessing a
family-based intervention programme for
assisting recovery from schizophrenia. They
contact people who are soon to leave hospital
after an episode of schizophrenia and are
going back to live with their family. They
work with them and their family over a nine
month span on the emotional and practical
problems which need to be addressed at
different stages in the course of recovery.
Their programme aims to provide real
continuity of help to families where a member
is recovering from a schizophrenic episode,
from coping with the after-effects of the
illness to subsequently assisting that person
towards involvements outside the home and
developing some sort of positive future for
themselves. First the general nature of their
intervention programme is outlined. Then it
is illustrated through a detailed case
example.

We work specifically with families where a member
is recovering from an episode of schizophrenia.
Some special issues arise in this situation. For
instance, family members are often bewildered and
anxious at the changes in the person who is just
home from hospital. They may be very uncertain as
to what the future holds for their relative or what
they should do to help. Likewise there are the
feelings of the patient who may be exhausted,
lethargic or disoriented in the after-effects of
the episode. Then there is the problem, which
recent research has established clearly, that some
common family emotional responses to this situation

36

actually risk triggering fresh psychotic symptoms.
So, straightaway, there are some strong reasons for
working with families who are facing this difficult
situation. This applies to any household where
someone recovering from schizophrenia is living
with people with whom they have had some connection
or relationship. So we would use the same approach
for someone sharing a flat with close friends,
though in practice it is predominantly family
households where we work at present.

Having said this, there are other good reasons
for basing our work with families, as well as these
problem areas. We seek to develop the potential of
families as an important positive resource for
people who may have lost many of their social
connections through a schizophrenic illness. Most
relatives, at least in the early stages of the
illness, really want to help their family member to
recover as fully as possible. They can in fact
contribute a great deal. Families are a major
resource for long-lasting social relationships, for
instance. One vicious circle consequence of mental
illness is that people steadily lose their social
contacts and relationships and tend to end up
isolated. Your family are people who are often
more likely than anyone else to stick by you, even
when as a result of your illness you are not very
socially rewarding. So helping people develop or
maintain contact and good relationships with their
families gives them an important long-term source
of links with other people, shared activities and
things like family occasions at Christmas or
weddings. This still applies, of course, if someone
moves out of the family home to live on their own
but maintains family links.

Another advantage of family links is that
families can have quite extensive social networks,
if you pool the contacts available to each member.
Between them family members may have openings to a
wide range of the opportunities and resources which
can be useful to someone trying to get back on
their feet following mental illness.

Then there's also an economic aspect in that
going to live with your family after a mental
illness protects you from what sociologists call
'downward drift'. This is the process whereby
people who suffer recurrent mental illness tend to
lose their accommodation and end up in poor
housing, sometimes in fact in lodging-houses, in
run-down parts of inner cities, where quality of
life is poorer in every aspect. Living with your

family can reduce the poverty, which often compounds the problems of recurrent mental illness, through access to the resources and facilities of the family home. It makes money go further by pooling income, and avoids the stigmatising or restrictive housing in which ex-patients without financial means can very easily get trapped.

Our programme for work with a family usually lasts nine months. It is directed towards three main concerns, which match quite closely the stages in which we work. One concern is the family's need for information and advice about recovery from schizophrenia and how they can help with this. Many families are understandably confused, mystified and frightened both by the symptoms of schizophrenia and by hearing that 'schizophrenia' is the diagnosis, if indeed they do get told this. Yet often they are implicitly expected to bear the burden of helping 'patients' get back on their feet following discharge from hospital. Unfortunately they are frequently given little or no advice on how this might best be done.

The family's difficulties will vary depending on the severity of the mental illness and how well the person is when they return home. A small proportion of patients will be still experiencing psychotic symptoms and consequently behaving in bizarre or disturbing ways when they are discharged. Many others will have secondary handicaps - grossly impaired social skills, extreme lethargy, and slowness or reluctance about daily living tasks. In our experience, the family is rarely forewarned about what to expect, let alone how to cope with difficulties that arise. They will most commonly have no information about the kind of problems or illness for which the patient has been treated. Added to this, we find that most relatives already have suffered considerable emotional distress themselves as a result of the patient's illness. Many relatives report anxiety states, disturbed sleep and feelings of depression and hopelessness in response to the changed and often disturbing behaviour of the person who has had a psychotic episode.

So one early mission is to give simple, straightforward information about schizophrenia and to help relatives with some constructive ideas for coping and about what to expect from the future.

The second of our concerns comes from a body of research on schizophrenia which has been building up in recent years. This has demonstrated

that a person's immediate social environment may
have a large influence on the risk that they will
relapse. When people who have had a schizophrenic
illness return to live in close contact with people
who are critical of their difficulties or who react
very emotionally to their illness, the chances of a
return of their psychotic symptoms are much
increased. Some aspects of the relatives'
criticisms may be a direct result of their
ignorance of the nature of the mental illness and
its symptoms. Their excessive emotional reactions
may take the form of self-sacrificing behaviour,
over-protectiveness, or severe distress and
worrying.

Generally a patient's whole family is likely
to experience considerable emotional disturbance
when the person is undergoing a psychotic episode.
These feelings can quite easily continue or revive
when the patient returns home. They may lead to
unhelpful ways of reacting to any difficulties
experienced in getting on with the patient. They
can also build up tensions between other family
members. So a second prong to our work is trying
to reduce stress in the home and working to stop
stress and tension building up so much that they
prevent relatives from helping the patient
constructively.

Our third major concern centres on overcoming
the restricted lives, inactivity and lack of
outside contacts, meaningful occupation or goals
which you find with so many people who've had their
lives interrupted by schizophrenia. We aim to help
people to get over the interruption caused by their
illness and progress as far as possible to the way
of life they would have been living, had their
illness not occurred. That, in fact, may sometimes
mean eventually moving out of the family home. So,
first we work to reduce stress and improve morale
and understanding in the home. Then we seek to
involve the family in putting their encouragement,
support and local community contacts behind their
relative first playing a more positive role inside
the home, then if possible resuming some past
interests and social contacts, developing some
networks and activities outside the home and
generally living a fuller life. We are concerned,
where possible, to help people get all the way to
roles and activities which are valued in mainstream
society. We might aim for instance towards
networks based on voluntary work or adult education
classes, rather than attendance at a psychiatric

day centre.

You could divide our customary intervention programme into these three components. Generally sessions 1 and 2 are concerned with giving information about schizophrenia. Sessions 3, 4 and 5 are concerned with identifying stress in the home and alternative ways of dealing with it. Subsequent sessions are concerned with the patient developing a fuller life, though obviously one returns to monitoring and discussing family stress intermittently. It's not something that you just drop.

In terms of general procedures, most of the time we work with the family all together. But at the beginning we always make sure there's a chance for any confidences to be passed to us. We will see parents together without the patient, for instance, fairly early on in case there is something they want to ask us without their son or daughter around. We may sometimes see just the parents together for a number of meetings, in fact. We will also discuss privately with the patient any reservations they may have about what the rest of the family learn. For instance, we would normally ask them to share the subject matter of their delusions during the family education process. But this might perhaps include something they wish kept private. We may also work one-to-one with the patient at any stage when this becomes relevant, maybe over one particular step forward. But most of the time we are working with the family, or core household group, together. Typically, we might see the family twice weekly for the first three months, then weekly for the rest of what is usually a nine month programme. At most of our meetings we see families in our office, for reasons of time. Obviously you get a fuller, clearer picture by making some home visits.

PROVIDING RELATIVES WITH INFORMATION

This is the initial component of our service. We describe schizophrenia as a stress-related biological illness which is diagnosed as occurring when someone reports that he or she is undergoing certain specific, highly unusual experiences - like hearing voices and suffering certain types of disturbance in thinking. The emphasis on biological causes may be helpful in alleviating any sense of guilt felt by relatives that they have somehow contributed to causing the illness. The specific symptoms which the patient experienced are explained to the relatives, sometimes with the patient's assistance. For the most part, relatives are unaware of hallucinations, delusions or disorders in thinking. They have only seen the patient behaving in uncharacteristic or bizarre ways and have had difficulty understanding why. We also explain very simply why the medication is prescribed, possible side effects, and its use to prevent relapse. We explain how stressful events may trigger off the illness and also describe ways in which the impact of such events may be cushioned. The importance of minimising stress and tension at home is also emphasised, including the detrimental effects of criticism and excessive emotional reactions. We advise relatives to make time for themselves and to try to use encouragement rather than criticism to assist the patient to recommence their usual activities. We actually have a short information document for relatives which has been published by the North West Fellowship, and it would be good to refer to.(1)

In our experience, relatives and patients report knowing very little about the diagnosis the patient is being treated for. Most have some idea of the name of the diagnosis, but in the absence of any further explanatory information find the label confusing or even frightening. The common idea of 'schizophrenia' tends to be associated with violence, split personalities, and very gloomy chances of improvement. We would offer the following guidelines to people embarking on providing an information service:

- Information is best given at an early stage in the illness, preferably at the first episode

- It should be offered to the patient as well as to the relative

- The information should be made as simple as possible and personalised to the patient's particular symptoms

- Follow-up support and time for further discussion should be offered after the information has been given

We should emphasise that relatives often find this information difficult to absorb or accept, even when it is presented in a very straightforward way. In the absence of any help or advice from outside agencies, in some cases for periods of fifteen years or more, it is hardly surprising that relatives have developed their own views and attitudes about the patient's condition, and that they are reluctant to relinquish these overnight.

ADVICE ON COPING WITH STRESS

This is the second component in the service we offer to relatives. It follows naturally from discussion on how stress affects the illness and how one needs to minimise tension in the home.

We begin by educating relatives in the nature of stress - how it affects the way we think, how we feel physically, and how it affects our behaviour and consequently the behaviour of others. Alternative and more adaptive ways of dealing with stressful situations are discussed, not only in association with the patient's problems but also with the many other stressful influences in everyday life. The emphasis is on coping practically with stressful moments in the family's day-to-day life, working on concrete examples. We may ask them to keep a 'stress diary' which records stressful incidents in between family sessions. We can then take this up at family discussions to look at regular sources of stress and to consider solutions.

We work on this using the same principles which psychologists employ in one-to-one stress-management counselling. We ask family members to take home sheets of paper and for each individual to record the situations when they, personally, feel stressed, for whatever reason. This follows from the rationale that reducing everyone's tension in the family is important for the well-being of the person who has suffered schizophrenia. Concerning each stress incident we ask each person to record:

- What actually happened
- The chain of events which led up to whatever triggered their stress
- How they responded to the stress: What they felt, what went through their minds, and what they actually did

We get them to study their responses to stress in detail so as to discover openings for trying more helpful alternatives. One aspect of response to stress is your physical reactions - tensing up, palpitations, feeling sick. For someone who becomes physically very distressed in this way, we might offer to teach them relaxation and breathing techniques. Another aspect is the way people's minds go during an episode of stress. They may be flooded with catastrophic thoughts of the "I can't cope. This is the last straw" variety. This can make them see the situation as far worse than it actually is and heighten their bad feelings. You can work with people on learning ways of thinking more positively in a stress situation - a different way of looking at it, maybe thinking in terms of constructive practical responses, or some other line which gets things in proportion and calms you down. Similarly with your actual behaviour there are ways of responding by which you just wind yourself up further. Pacing up and down from agitation, for instance, will just increase your physical arousal, your heart rate and blood pressure and compound your feelings. Much better to sit down, relax and breathe slowly. That way you may also stop yourself acting impulsively and doing things you'll regret. Obviously, if you respond to stress by shouting at someone or storming out of the room, you are stoking up the situation and maybe triggering responses from the other person which, vicious circle fashion, are going to increase your own stress still further.

So we get each family member to examine the sequences of events which make them feel stressed and how they customarily respond. Now while these principles of monitoring stress and discussing alternative responses are the same as in individual work, there is a whole new dimension to doing it in joint family discussions. Not only can members learn from each other but much of their stress stems from common issues and incidents and interacts together. One person's response to stress may be the trigger to another person's stress reaction and so on, for a sequence which may last days. Sometimes they grasp quickly and vividly the cause-and-effect sequences by which they affect each other negatively and stress builds up in the household. We work on unravelling this cause-and-effect sequence and propose alternative ways of responding when familiar situations recur. Then at the next meeting we can ask how this went and propose a modification if it did not work.

It is important to establish clearly the

rationale for other family members discussing their
own stress and emotions in order to gain their
co-operation. We have encountered fears that this
means we think they share some of the patient's
problems or maybe are in some way the source of the
problem. We take care to clarify the reason for
asking them to do this: "Research has shown that
people who are recovering from a mental illness
need to live in a home where stress is as low as
possible". Occasionally if other family members
seem anxious about getting involved in this part of
the programme, we defer it till we have gained
their confidence. While the particular process of
teaching how to reduce stress comes at this quite
early stage, it is something we return to
intermittently throughout our subsequent work with
the family. We need to monitor stress regularly.

TOWARDS A FULLER LIFE

This is the final goal of our intervention
work. As mentioned earlier, we want to help people
to regain functioning, to get back to pursuing a
life which includes goals and satisfactions which
really matter to them and, as far as practicable,
to take up again the threads which their illness
may have forced them to drop. We work with the
family as a whole on this, using other family
members for their knowledge of the patient's past
strengths, their access to local community
contacts, and for practical and moral support.
A key stage is to develop some positive goals
- goals which are both practicable and which the
patient would really value achieving. We use as a
central question: "If this illness hadn't happened,
what would you be doing now? What sort of life did
you lead before your illness - what activities,
what interests, what circle of friends - and what,
generally speaking, might this have grown into?"
We discuss this question with the family together.
They also discuss it between sessions because it
takes time to put together an answer if a person's
life has been severely constricted for so long that
it's hard to imagine them doing very much at all.
We aim to set in motion a process of remembering
the person's past activities and achievements in a
constructive way with a view to strengthening
interest in living a fuller life.
We seek to establish some general aims which
the patient really wants and which seem
practicable, given time and careful work, even if

they are far removed from present levels of
functioning. We draw up a list of needs which must
be met in the move towards this. They might
include the need for social contact, friendships
etc, occupational activities and interests,
independent living skills and, if appropriate, a
home of their own.

We also ask the patient and other family
members to compile a list of relevant resources and
strengths. These would include the person's
interests and abilities - often those practised
before the onset of the illness - available
community resources, friends, or friends from the
past, or other agents who might plausibly be
willing to help.

As far as possible we would encourage the
patient and the family to seek ways of using these
strengths and resources in order to meet the needs
listed. For example, although the standard answer
to lack of activity in someone recovering from a
mental illness is to go to a day centre, this might
be quite inappropriate to the person's needs and
fail to build on their existing resources. Far
better to identify past interests and social
contacts and to marry these with resources existing
in the community - say for example, spending time
with friends or attending classes at an adult
education centre in subjects in which he or she
used to be interested.

We work on setting clear goals for meeting
these needs and break them down into easily
achievable steps, sometimes planned out at family
discussions. Often there seems an enormous gap
between how a person functions after several mental
illness episodes and what he or she used to do.
Having clear goals to aim for and breaking these
down into small attainable steps can provide a
feeling of progress in a relatively short time.
This can lead to increased confidence and
motivation. Saying to a person who has become very
socially withdrawn and who has no regular social
contacts or current interests "You should get out
more" is very unhelpful. It can only increase the
person's low self-esteem and feeling of failure.
Where they might go to needs to be carefully
discussed. How they might achieve this in small
stages needs to be worked out. A small step might
be simply to find out addresses of a particular
club of interest. This might need to be made
easier by the help of a friend or relative
accompanying the person to the library to seek out

such information.
      Two qualifications need mentioning.
Particularly with people recovering from
schizophrenia, it is important to distinguish
between relatives being contructively involved in
helping and the sort of intrusive or critical
behaviour which threatens relapse. Trying to help
too much or in ways which violate the patient's
autonomy can amount to the over-protectiveness and
intrusiveness which are known to increase risk of
relapse. Sometimes parental keenness that the
patient seek a more active life or resume
particular interests or goals can amount to a
critical attitude to the way the person functions
at present, another high risk factor for relapse.
Our sort of family work needs to check that family
involvement does not head in these directions.
      While we use a lot of help from families, we
recognise certain areas where a family member
really should not be involved. Sometimes these are
situations where maybe a professional or a friend
could intervene appropriately, but not a family
member. Sometimes, too, it is something which the
person should be managing on their own. We need
also to keep an eye that family involvement does
not turn into stressful interference or pressure.
In a sense, our way of involving families can
defuse and channel constructively some of the
emotions which lie behind harmful family attitudes.
At the roots of over-protectiveness, criticism or
nagging can lie deep family concern and a longing
that a person gets back to what they were before
the illness. Our approach offers constructive
outlets for the wish to help and boosts family
members' morale because our gradual, planned
process shows them clearly that their relative
really is making progress.
      Also, we have to very much adjust our goals
and family involvement depending on the family and
the level of the patient's recovery. Goals for the
patient, who for example remains very deluded and
is markedly handicapped because of this, may be
more limited than those for someone who no longer
has psychotic symptoms but is lethargic and
socially isolated. Sometimes in the former
situation, say, if a relative is very disturbed by
the illness and has become very isolated
themselves, it may be more appropriate to work on
meeting the relative's needs, rather than
increasing the patient's functioning. These needs
might include the relatives taking up or resuming

46

more social contacts and interests outside the home
- things that have been abandoned because of
worries and excessive concern about the patient.

THE INTERVENTION PROGRAMME IN PRACTICE

Susan was a young woman, aged 25, whose
life had been interrupted since her first
schizophrenic breakdown at 21 years old. She'd had
three subsequent breakdowns, roughly one a year
over the last few years. By the time we
encountered the family after her fourth hospital
admission, Susan's whole life had been affected.
She had no friends, no social life, no boyfriends.
She'd had no job for five years. She had been
living at home continuously since her first
breakdown. She spent much of the day in bed,
rising to go out and buy cigarettes, then back for
naps and finally off to bed early in the evening.
But before her first breakdown she had been a
popular young woman with lots of boyfriends and had
successfully left home and set up a flat of her
own. She had been at college, studying for a
qualification in languages. All that had been
brought to an end by schizophrenia. These social
consequences of her breakdowns had in fact been far
more damaging than the actual breakdowns.
She was living with her mother and father.
There were two other children who had left home.
Her mother was working part-time, while her father
was unemployed and spent most of the day at home,
doing the housework. Susan's mother cared for her
very much but had become over-involved with her.
She'd become excessively protective and rather
intrusive. She could get very emotional and upset.
She did most of Susan's laundry and cooked her
meals. Sometimes she tried to take her out places
to provide more interest in her life. Because her
mother spent so much time on Susan, she had rather
split the family - particularly concerning her
father who was quite depressed himself over his own
unemployment. He felt his wife was neglecting him
to look after Susan. She accused him of
criticising Susan too much, and not doing enough
for her. It was in a number of respects the
typical fraught family situation which research on
schizophrenia warns against, particularly
concerning the relationship between Susan and her
mother.
Initially, just as described earlier, we spent
time with them explaining the nature of Susan's

illness. In fact they found this easy to grasp.
We explained to them general ways the family can
help and how being too emotionally distressed
certainly didn't contribute positively. We aimed
at helping them get the future into proportion.
For instance, to understand that another episode of
schizophrenia was entirely possible but it wouldn't
be the end of the world. Susan's mother was so
frightened of relapses that she would weep even
when talking about the subject. It was very
important to help her towards a calmer attitude
towards relapse as part of reducing tension in the
home. In fact, Susan's hospitalisations had been
quite brief and it was the constriction of her life
in between relapses which was a much greater
problem. These information-oriented sessions took
place with all three of them present.

Next we started work on reducing tension in
the home. In this instance we spent the next four
sessions with just the parents. During that period
we actually got them to monitor the occasions in
between our sessions when family members became
upset, annoyed or emotional for whatever reason,
whether to do with Susan or not. They would record
it and we would review ways to cope with such
situations at the next meeting as a start to the
process of reducing tension in the home.

Susan's mother's stresses all revolved round
Susan. A typical sequence would be that she'd come
home from work and immediately ask her husband,
"How's Susan been?" He might reply "Oh she's just
been sitting around all day", and this could lead
to an argument. Generally Susan's father did the
housework and Susan's mother was the wage-earner.
Susan herself had no role available in the family.
She was basically a passenger in the home.

We got them monitoring and reporting stress
incidents of the sort described and to look at ways
of avoiding some of these things building up. We
had limited success in this area. We certainly got
them to understand how these things blew up. We
did help Susan's mother to control her anxiety.
But we didn't make much headway on reducing
arguments between the parents. That didn't matter
in itself because we're not there as family
therapists to make everyone's relationship
'perfect'. We're there, rather, to help develop an
environment which is supportive of Susan's mental
health. But what did matter was that we hadn't
reduced the types of interaction which risk
recurrent symptoms of schizophrenia quite as much

as we had hoped.

For the next phase, helping Susan towards a fuller life, we worked with all three of them together. It's worth stressing how in this phase we are concerned with the strengths and positive features of the family, not with its problems or any unfortunate ways members interact or any other of the negative aspects of families which too often are the exclusive focus of family therapy. This stage is quite different. We are seeking to utilise the resources of all three family members, Susan included, to help Susan out of her rut. We start by working together to identify Susan's positive assets, her past and present interests, resources like people who could help or opportunities she could take up. It is a very interesting exercise because even if someone seems to have nothing going for them, when you look back you come across strengths which you can build on. For Susan her resources included:

Her family, ready to help her, including a brother living in Wales who proved useful later on when she was able to go down there for visits.

Her hobbies and interests - she'd had really quite a lot up to the time she became ill. She'd been keen on sport. She'd travelled a lot. She'd been very fond of music, visiting jazz concerts and the like. She had been interested in wholefoods and some other vaguely hippy pastimes.

She had been keen on studying, liked reading and had a penchant for spending time in quite intellectual pursuits.

She had been able to make lots of friends and had been known as affable and sociable, though now she had contact with no-one. She used to be popular with boyfriends.

Her present day interests in working with people. She wanted to work helping people in some sort of way. This was the focus of her interest in jobs for the future.

Academic qualifications were another asset - 'O' levels, 'A' levels and an HND. She had experience of working as a technician in a language school.

She could drive a vehicle.

So we listed her resources. Using discussion in a family group is always a good way to do this because you have each of her parent's separate memories to pool information on her past ventures and to jog her memory.

Next comes our key question: "If your illness hadn't happened, how might you be living now? How would it be different from the present?" Susan was able to identify things like: she would have friends, she would be going out a lot more, she'd have a job, she would live in a flat of her own, she would pursue some of her old interests.

This becomes our general direction - the way of life which might have been hers but for the illness. It is possible to work within this framework without raising unrealistic expectations. We have to work out how much might be realistic and then devise together strategies for working very gradually in the direction of these goals. This approach gives us clear goals to work towards and goals which the person identifies as genuinely their own aspirations, things they really want to do.

The next step is to summarise her needs in discussion with the family, the changes she needs to make if she is going to move towards these goals. Here it is important to get the parents' comments on what they see as holding her back. They commented on how apathetic she seemed and how she never seemed to want to do anything. We make a point of translating such remarks into positive goals - ie. that Susan's first needs are to be more active, to do more for herself, to have some meaningful occupation, to have some interests in life. And it was certainly true that her present life-style was a long way from her goals. Her day would start around 10.00 am. She would hang around until lunch. Then go out for a packet of cigarettes. Then she would pop back to bed for a nap or two in the afternoon. Her day finished early, as she liked to spend the evenings in particular in bed. She had had no activities or contacts for so many years. At one time she had been attending a day hospital but decided against this. Like so many of the people we have contact with she did not want to be associated with other people who had been mentally ill.

So we had agreed with the three of them a list of basic goals, what Susan would need to do if she were to achieve them, and the strengths and resources which could help her there. The next step was to agree which of her needs to work on first. We decided with Susan to start on basic occupation and move on to interests and social contacts.

We started with the idea of her doing useful things around the house. We discussed with her general principles of trying to move gradually towards her overall goals. We said to her "You want to live in your own flat. What will you need to do for yourself?" We talked about cooking, cleaning, laundry, shopping and so on. At one stage we put it to her: "There are certain things you must take responsibility for even though you are living in your parents' house. Your own laundry is one. Doing some of the cooking is another. Also, you really should contribute to some of the gardening." She took this up quite well and we were able to work with her to plan taking on more and more appropriate responsibilities. We were careful to get the family to define this as Susan taking personal responsibility for parts of her own life, rather than in the role of a daughter helping her father with the housework.

We work on the principle of defining a sub-goal clearly - like that eventually she will do all her own washing, will cook a particular number of meals a week, and do certain named gardening tasks. Then you start very gradually towards one goal at a time. You have a clear framework but you make very small demands to begin with and give lots of support or even do a particular step alongside the person. Then, once they are established doing that, you can move on to the next stage.

So deciding what sub-goals to work on and how to approach them is discussed at family meetings. We would reach agreement as to what task Susan would take on next week, maybe roughly when and how she would do it and any help another family member should supply. And at the next family meeting we would hear how it went. It is always important that each stage of the task is something the person themselves names as feasible and that it's something they actually want for themselves.

For instance when it came to Susan doing some cooking, she didn't want to cook the family's standard meals. She wanted to devise meals of her own choosing, buy the ingredients and cook these instead. So, of course, this is what we encourage at the family meetings. She was developing an interest in something. At one stage her old interest in wholefoods, mentioned on the resource list, revived. She began baking a lot of bread and would spend quite some time shopping in different places for various ingredients, another more active, constructive thing in her life.

Besides being more active and looking after herself, another need high on the list was Susan's lack of friends, lack of any contacts outside the home. We discussed this at the family meetings. We were all agreed that Susan needed to socialise more but her parents could also see that there was no way that she could just go out and meet people. At the least she'd need a supportive friend and she didn't have one. Her parents cared, though, and they were among her resources. We agreed that to make a start Susan and her father would work out a suitable evening and go to the pub together before the next family meeting.

This worked and in fact it became a regular occurrence that Susan and her father went to their local pub together. The ultimate goal wasn't for Susan to go out with her father but with peer group friends, too. But we agreed that as part of Susan venturing out more and participating in mainstream social activities, like pubs, it would be valuable for these outings with her father to become part of her routine. There was absolutely no way, of course, that Susan could have started off going to the pub on her own. That's difficult for very many people. But much later, when Susan was feeling better on a number of counts, the confidence she had gained in pub-society through these pub visits with her father actually enabled her to meet people or re-establish contacts with neighbours. Her old, affable personality returned gradually and she was able to visit pubs on her own and meet people and chat to them, then and there. She even worked out simple strategies for coping with psychotic symptoms which occasionally returned to trouble her in such situations. Sometimes, for instance, she would be sitting in a pub and experience thoughts she knew to be delusional about creatures speaking to her. She would just say to herself: "I'll have one drink. Then if I'm still feeling like this, I'll go home. If it's passed by then, I'll stay".

Susan's pub outings with her father laid the foundations of what much later became, thanks to her personality and the locality where her family lived, an important, readily available social outlet. But it needed this gradual, supportive start. It's an example of how even with someone who actually has the potential for socialising, based on past experience, you need to progress very gradually, with support and with clear, practical, feasible plans as to how a person who was as withdrawn as Susan can take the first steps. Just think how unhelpful it would be to lecture someone like Susan with: "You need company. You need a social outlet. Why don't you go out and socialise more?" You have to think out a clear, concrete initial opportunity which the person can actually grasp.

So you see the sort of role the family can play in this process. There is direct help, like Susan's father going with her to the pub. There is the sharing of extra information on the person's past - the abilities, interests, achievements or contacts which they have forgotten or lack confidence to name. There is the sense in which working with a family enables processes which you have started in the session to continue with their own momentum in between sessions. So, for instance, after we discuss former interests and hobbies with the family, we may say: "You can't always think of things to order but over the next two weeks other things may come to mind". And we give them sheets of paper to carry on after we've gone and we review these next time. Then, there is the encouragement and support and co-operation which comes from involving the family. This family knew exactly where Susan was trying to head. They understood and had a part to play in all the steps she was trying to take within the home - even if that part was quite often to step out of her way. And very important, too, was the way they supported her morale. It was a long, slow process of building up her life again and at times Susan got quite fed up and depressed. After a couple of months, as she became more active, this opened her eyes to how much her life had shrunk since she became ill and how she was functioning at only a fraction of her former abilities. Her parents were able to support and encourage her through these temporary spells of depression.

It is worth pointing out some of the limits to family involvement. We did make a point of seeing Susan on her own from time to time, just to check that she really did want to do some of the things coming up at family meetings and was not just responding to the quite strong group spirit which developed. Also, there are some situations where involving a family member as a helper risks turning into intrusiveness, over-protectiveness or nagging. One example arose in connection with Susan's later interest in doing some studying - another feature from her list of resources. This grew out of her increasing concern for a job, a career. She became interested in studying for more qualifications as a stepping-stone to better job prospects. We agreed at the family session that she would bring to our next meeting information from the local library on courses and evening classes so that we could discuss what might help her. Now eventually she ended up going to 'O' level Spanish classes two days a week for some months. But she nearly got stuck while setting this up. Like so many of the people we see, she had great difficulty in initiating things, in starting anything off. Maybe it is to do with lack of confidence. Maybe it is linked to deficit states following schizophrenia. Whatever it is, situations arise when someone needs to be ready to lend a hand to get something started. But in this instance we felt it should not be a family member who did so.

Susan took the first step herself, finding out what courses were available. But the next stage was phoning to get times for starting and this she just could not do. So we offered to help her over this stage, if she wished. She insisted she could do it herself. One of us told her: "I'll ring you by Wednesday and if you haven't done it by then, I'll do it for you". But she actually managed to do it herself by then. In fact that was her over her block. When the much more demanding task of enrolling in the course came round, we offered again to help but she was able to do it first time herself.

The intervention we made here could risk being intrusive if coming from a family member. Action was necessary to help Susan from getting stuck but it needn't have been from a mental health worker. A friend could have done just as well. But for a parent to do this could risk a valid, necessary intervention getting mixed up with nagging, intrusive or infantilising behaviour. This sort of intervention should be understood as qualitatively different from nagging. It should involve a clear, agreed procedure of steps to be taken by each party, like a contract.

Susan made her biggest step forward through a
voluntary job. This arose from her agreeing that
she needed more to occupy her. When we went back
to the resource list we noted how she was
interested in helping people as a general line of
work. We discussed with her how some appropriate
voluntary work might help her towards this.

Now we had some links with a local charity for
elderly people which needed volunteers for its day
centre. But the process of Susan getting there,
after she'd declared an interest, had to be tackled
very gradually. You couldn't just say to Susan -
or indeed to many people leaving a psychiatric unit
- "Ring up such and such a charity and make an
appointment to be considered as a volunteer". That
would be just too much for her, quite clearly so.
At this stage Susan was very nervous. She was
going through a phase when she was finding it very
difficult to mix with people. One of us arranged
to meet her at the day centre and introduce her to
the organiser. She was very open to the idea and
we set up an arrangement whereby Susan would try
spending an afternoon there - not a whole day, in
view of limiting the demands on her initially.
But, in fact, being there on her own the first time
was still just a bit too threatening. She wasn't
able to bring herself to go there. So we set up a
second half-day arrangement and said that one of us
would meet her there and stay with her for part of
the afternoon at the centre. That proved enough
support for her to turn up and, indeed, stay at the
centre for the second part of the afternoon on her
own. She had wanted to do it all along. It was
just a matter of organising the opportunity in a
way which reduced the threat sufficiently for her
to take the first step. In fact after that first
afternoon she was able to subsequently go alone -
first for another afternoon, then on to two regular
afternoons a week. After a while she attended for
full days at a time and, eventually, made a
full-time commitment which was to lead to paid
employment.

So this fairly simple intervention was all
that was needed to open this major opportunity for
Susan. But without it she would never have got a
foot in the door. We felt that, while Susan's
mother would have readily taken time off work to go
with her that afternoon, it was actually preferable
for one of us to take that role, considering the
nature of their relationship. It would actually be
a world of difference from Susan going to the pub

with her father for her mother to hold her hand on an occasion like this. A friend, though, would have been perfectly appropriate to accompany her, better in fact than a mental health worker.

Susan's duties during her first phase of voluntary work included making tea for elderly people, helping them to and from the bus which brought them to the centre, helping them to the lavatory and so on - generally rather like a nursing assistant. As she became liked and trusted by the staff, she got the job of driver's aide, accompanying the centre's bus to pick people up in the morning, help them down the path and onto the bus and then taking them back home in the afternoon. Early on during this voluntary work she was going through a period when she was finding mixing with people very difficult. She found her role at the centre allowed her contact with people without too much requirement to interact with them if she was finding it difficult. She could easily back off from contact, when necessary, without breaching the role required of her. In actual fact she was well liked at the centre and regarded as mixing well. She was not identified by other people as recovering from a mental illness. We had explained her illness to the organiser in Susan's presence but no-one else had been told.

Susan went on to commit herself to work there three full days a week. Round that time she became pretty fully occupied, because she took up 'O'level classes on the other two days. Then they asked her to actually do some driving for them - ability to drive had in fact been another of her strengths on the resource list. She later moved on to working there five days a week, still as a volunteer.

Shortly after, they offered her three days a week paid employment as a driver, which she has taken up. So now she has a job - if only part-time and for one year. It will at least give her a good reference as a reliable and friendly person who can take quite some responsibility in a job of social importance.

Eventually Susan got herself a Council flat. This came after our nine month formal programme had finished. Independent living in a flat of her own had been down on our goals. The way we had left it was like this. She had put her name down on the Council Housing List. She wanted a reasonably pleasant flat, not the sort of rough, problematic, hard-to-let flat which she might have been offered if we'd been pressing for something soon. We were all agreed that a problem flat would not be a good idea. So the general understanding was that she wouldn't push for early rehousing but would stay in the family home for a while, where she was comfortable and now had a job and a very much fuller life. If she got offered a decent flat, she would consider it. And that is what happened. When she got the offer her mother, characteristically, rang us for advice. But it seemed a natural course of events for her to take up the offer and she moved in. She now has her own home and a job, though Susan would be the first to admit that some areas of her life are restricted. Some of these are to do with the financial constraints and the general problem of obtaining full-time work after her year's contract with the charity finishes. Some are associated with the difficulties in establishing a social network after such a long period of social withdrawal. However, she is coping well with the demands of independent living, and, in the short term at least, the bridge between her parents' home and her own flat was successfully crossed.

At the nine month point we offered Susan and her family further contact if and when they thought it would be helpful. In Susan's case we also emphasised that future relapses might well occur and rehearsed procedures for coping with such eventualities.

Working this way with people who suffer from schizophrenia has taught us many new possibilities. The biggest surprise has been how far people can go, how with this gradual approach many people can make a much better recovery than we had ever expected and move far further in terms of levels of social functioning. It can prove so worthwhile to put in time with people who have quite serious psychiatric histories, like the people with whom we work. It really does yield results to stay with them for a while to help open the sort of opportunities which are too often dismissed as impossible or irrelevant for people with such histories of illness. Too often psychiatric services either abandon such people or else treat them like children. Either they just abandon contact, aside from medication, when a person goes home from hospital, maybe to a pretty demoralising home situation. Or they send people to day care facilities which understandably do not serve the needs of all patients and can add to the patient's social segregation. But we have found that if you stay with people as they recover from an episode of mental illness and work with them on socially valued, mainstream, adult opportunities, you can help them go a long way forward. Given a period of appropriate help, some people can take steps no-one ever thought possible. And for the very disabled person even very small changes can be very important to them and their family.

Links to community resources are outstandingly important in this work. Among our most important resources have been community centres and evening and day Adult Education classes. They have proved useful for a lot of the people we help because they combine interest in some kind of activity or occupation with an opportunity to meet people - something which can bridge that gap from doing nothing to having a social life. There are so many stages to a person getting established in something which suits them. Gather information on relevant opportunities. Clarify which options might be right for that person. Build up confidence to try one out, and so on. It would be a very great help to have some sort of directory of local resources or someone to help us find out what opportunities are available. It would also help to have some sort of befriending service which could accompany and support for the first couple of times those people who really cannot manage the initial steps on their own. This would be of very great value to us - a service which identifies what is available in a normal community, allows people to pick opportunities for themselves and offers some practical choices for how they can get access to these.

NOTES

1. Christine Barrowclough, Nicholas Tarrier, Susan Watts, Christine Vaughn, Hugh Freeman: 'What is Schizophrenia? Information for Relatives', published and available from North West Fellowship, 46 Allen Street, Warrington, Cheshire WA2 7JB

Chapter Three

USING OPPORTUNITIES IN THE COMMUNITY

Carol Williams

Editorial Introduction

In 1979 in the West London Borough of
Hammersmith a new advice project for unemployed
people took on exactly the issues mentioned at
the end of the preceding chapter. Carol
Williams started a project called 'Alternatives'
which was funded to help people who were aged
over 45 and had been unemployed for a long
while. It aimed to help them overcome social
withdrawal and demoralisation, to build contacts
outside the home and generally to lead fuller
lives. While intended for a broad public, in
its first year a third of its users volunteered
information on their own mental health problems.
Substantial numbers had left psychiatric day
units or a local alcoholism project and were
wondering what to do with their lives now. The
approach which Carol Williams developed may have
relevance both to people seeking to provide a
similar service for the general community and to
mental health workers who want to incorporate
such a role in their own work.

Some idea of the aims behind 'Alternatives' can be
conveyed by key phrases from our list of objectives.
This was drawn up by the voluntary services
committee to which I was answerable for the project.

"To provide a service for people aged forty-five
and over and for whom there is no immediate
prospect of employment....In the absence of
employment to work with clients to re-create a
sense of self-esteem through leading an active
life of value to the community....To enable
clients to combat their depression and sense of
isolation. To provide information about
activities in line with individual clients'
interests...To provide contact outside the
immediate family. To develop public awareness of
the problems of the unemployed.... To negotiate
concessionary charges for unemployed people as
is done for other identifiable low income

59

groups."

I developed my approach by trial and error,
according to what seemed to work in this unusual
situation.   I'd never thought before about how you
go about helping someone use their leisure time.
I just started with an office where I could see
people and I got my first clients by publicising the
service through hand-outs which asked unemployed
people whether they wanted to do more with their
lives. Later I had many by referrals. At first six
initial clients and I handed out leaflets about the
project outside Post Offices on Fridays - Giro day.
We got surprising numbers coming along from this, so
many that we had to stop doing it every now and then
until I had coped with the responses we had aroused.
Later I was getting referrals from social workers,
day centres and other agencies. I would get invited
to give talks at day centres to groups of people who
were likely to be leaving soon and at various Social
Services clubs.
    When I started, I didn't know what I was going
to do. I learned by listening to people talking
about their experience of work and unemployment,
about what they were doing now and what they felt
was lacking in their lives. I ended up with an
approach I called 'Leisure Guidance Counselling'.
It had two main elements - an information bank and a
counselling process. The information bank was a
huge list of local opportunities of every kind -
every sort of club, group, adult education class or
whatever. I built this up from all sorts of
sources. Whenever possible I tried to add to the
card about each activity or opportunity some
feedback from someone who'd tried it out.
    The other aspect, the sort of counselling
process which emerged, came rather as a surprise to
me. It is quite a sensitive and lengthy process. I
don't know whether you have discussed someone else's
spare time in this way. I never had before and I
was really quite astonished about how difficult this
was and how sensitive is one's use of time. People
found it difficult to talk about the gaps in their
days and weeks and about how they didn't have any
social life or couldn't account for how time passed.
    I worked by trial and error and what I ended up
doing was seeing each client individually,
originally for an hour each. I would sit down with
them and talk to them about time and about work and
about what they were lacking now. Then I used to
try to work in quite a structured way.

I would give them a sheet marked like a
timetable for each day of the week, Monday to
Sunday, and divided into morning, afternoon and
evening. I would ask them to fill it in and work out
what they were doing in a typical week, maybe using
the week which had just passed. That would include
really everything, including things like doing
housework and chatting to family members. We would
talk about how they felt about different aspects of
their week and where the gaps were. Then I would
work with them to fill some of these gaps gradually,
to help them choose activities which they wanted to
do.

One thing I found very important was to leave
the act of choosing to them. It helped for me to
let them think aloud about what they might want to
do. It helped for me to present them with cards
about different local activities, education classes,
clubs and so on. But they had to initiate the
actual choice themselves. It didn't work for me to
suggest doing a particular thing, even when that
might be a really clever idea considering that
person's character and interests. I learned to keep
quiet about direct suggestions. No "Why don't you
go and do such and such?"

Quite often when starting to work with someone
I found it useful to emphasise the idea of putting
in pleasurable activities in your week, however
small, particularly just after stressful or
wearisome activities. So often the people who came
to me had no places in their weeks where they
experienced any pleasure. You got an impression
from some of them that they felt they weren't
entitled to it. So quite often initially I would
suggest that they looked for ways of introducing a
treat or two into their lives, preferably something
to look forward to after a difficult or stressful
part of the week. For many people that meant a treat
after signing on at the Employment Exchange.

Sometimes people would be completely blank
about any activities they might want to do. Not for
years had they engaged in any hobbies or any sort of
interests or pleasures. What I'd do, then, would be
to ask them to think backwards - to teenage years,
schooldays, to childhood - and think about their
interests and activities then, to think about
something which had given them pleasure in those
days. And then we might work back from those old
interests to something which perhaps connected with
them in the present. So many people actually give
up their leisure pursuits when they become adults.

61

Work and resting from work becomes the whole of their life. Then, when they haven't got work, they have nothing to fall back on. I found it could be very helpful for people who were blank about leisure activities to think back to childhood in this way to get in touch with the side of themselves which had once been able to enjoy things. Many people respond very warmly to this question. And if you give them a little time to reminisce on childhood or teenage pursuits it can have a sort of revitalising effect. I remember, for instance, one man who had been blank about what he might want to do. But he came to life after we had talked for ten minutes about the wood carving he'd done as a boy. Soon he was seeking a woodwork class through Adult Education.

Something else I found helpful was that when anyone went off to try a particular club, group or class, I used to ask them if they would come back and tell me about it so that I could tell other people what it was like. Now this served two purposes. It helped me to get information about clubs and it also meant that, if they didn't like it, they came back so that they could try something else. I always used to say "I don't know what the club is. I don't know what you are like. I don't know whether it is going to suit you". Very often it took two or three goes to set up one activity. It was very slow and I continued to see people for about an hour a week, more if I thought it was necessary, but that was average. You can see that I couldn't see that many people.

There is no way, though, that you can go quicker than this, if enduring results are to be likely. On this business of offering a number of options for the same activity, think of the long-term contribution an activity can make to someone's life if they do become truly rooted in it. I remember one man, for instance, who wanted a chess club. On the first two clubs I found him, he came back to me unhappy about the other people and the atmosphere. But with a third club he found his niche. When you consider what a regular club can give in terms of friendship, sense of belonging and so on, you can see why it's necessary to take the slow way and help someone find activities where they really do fit in, if we are serious about enduring opportunities for a fuller and a better life. Another example was the requests I used to get for dancing classes - quite a common one. Now dancing classes come in all shapes and sizes specialising not just in different types of dancing, like they will tell you on the information sheet, but also in different social atmospheres with different classes often attracting participants of a particular age or background. Obviously it matters a lot to someone which class they get to if we're talking about opportunities which can put a real sparkle into their life or from which a social network might grow. So you need to collect a variety of choices for things like this and to respect people's need to pick and choose somewhere they feel at home.

I found it necessary to work regularly and in a fairly concentrated way with each person over quite a period of time. I found it essential to work on building up one activity at a time. Only when it was really ensconced in someone's routine was it worth introducing another activity. Particularly for people who have done nothing for years, it is counter-productive to try to move from inactivity to an action-packed week all at once. They will give the whole thing up in despair before long. For a person who has been venturing out really very little, just keeping up a single venture a week in the beginning is quite enough to give them a focus in life and as much as they are likely to persist with for quite a while.

Another thing I found often necessary, particularly with people who seemed very vulnerable, was to go with someone first time to a new activity to help them get over various inhibitions and fears which might stop them trying new things. Either myself or a volunteer might go along with a person first time, rather than just saying things like - "There's this marvellous adult education class, go along". I myself find adult education quite difficult to go to. Those forms - you need a PhD to fill them in. Then you have to stand in this long line. Then you have someone who asks you questions you really cannot answer easily because you don't know whether you are going to like the class and anyway you would rather not pay until you are sure you do like it. Knowing the ropes is important, too, because in fact you are not obliged to pay for adult education until you have been to one class - though the adult education people may very well not tell you this.

So I used to go along with people on their
first session and sit with them in the class and
then if it was possible I'd ask them to come in
and see me the next day and talk about it to see
if they were happy with it. It sounds very
laborious. It was, it is, but it did work
better. I tried out not doing that. I got very
worried about being over-protective, taking
people by the hand like this. But I found that
things like clubs and groups can be really so
frightening that it is no good expecting someone
who is vulnerable to do it on their own. So I
ended up discovering that in fact this is the
best investment for worthwhile results.

So that was my approach. One-to-one
counselling over quite a number of sessions,
developing a trusting relationship, establishing
very gradually and one-at-a-time leisure
activities which were chosen by the client from
the information bank to fill the gaps in their
week which we identified from the exercise with
the blank time-table. And, of course, giving as
much support as proved necessary. I used roughly
hour long counselling sessions, which seemed
right for the sensitivity of some of the topics
one got into. Groups never seemed right to me for
this purpose. Leisure guidance counselling seems
to me to be about a person working out their very
individual structure for their private life and
that I think is best done one-to-one.

So it was a time-intensive process, working
carefully with a smallish number of people over a
period of time till they were getting really
established at a couple of things and life was
looking up for them. I discovered it was most
effective to concentrate on a few people at a
time, really get them settled, than to try and
spread yourself thinner across more people.
Really, once the process was working, it could
make a very big difference to a person's life.
To give an idea of the sort of time-scale that
could be involved I would cite one woman who was
attending a mental health day centre. She was
about 30 years old. I don't know what sort of
psychiatric problems she had suffered - that was
none of my business. But she had been ill on and
off for years and years. Her marriage had broken
down, her relationship with her children had
broken down, and she was very isolated. The day
centre was very important to her and she was
finding it very difficult to move outside the day

centre. She came to see me and we sat down and
we went through the time-table and so on. We
ended up with her spending quite a lot of her
time doing various types of voluntary work,
though normally voluntary work would be something
I would suggest to someone only quite late on,
after they've got easier, more pleasurable
activities established, because I think you have
to be quite strong and motivated to do it. But
she opted for voluntary work and with a
combination of some voluntary jobs and adult
education classes she was able to eventually
restructure her life without the day centre,
which I do not think was an easy task for her.
It took about six months of us working together.
When I last heard of her, not only was she
keeping these activities up but she had actually
become involved in additional things. So what I
had done was to help her set up a base from which
she was able to progress on her own. She was one
of the people whom I felt I had to accompany to
every group and class initially. It certainly
bore fruit.

Just as important as the counselling side is
the more obvious one of building up a really good
information bank on local opportunities. It
takes time, though it's quite possible to start
with scanty local information and build it up as
you go along, getting help from some of your
clients in doing so. You can work together in an
equal relationship. In fact I found some people
who originally came to use the service became
very helpful in gathering information. Another
possibility is to recruit volunteers. Going
round trying different clubs and classes and
reporting back is really a very attractive
voluntary job for many people, easily enough to
motivate competent volunteers. Likewise for
keeping the information bank up to date since
many of these things change so fast.

There were a couple of particular aspects of
being unemployed to which I found I needed to be
very sensitive. One was the great limits imposed
on leisure activities through shortage of money.
You need to be looking for activities which can
be done within a Supplementary Benefit income and
to bear in mind all the time the cost of extras
like travel. I did some work on negotiating
local concessionary rates for unemployed people
on the same principles as for other identifiable
low income groups like pensioners or students. I

would approach the manager of a sports centre,
for instance, and ask if there were concessionary
rates for pensioners, which was invariably the
case. How about unemployed people then? Quite
often we got it. We even had some success with
cinema managers giving concessionary tickets to
the project. Really very small sums of money are
crucial to whether someone on Supplementary
Benefit is able to develop a leisure routine at
all. Anyone working seriously in this area must
keep an eye on costs all the time.

Another issue was to convey clearly that to
plan your unemployed time constructively did not
mean you were giving up all hope of a job. For
someone, say, leaving a day centre following a
long stay after a serious illness the idea of
education classes, community centres and the like
meant adventure, living more fully, progress.
But for someone only recently unemployed or
someone much younger it could feel like a step
backwards to be, as it were, planning as if you
were going to stay unemployed. The idea of
developing their leisure time could conflict with
their hopes that they would get a job soon, as if
it were a choice between the one or the other.
You know how when people are keyed up and hopeful
about getting a job, they can act as if they
might be back at work by next week and don't want
to discuss other possibilities.

The first thing I'd say to people with
strong hopes or desires for a job was : "Let's
start by planning some activities for evenings
and weekends which you won't have to give up if
you get a job". Another thing I sometimes did was
this. I got the current statistic for how many
months unemployed people spent on average between
jobs. I would sometimes say to people: "If you
have only average luck, you'll have many months
spare before you get your job". Then they'd find
it easier to discuss planning to use that sort of
time-span without giving up hope of becoming
employed again.

In fact I think it's particularly important
that people who are looking very hard for work
should carefully plan leisure and pleasure
activities to keep up morale. Seeking work
nowadays can be an arduous and soul-destroying
business. There is in fact only a limited number
of hours per week which can be used in genuinely
productive job search. But you find unemployed
people spending all their time doing this, doing

it in an increasingly desperate, wearing and
unproductive fashion, then giving up. I would
see Leisure Guidance Counselling playing a useful
part in allocating particular parts of the week
to carefully planned job-seeking and backing this
up with planned leisure activities which can
support morale.

There was a refinement I sometimes added to
the blank timetable exercise for examining the
structure and gaps in your week. It concerned
the different psychological rewards which
different activities give. Quite often the
combined work and leisure activities of employed
people offer a nice balance of some activities
which give status, some which give structure, and
some which give satisfaction. Let's not glamorise
employment and imagine any job creates such a
balance. But quite often you do find that
employment introduces elements of structure and
status into a person's life, while leisure
activities in the main supply the pleasurable,
satisfaction side. For some people it is missing
status and structure which is the most
demoralising aspect of unemployment. Sometimes I
would help people pinpoint particular elements
which they felt were missing in their present
lives, then discuss ways of filling these gaps.
I might, for instance, ask clients to rate each
activity they put on their week's timetable in
terms of whether it gave 'status', or
'satisfaction'. We might discuss the balance and
whether this brought to their attention anything
they wanted to work on.

By 'status' I mean activities that you feel
give you status in the eyes of others, that make
you feel important, that give you self-esteem.
By 'structure' I mean activities that create a
time-structure in your life, which map out a
timetable of activities which have to be done at
a particular time. So, for instance, commitment
to an adult education class gives a fixed time
for going to that class, whereas playing the
guitar at home whenever you feel like it does
not. 'Satisfaction' is just activities which
give pleasure in themselves. It can even be a
very passive activity, like favourite TV
programmes which, by the way, also bring not a
little structure to many people's evenings.

People differ widely in what they seek
concerning 'balance' of such elements in their
lives. So there are no rules. But discussing

this can sometimes helpfully put someone in touch with something they're missing and give an idea about a solution.

One thing I found came up regularly was how hard it is to find activities outside employment which give you a feeling of status. Often that was an area where people were lacking. Of course there are ways people can get status while unemployed - maybe as youth club leaders, Sunday school teachers, through competitive sports, winning vegetable-growing competitions or whatever. But it isn't that common. You may need to work together about ways of getting it which are up that person's street.

Structure is something other people find themselves lacking. Often it's events where other people are in some way expecting you at a particular time which provide structure. So, for instance, if a client had gone through their week's timetable and it turned out they had nothing much which structured their time, I might ask them how they experienced this. Did they think it mattered? I might ask them about some time in the past when they had experienced much more structure and to compare now and then. If they found this thought-provoking, we might end up discussing ways they could introduce more structure to their week.

I must stress that in my Leisure Guidance Counselling I never laid down laws about what people needed or what my clients' lives should look like. Asking about balance between 'Status, Structure and Satisfaction' is just a tool for clients to try for size and to use only if they think it fits their situation. In Leisure Guidance Counselling you don't try to impose anything. You offer things to people who have taken the initiative to come for help in this area. Everything you do must keep in step with the client's initiative. So you point out a gap in someone's life, but you wait to hear how they experience it. You offer an awareness exercise about their everyday life, but what happens next depends on the conclusions they form. You offer information - as they request it. Everything depends on working with and respecting the client's initiatives and autonomy in this normally very private area. Without the client's initiative staying alive and well and in charge of what happens between the two of you, Leisure Guidance Counselling cannot bear fruit.

Chapter Four

NEW ROLES AND ESTABLISHED SERVICE STRUCTURES

Charles Patmore

Editorial Introduction

Previous chapters have discussed ways of
helping vulnerable people to get a foothold in
mainstream roles and activities. But how easy
is it for mental health workers to provide
such help, given the traditions and structures
of the services they work in? Using day
centres and day hospitals as an example, this
chapter analyses features of services which
can make it hard to incorporate such roles in
rehabilitation work. It points to the need
for some background changes in how community
mental health services are structured and
managed.

If asked the question, almost all mental health
professionals place high value on a client getting
involved in social or work activities in the
community in everyday life. But of those many
workers - whether social workers, community nurses,
psychologists, OTs, or day hospital or day centre
staff - it is relatively few who make this a direct
practical goal in their everyday work.
Chapters Two and Three convey the sort of
worker roles and investment of time which can be
required to do this - the combination of
counselling concerning hopes and goals, assistance
with finding opportunities, and direct practical
support, even to the point of accompanying
individuals to voluntary work, adult education and
the like. It is true that some mental health
workers have always assumed such roles. But many
others either omit this function altogether or else
perform it in perfunctory ways, like outings in
groups or impersonal information sheets about local
resources for people leaving hospitals or day
centres. Is lack of time the whole explanation?
Pressure from many competing demands can offer
explanation where a busy admission ward is
concerned. But questions about priorities really
must be raised when one finds this with community
based staff with social rehabilitation and

aftercare functions - sometimes actually in units
with phrases like 'help people integrate into the
community' in their founding briefs.
       Why is this element so often left out?
Further explanation than shortage of time is needed
for why so many workers do not take the relatively
commonsense path towards developing such a role.
Could any structural or organisational features of
community mental health services be stopping them?
It is important to seek out any such features or
dynamics and consider how to tackle them.

CAN DAY UNITS LOOK OUTWARDS?

> "... the centre should not be allowed to
> become a closed community which seeks to meet
> all its users' needs; rather it should be seen
> as a focal point from which they may move out
> to use general public services. Libraries and
> the adult education services are examples."

> From 'Organisation of day centres' in 'Better
> Services for the Mentally Ill' HMSO 1975

> "Clients should be encouraged to use community
> resources wherever possible, evening classes,
> clubs, libraries etc. in preference to day
> centre resources. Staff should also be
> prepared to involve the total family in
> whatever treatment plan is deemed necessary
> and to encourage communication between the
> identified client and other areas of his/her
> life. Staff also need to be aware they
> themselves are part of the community and do
> not exist solely within the walls of the
> building."

> Day centre policy document, West Midlands
> community mental health project, 1979

Day units are worth spotlighting in connection with
this question. They are a major element in
community mental health resources. Between them,
NHS day hospitals and Social Services day centres
offer over 20,000 'places'. Many policy documents
on day services emphasise promoting users' contacts
with people and opportunities outside unit
buildings. Indeed for many users these services
are the final 'stepping-stone' from hospital to
life independent of helping services, so this makes
very good sense. Users may need help in many areas

of life - family links, welfare benefits, training
for employment, developing new interests or joining
groups or classes in the community. But often the
help day units provide in such directions seems
limited, even in units run by very dedicated and
able staff. Back in 1976 the National Day Care
Project noted signs that day hospitals and day
centres were rarely helping people make changes in
their lives away from these units.

> "Only about one user in twenty - regardless of
> type of day unit - mentioned that the day unit
> had affected any of the following matters
> concerning their life outside the unit.
> First, there was the question of their ability
> to cope with social situations outside the day
> unit eg. 'I'm more considerate of other
> people and do more for my parents'. Second,
> there was their ability to perform new skills
> of the type one might learn at an adult
> education class. Third, there was the issue of
> their ability to take on new roles or revive
> old ones (for example, as father, wife,
> worker, or friend). Since it is precisely in
> areas such as these that people who are
> suffering from self-perceived mental disorders
> might be expected to have difficulties, it is
> perhaps surprising that so many users
> concentrated on describing their status within
> the day unit rather than on their lives away
> from the unit. This area needs more
> investigation, for as one man commented: 'The
> only snag is when you go away from the day
> hospital and go back home you're surrounded
> by things and people that were there when the
> trouble started.'"

> Carol Edwards and Jan Carter 'Day services and
> the mentally ill'(1)

Furthermore while only a fifth of users lived
alone, they found that family networks received
little attention. "We found that only a quarter of
day hospitals, a tenth of day centres, and no
voluntary units were in contact with families on a
monthly basis."(2)
    But that was in 1976, the only large scale
investigation of day services. More recently,
though, it is plain that many day unit staff have
become acutely conscious of the 'nothing to move on
to' problem which their clients now often face.

They have looked around hard for solutions.
Nevertheless their efforts to help people develop
opportunities and resources outside the centre seem
a curiously uphill struggle. The results often
seem not to do justice to good intentions. Visit,
enquire and judge for yourself, but it is
relatively rare to find day hospitals or day
centres where anyone is receiving really sustained,
individual-focussed, practical help on developing
important involvements in their life outside the
unit, like that illustrated through earlier
examples. Of course there are notable exceptions.
But, as a rule, it is quite rare. What you will
find, though, is plenty of centres with regular
staff-led group outings to facilities like swimming
pools, libraries, museums or sports centres or
which give noticeboard information on community
resources. These do, of course, make a
contribution. But it is important to distinguish
such help from the process of working carefully
with an individual over time on engaging with the
sort of opportunity which might become a major
long-term resource for that person. It is the
latter which many day units seem to find hard to
incorporate within their work.

Why should this be? Could any aspects of
today's models for day services be preventing staff
from developing such approaches? Commonsense
suggests, for instance, that how a day unit is
organised must have some bearing on how easy it
will be for staff - or users - to work on
developing outward connections. Even if the effect
is only marginal, there must be some day units
surely which are more suitable than others for
doing this sort of work. There must be some
features which would be an advantage to any day
unit which seeks to assume this role. Likewise
there must be features which do not assist this
sort of work or, on balance, actually hinder it.

WORKING ON OPPORTUNITIES AWAY FROM THE CENTRE: WHAT
HELPS AND WHAT HINDERS?

One very basic requirement for such work is
that staff must want to do it and see it as part of
their role. Another is that they must have the
necessary time and practical opportunity to perform
it effectively.

In respect of the latter, note how staff as
well as users would need to be engaged away from
the day unit. Staff would, for instance, need to

spend time out in the community to collect
information on opportunities, liaise with people
who manage community resources, accompany people
first time to things like evening classes or
recruit volunteers to do so. Other tasks which are
part of helping users develop opportunities and
quality of life outside the centre include working
with families, sorting out welfare benefit
problems, pursuing possibilities for rehousing,
employment or training. All these need tackling in
conjunction since so often one affects another.
Day centre staff may need at least to start the
ball rolling themselves, if any assistance is to be
available. Rarely nowadays can people attending
day centres also get such help from field social
workers.

The general effect is to draw staff time away
from a customary day centre programme and into
one-to-one work with clients and roles outside the
centre. There will be occasional need, too, to
work a little at evenings and weekends, which means
time in lieu taken elsewhere in the working week.
A more outward orientation would, therefore, take
significant staff time away from a conventional
Monday to Friday activity programme inside a day
unit building.

So what features of a day unit might equip a
staff team well for working in this direction?
Alternatively, what features might make it
relatively unlikely that staff either could or
would work in this way?

STAFF TIME COMMITTED TO MANNING CENTRE BUILDING

The more that staff time is locked into
providing services within the building, the less
will staff be able to work outside it. Certain
models of day services commit much staff time to
particular roles within the building. For instance
some units rest on very structured timetables of
staff-led activities. But just as important are
certain constraints sometimes imposed by employing
authorities. Social Services day centres are
usually set an average daily occupancy target, for
instance. A centre may be set up with an
expectation that on average, say, 40 people will be
attending each day over a five day week. In some
Authorities the building occupancy figures become
senior management's over-riding concern.

Average daily attendance figures may be
expressed as whatever percentage of the centre's

occupancy target is being achieved. Some Social
Services Departments regularly compare these
percentage occupancy figures between all their
centres, including centres for elderly and
physically handicapped people. Centres which are
consistently furthest from their target risk losing
posts to those who score well. They may even face
closure. A centre with a high occupancy target may
need to commit a great deal of staff time to
running activities inside the building if it is to
bring in the numbers required. It may have no
choice, for instance, but to run a full programme
five days a week to reach this daily average. Nor
does this just mean that staff lack time to work
with individuals on involvements outside the
building. Success in the latter also reduces
attendance figures and hence can actually generate
problems. It is, of course, essential for
management to monitor how much service a given
resource is providing. Day services can certainly
be prone to underuse and some staff teams are
narrowly selective of referrals. But using
building occupancy as the measure of service is
peculiarly counter-productive for day services.
Here is the viewpoint of the Manager of a large
Social Services psychiatric day centre.

> "My centre has 75 places which has meant an
> expectation from the Department that we should
> have 70 to 75 bodies in each day. Now it
> seems to me that that is fair enough if you
> have a day centre that is bringing in people
> five days a week and a lot of day centres do,
> certainly those for the mentally handicapped
> do. You will have very little turn-over.
> People are not going out to employment.
> Basically the centre is the level at which
> they are going to be functioning for a very
> long time. There are going to be very few
> people moving on. It's when you get to this
> ball game of people moving on and people going
> outside to practice things that they've done
> in the centre that you start getting
> fluctuations in your daily attendance. There
> will be visits to the DRO, going down to sign
> on, going to the GP and groups, clubs or
> classes that the person is going to as part
> and parcel of their getting away from the
> centre. So they miss a day, here and there.
> And the constructive things they are doing
> don't show up on your statistics, so the net

result is that this cuts your daily average
occupancy figures. So instead of getting 70
or so a day you only get about 60. But these
factors about clients weaning themselves away
are never taken into consideration when usage
of the centre is being talked about. Senior
management considers that the centre is
operating at 15 under capacity because it
should have 75.

I don't know who decided on that 75. Our
daily average of 60 people actually represents
a larger number of people whom we see each
week. We are maintaining in the community 135
people and that daily figure of 60 is just a
mathematical production. Another factor is
the flow through of people. That doesn't show
up on the figures by which they assess you.
The only statistic which goes forward to
senior management and the Finance Committee is
that average daily attendance one. That shows
60 people. What it doesn't show is that that
sixty has in fact changed each week as two new
people have joined and two have left on
average.

So these occupancy figures don't take account
of people being helped to do constructive
things outside the centre. They don't take
account of the actual number you are working
with. And they don't take account of your
achievements if you help people move on. It
seems to me that if this persists you run the
risk of keeping people in the day centre to
meet occupancy targets. There are times when
I have said, and our staff group have said,
'OK, we'll hang on to people.' I think there
is evidence at this moment that there are
people in our day centre who could be moving
on to things like Age Concern, adult education
and so on, but we are reluctant to do this at
the moment because we are at the period in the
year when attendance levels always naturally
dip, from June to September. Our occupancy
targets, though, don't dip."

Another way staff time can be locked inside
the building is through commitments to be available
five days a week for certain individuals who have
nowhere else to go. Some day hospitals must have
staff on hand to provide at short notice for

in-patients from nearby units. Likewise some day centres are committed to offer shelter and activities to residents of particular hostels whom hostel rules force out all day, five days a week.

Obviously a massive obstacle faces any day unit where the employing authority actually forbids staff to work outside the unit building. Usually such vetos aim to preserve traditionally conceived boundaries between 'Day Care' and 'Fieldwork'. This used to be principally a Social Services management practice, with NHS day units less prone to such constraints. Recent years, though, have seen much greater flexibility in the Social Services sector. In contrast, such restrictions may be spreading in NHS day units, owing to some narrow management perceptions of their role vis a vis the growing Community Psychiatric Nurse service. In some places day hospitals are being pressed to formally limit their work to their buildings and leave the rest to the CPNs.

Day units will find an outward approach difficult the more staff are tied to working within the building for any of these reasons. It will be much more practicable in centres where obligations and staffing permit, say, a couple of staff to be working outside the building at any time in the week or, alternatively, if senior management can permit the centre to be closed for two, three or four half days a week so the staff can pursue the service's goals in the wider community.

SIZE OF CATCHMENT AND DISTANCE FROM USERS' HOMES

Promoting natural support systems requires helping users find opportunities within reach of their own homes. An ideal situation for researching resources would be where all centre users come from one fairly compact community so that one really thorough pool of information and contacts can serve everyone who comes to the centre. Specialising in one community's resources will lead in time to a formidable network of personal contacts with people able to open opportunities, like community workers, employers or clergymen or volunteer organisers. Also helpful, of course, would be a centre building located in the heart of the community it serves. Another bonus for users' social opportunities is that friendships formed at the centre can continue naturally and easily since everyone lives close by. Some former users, too, may become important parts of the

resource network. Contact with them will be easy
to maintain through close physical location.

In the opposite direction, the wider the
catchment, the more separate localities it will
contain and the harder for staff to research any of
them well. Distance from the centre building will
make it harder for staff to form personal
connections with influential people, community
centres, adult education institutes, etc. It may
be harder, too, for them to join users in ventures
in their own localities.

Relatively few day units serve just a single
compact community. But there are a fair number
which serve no more than two or three distinct
localities. For these it is readily practicable to
build links to opportunities within those
localities. It will be harder, though, where
another common arrangement is concerned. This is
where two or three centres all serve the same large
catchment but specialise in different services
thought to suit different sub-groups among people
recovering from mental illness. Clients are
matched to a centre on this basis rather than
closeness to their homes. There are some day units
where all geographical factors conspire against
staff working on outward links - like some day
hospitals on out-of-town large hospital sites which
serve very large catchments. One can readily
understand why some staff in such situations
gravitate to a building-centred model of service as
the only practicable proposition.

THE CENTRE'S PHILOSOPHY MUST VALUE USERS' OUTSIDE
NETWORKS

Many staff teams have some shared
understanding about how their service helps people,
about what are its most important elements and the
criteria which signify that a client is making
progress. Staff are more likely to work on users'
outside involvements if this relates to the team's
values about their particular role in the process
of recovery. Of course every day care worker
applauds people living a fuller life outside the
centre. But whether the team's philosophy promotes
this as part of their job is quite another matter.
Therapeutic Community models, for instance, direct
staff attention to clients' relationships and
behaviour within the centre community. Helping
people to increase involvements away from the
centre may seem at a complete tangent to the agreed

role for staff at such a centre. Sometimes, even, it might seem to challenge the whole emphasis of the therapeutic community on working on day to day happenings within the centre. Likewise staff at a unit where industrial contracts are important will understandably be unlikely to consider such a different role. In contrast, a centre pledged to a Normalisation philosophy should readily become interested in how users can participate in mainstream activities and social institutions. Behavioural ideologies can sometimes be quite fertile ground. Behavioural principles, for example that learned assertiveness or social skills need to 'generalise' to real-life situations, can endorse work with clients on social opportunities away from the centre. A team member introducing, say, some form of leisure counselling need not appear to be running a side-show unrelated to their colleagues' efforts.

Certain models of mental health work can specifically encourage staff to promote users' opportunities and personal networks in the community. Others, though, channel staff attention and energy away from this and define the important areas for intervention as lying elsewhere.

STAFF OPENNESS TO NEW ROLES

New skills, knowledge and aptitudes are needed for some tasks involved in outward-oriented day services. For some roles, for instance, a community worker's experience of informal community institutions and networks may be better preparation than any mental health profession's training. A day centre will be better equipped for an outward role if its staff are enthusiastic and open to these new roles. It may help, too, if it can employ some staff with relevant, if unorthodox, backgrounds. An example might be local people who lack mental health experience but are rich in local contacts.

The task will be harder the more a centre's staff are committed to any of the specialised staff roles or expertise which have been generated by conventional, building-based models for day services. Some staff join day services specifically from commitment to a particular skilled role - for instance leading psychotherapeutic groups maybe, an instructor in a particular craft, or to manage industrial processes. Understandably they may have reservations about giving time to new and different activities which are focussed outside the centre. At day hospitals the formal assignment of posts to nursing, social work or occupational therapy roles sometimes adds complications. These qualifications may hamper recruitment of local people with highly relevant contacts and knowledge. They may encourage staff to demarcate their roles according to traditional professional identities. This could mean that occupational and social opportunities outside the unit are seen as the OT's business only, if anyone's at all. A special regret in this context concerns the way some OTs working in mental health have been developing their role over the last decade. A sizeable minority have pursued an identity as specialists in particular psychological therapies, like psychodrama, art therapy or relaxation techniques. They have rather turned their backs on using everyday roles and activities in the community as their focus for helping people regain functioning. Thankfully, though, a reaction is now under way. Some community-oriented OTs are now vigorously involved with employment and mainstream leisure opportunities.

OPPORTUNITY TO GRADUALLY DEVELOP OUTSIDE NETWORKS

At some stage a day centre programme should become very part-time and leave sizeable gaps in a user's week. Client and key worker can then work together on gradually filling some of these gaps with valued involvements away from the centre. For many people, anyway, part-time attendance is appropriate right from the beginning. A key feature of an outward approach is that 'leaving' involves gradual reduction of time at the centre, as a person establishes themselves elsewhere.

Counter-productive are any centre practices which involve people excessively with the centre or which prevent staff and users from working together on gradually establishing a life away from the centre. This includes the most traditional pattern of day unit attendance: five full days every week until an abrupt discharge date. Nowadays blanket patterns of five day attendance for all clients are relatively rare, compared with the high levels shown by the 1976 National Day Care Project survey. But, clearly, where a centre is engaging a user all week within the centre building, staff are obstructed in a basic, obvious way from helping that person explore alternative ways for spending those days. Reasons why some centres still have everyone coming five days a week include staff ideology, demands from users, pressure for high average numbers of daily attenders, and commitments to hostels or families of users which want them elsewhere in the daytime.

Common sense suggests such factors will affect whether a particular day unit helps or hinders staff becoming involved with issues facing users outside the centre building - jobs, leisure activities, voluntary work, family problems, training courses, benefit or housing difficulties. Of course there are many other possible influences. Logic suggests, for instance, that common ground between staff and user sub-cultural backgrounds should help. Assisting involvements outside the centre requires understanding of common aspirations, interests and way of life of people of similar age, social class, ethnic identity, or local sub-culture to the person with whom you are working. Staff teams will be better equipped if their composition roughly matches the major sub-groups represented among users. This goes for the many older generation working class people among day service users, just as for West Indian or Asian people. Another influence might be staff willingness to take on occasional evening and weekend tasks. This inevitably comes up if a team directs itself to helping with involvements away from the service. Nowadays many day service staff willingly work flexible hours. But back in 1976 the National Day Care Project noted how a quarter of staff had entered day services specifically because the traditional 'day care week' offered escape from evening or weekend shift work. Maybe in a few places this could still be an issue.

WHAT HELPS CENTRE USERS' OWN INITIATIVES?

Such factors may influence whether a day unit puts its staff in a good position to help users in improving their opportunities away from the centre. But, leaving aside help from staff, there are day centre users' own private initiatives. Logic suggests that, even if it is only a marginal effect, some day centres will make a better base than others for a user to take his or her own steps towards involvements elsewhere. What features might matter here?

Many in fact will be just the same as assist staff for the same purpose. For instance, a centre with a compact catchment means friendships and contacts made through the centre can continue more easily outside than if much travelling were involved. In particular, users need opportunity to disengage gradually, through part-time attendance, and put roots down elsewhere while support is still available. Some day centre users describe quite explicitly how they organise their own 'leaving' process in a careful, systematic fashion which depends on the opportunity to disengage gradually. A sudden switch from a high level of attendance to an empty week requires people to develop alternatives very fast, within a few weeks, while their reserves of confidence and well-being last. It is rather like expecting unemployed people to develop new support systems during the brief 'holiday' period which often follows job loss.

A particular complication can face someone who lacks any single major alternative to the day centre like a job, a training course or a major family role, which can become a new focus in life. This is the 'magnet' pull exerted by the friendly atmosphere, daily structure and social identity given by many a day centre. Detaching yourself from a routine with a thriving day centre may be considerably easier with the pull of a major alternative like a job. It may be hard if you have to motivate yourself to give it up bit by bit for an assortment of Adult Education classes, voluntary work, visits to friends, housework and shopping. Indeed, day centre users trying this do describe dilemmas when favourite centre activities clash with outside opportunities. Centres where the majority of users spend most of their time together are, perhaps, especially hard to disengage from. Taking time out may conflict with the dynamics of the mini-community that can develop. In fact the same warm, cohesive atmosphere which is vital to drawing a new user out of his or her shell can also subsequently stop people from separating. This is an old, familiar problem, as old as helping relationships. Therapeutic Communities for instance, which often manifest strong 'centripetal pull', often utilise special leaving arrangements intended to cope with it, like precise leaving dates agreed by contract long in advance. What is new today is not the appeal of staying with your day centre but the relative unattractiveness of moving on from it. Until recently jobs were readily accessible which could offer such a rapid, comprehensive change in your way of life and

financial and social status that they could supply
a strong, counterbalancing motivation to leave day
centres.

Another issue is whether a centre publicises
any philosophy about developing involvements
elsewhere or discusses with individual users a
timescale round which a person plans to reduce
contact with the centre. Practices like staff-
initiated discharges at very short notice are
plainly counter-productive to clients planning and
managing their own futures. Likewise, positive
initiatives are inhibited if users see that early
flickers of health earn you a rapid discharge and
withdrawal of all support.

These are commonsense suggestions about
influences which facilitate or restrict a day unit
in helping users develop opportunities and
involvements elsewhere. Consider any day centre or
day hospital you know and assess for yourself the
relevance of these suggestions. Consider what the
centre does at present to promote opportunities and
quality of life elsewhere and how much room there
might be to increase this role.

Some of the issues mentioned apply only to day
units. But others apply equally to whether a field
social worker or a community nurse takes up work on
clients' opportunities for occupation or social
contacts. The size of a fieldworker's catchment or
'patch' will clearly influence how far they can
develop informal local resources. An individual's
professional background, their view of how mental
illness is best helped, and the professional skills
they value most - all these will influence how far
they see occupation, social networks and material
resources as important to mental health and part of
their own job.

MODELS FOR MENTAL HEALTH DAY SERVICES

Where older day units suit an outward-looking role,
luck rather than planning may be the reason. Until
the end of the 'seventies such a consideration was
rarely evident in how day units were actually
designed, even when it did figure in planners'
statements of aims. British mental health day
services have evolved in fact from models which
emphasised services and processes inside their
buildings. Day programmes, which often reflected
needs and problems arising in in-patient care,
became used for community residents, with their

different needs and opportunities, with relatively little modification. For instance, Therapeutic Community concepts, which have influenced a generation of day units, developed in part as an attempt to handle and harness constructively the tensions which develop in the total environment of in-patient units. Many features of day hospitals were transferred from day programmes developed to treat or occupy in-patients in large, remote psychiatric hospitals, where contacts with patients' networks outside the hospital are notoriously difficult. Furthermore, despite serving day-patients living in the community, many day hospitals were actually established on the sites of large psychiatric hospitals - a third of day hospitals at the time of the 1976 survey. Currently, though, many are to be relocated.

Many Social Services centres were founded on models which share similar Therapeutic Community, Occupational Therapy Department or industrial workshop pedigrees. In all such centres the important process, the process which fulfills the service's purpose, takes place inside the building. One logical consequence is the custom of measuring a day facility's workload through the numbers of people inside it. Other consequences include many of today's norms concerning staff/client ratios and staff qualifications, job descriptions and levels of pay, as certain job titles in today's Social Services centres attest. Many basic parameters of today's day units like size, location and catchment were established with fundamentally inward-looking models of the service in mind.

A major formative influence on day units was a long period of low unemployment during which their users regularly moved on to jobs. Up to 1975, when 'Better Services for the Mentally Ill' detailed policy on day services, unemployment rarely passed 4%. At the 1979 General Election it was not quite 6%. These relatively low levels of competition mean even quite disadvantaged people get jobs (see Chapter 1). Day centres were in fact intended to use these readily available jobs as a major goal in the rehabilitation process as indicated by DHSS circulars of the period (see page 5). Access to employment meant that a day unit could be helping people move on to opportunities and supports after the centre without necessarily working directly with an individual on actual changes in their life outside the centre. The 1976 findings of Carol Edwards and Jan Carter about the limited gains

named by day centre users need to be considered
from this perspective (1). They noted that users
emphasised improvements in personal confidence and
morale, getting on with other people within the day
unit and having a daily routine. They comment on
low feedback on changes relating to life away from
the day unit (see pages 10 and 71). But the former
has special value if a key aim is to help users fit
into the routines and relationships of a large
social unit, take on increasing challenges and
responsibilities, then transfer new confidence,
attitudes and social skills to the more demanding
social unit of the workplace. This can apply just
as much to today's majority of day units, which are
based round social therapies, as to the minority
where industrial work predominates. Indeed many
features of 'traditional' day centres, which are
currently often criticised, make sense if the
centre aims to help people adapt to the routines
and social expectations of employment. These
include timetables of structured group activities,
commitment to punctual and regular attendance for a
full five day 'working week', and leaving the
centre in a single step without gradual reduction
of attendance - often when a person was going
straight to a job the following week. In fact an
emphasis on alternative weekday activities could be
seen as controversial if there are jobs waiting.

A major theme at many conventional day units
is that of the centre as a sort of miniature
community. Here users can gain experience of
belonging socially and getting on with others and
can develop a new, positive self-image which is
reflected back from this mini-society which accepts
or values them. Social skills and capacities for
positive social roles are developed through
activities within the centre community on the
assumption that they can transfer to opportunities
outside. An information sheet for referrers to a
London Social Services day centre in 1980 put it:-

> "The Day Centre is run on therapeutic
> community lines, members of the Community
> being encouraged to make more satisfying
> relationships with each other and to take on
> practical tasks and responsibilities
> concerning the day-to-day running of the
> Centre. By taking, for example, the position
> of chairman of a Community meeting, or cook,
> clients are given the opportunity to develop
> or rediscover the kinds of skills useful in

everyday situations.

The Centre provides people with the opportunity to develop in the following areas:

i)   Confidence in making and sustaining relationships
ii) Social and practical skills
iii) A realistic awareness of personal potential and limitations
iv) Confidence in making decisions and consequently greater independence."

This contrasts with supporting a person in an actual situation in mainstream society where there is opportunity for a positive social role, like home cooking, adult education classes or voluntary work. An obvious danger of the day centre-as-community model is that without a bridge to opportunities elsewhere it can be very inward-looking. When the bridge provided by employment disappears or diminishes, this model of day centre must be questioned.

All said and done, there are in fact some very good reasons why day units often face difficulty in helping people develop networks and resources elsewhere. Certain features and dynamics of the conventional 'age of employment' day centre seem to draw the energies of both staff and clients into the centre and away from the community outside. A staff member who seeks to work with individuals on opportunities to replace the day centre can sometimes find that just about everybody else's concerns take them in the other direction. Clients may have their time committed to activities and friends within the centre. Colleagues may feel a hand short for running the programme in the centre building. Senior management may insist that the daily occupancy figure be maintained. If this analysis is correct, we need new models for mental health facilities. We need models whose starting point is how users can build up informal resources away from the centre.

NOTES

1. Carol Edwards and Jan Carter, 'Day services and the mentally ill', chapter in 'Community Care for the Mentally Disabled' Ed. Wing & Olsen, OUP 1979

85

2. Carol Edwards 'Research looks at practice difficulties', in 'New Directions in Psychiatric Day Services', MIND Publications 1980

Chapter Five

THE ERCONWALD STREET MENTAL HEALTH PROJECT

Editorial Introduction

Alternative approaches to day services have
been appearing which reflect the need to build
bridges to everyday opportunities and
involvements away from the service. The
Erconwald Street Mental Health Project is one
example. It was launched in 1980 with funding
as a Social Services day centre in
Hammersmith, London. It was intended from its
inception to establish an outward-looking
atmosphere, for staff to work outside the
building and facilitate users developing
activities, relationships and resources
outside the Project's building. In the
ensuing six years it has developed and
maintained such an approach with an impressive
consistency. In the first part of this
chapter Nigel Jones, who was the Project's
first manager, describes the principles by
which it developed during the first years of
its life. This draws from a transcript of a
1982 presentation about the project. In the
second part, Christine Embleton, who has been
manager since 1984, gives a detailed picture
of the day-to-day functioning of the Project
in 1986.

PART ONE: A CORE AND CLUSTER MODEL

Nigel Jones

One of our major concerns is to enable people who
use the project to engage in activities similar to
those chosen by socially valued people of like age
and cultural background and to do these in the same
sorts of places and company. To engage in
activities which they and their peers value and in
the natural life of their families and communities.
This Normalisation philosophy underpins the
Project.
    One thing that means is an outward direction -
outward to events, people, places outside the day
centre, or to activities which we may have set up

initially but which have become valued activities
in their own right, not part of any 'psychiatric
day centre programme'. We are concerned to avoid
building up the sort of dependency on the centre
which would mean that in three, four or five years
time the day centre is the basic focus of people's
lives. We are concerned that the centre becomes,
when people are ready for it, a base for moving on
to opportunities outside, that there are ready
pathways to valued involvements elsewhere.

It's a joint-funded project, managed as a
local authority day centre. It's based in a
largish house in the middle of one of the two
council estates where many of the people who use it
live. It has a staff of six and a secretary,
part-time. We are open to around 25 people coming
each day. Not everybody comes every day, so we see
about 80 people altogether and another 20 people
whom we are in contact with one way or another. We
are open to day centre members only four days a
week. On Wednesday, instead, we have a staff
meeting all the morning and the afternoon is given
over to services specifically for people who are
not in regular contact with the centre. Thus from
the beginning we have built in the idea that people
can't be dependent on the centre for a five day a
week total experience. Most people come no more
than three of the other four days. Some people only
come for one session - they might only come for one
particular group each week.

The jargon for our model is the 'Core and
Cluster approach'. Very basically that means that
we have some sort of central service, the 'Core',
inside the centre building where people can come,
say, just after they leave hospital. It can be a
sort of refuge place, a safety-net where people who
are troubled can be received. It is a place where
they can be made at home and can engage in some
groups and basic activities which can help them
gain confidence, get to know others, feel less
dislocated. Outside the Core our work radiates
out, as the diagram suggests, to opportunities in
people's everyday lives which can become valued
activities or otherwise support mental health.
This is the 'Cluster' - activities or connections
which can remain valued resources in someone's
everyday private life long after he or she has
moved away from the 'Core' provision within the
centre. Some of the 'Cluster' activities are
opportunities which an individual develops or makes
more of in their private life, like a hobby or an

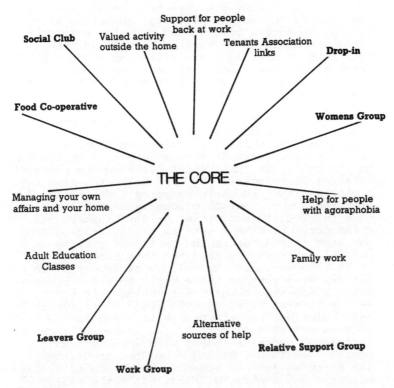

ERCONWALD STREET MENTAL HEALTH PROJECT

'CORE AND CLUSTER'

Social Club

Valued activity outside the home

Support for people back at work

Tenants Association links

Drop-in

Food Co-operative

Womens Group

THE CORE

Managing your own affairs and your home

Help for people with agoraphobia

Adult Education Classes

Family work

Leavers Group

Alternative sources of help

Relative Support Group

Work Group

Figure 5.1

89

adult education class. Others are activities which
we have helped to set up - for instance there is a
food co-operative run between the local Tenants
Association, a local club for elderly people and
members of the centre. That's a weekly event every
Friday in which many local people take part and
there's a chance to get involved with them through
the work of buying, bagging and selling the food.
Some Cluster activities take place within our
building, like this food co-op or an evening social
club, but many are outside it. What they have in
common is that they are ways members can satisfy
their needs for valued activity, to belong with
others, to have a role and so on - the sort of
needs which all of us have as long as we live.
Such ways of meeting these life-long needs can
naturally become a permanent part of someone's
life, if they wish it, because they are the sort of
ways of meeting these needs which are valued in our
society.

So an important idea for us is that people
gradually move outwards from Core to Cluster, that
they gradually shift their time and involvement
from the Core activities to a couple of things on
the Cluster. We think about 'leaving the centre'
as a gradual process, not someone coming five days
a week and then suddenly stopping. We see leaving
as being about a person gradually becoming more and
more involved in activities on the Cluster. We
think about it like a see-saw slowly tilting from
one side to another as the centre of gravity of a
person's life shifts from the Core programme to
activities outside. We believe it important to
discuss with someone quite early in their contact
with us how they might start making this shift.
Really this shift in how you spend your time is the
essence of how we help people to overcome the
intense social dislocation, isolation and lack of
sustaining social networks with which so many
people come to us. Moving from Core to Cluster
isn't for us just an appendix to a main programme
within a day centre building. It's the really
important business of a person acquiring networks
they did not have before.

We intend that people who have left should be
able to quickly and informally return to the Core
if their problems return or if they face a sudden
crisis. It's always there as a safety-net, without
grand re-referral procedures. So in that sense,
too, the process of 'leaving' doesn't have such a
sharp cut-off point. Some people, with cyclical

mental illnesses, may regularly move backwards and forwards between Core and Cluster, gaining through more satisfying lives between episodes of illness.

We are also concerned that our service should be able to help people who only need quite a little from us. We find there are some people who need only a little informal help because they have quite a lot going for them already if only we can help over one particular problem. So sometimes we use some Cluster activities on their own to meet the needs of people who shouldn't be involved in the centre to the same degree as someone whose life has been seriously disrupted by a stay in hospital. Some work goes on with people who never come to the centre building. Going through the different elements on the diagram:

THE CORE

It is a base for people first coming to the service. The administration takes place there. Some assessment is done there, though we also always make a point of seeing a person initially where they are living to get a fuller understanding of their reality and resources. That is really essential, actually, to get a full picture of what a person does all day, the connections they have - or the lack of them - the environment they live in, to guide you on their needs. But back to the Core. It is a base, a refuge, a safety-net to which people can return when troubled. We run some quite traditional day centre activities in the Core, within the building. We have craft groups, art groups, a problem sharing group, that sort of thing.

Working round the Cluster activities:

THE WORK GROUP

This works completely outside the centre building. It meets one day a week doing painting and decorating on Housing Association houses locally. It can be for people currently attending the centre or people who used to attend the centre. It can also be for people who have never attended the centre but, say, have been referred to us and this seemed, just on its own, the sort of opportunity they were looking for. The group meets on site, wherever it is due to be working that day, not at the day centre. We are hoping to get the

group a base of its own, a room in a building
attached to a local church. Even now with the work
group as it is, there is not a lot of contact
between the people who work in that group and the
actual day centre. For instance, when lunch
happens people in the work group go to the local
cafe. They don't go back to the day centre. They
do what would be an appropriate thing for people at
work to do, which is to go off to Fred's Cafe and
have lunch and then they come back at half past
four, five o'clock, if they come back at all. So
it is the idea of actually building something which
has a life of its own and has little connection
with the centre in the middle of the diagram. We
see the work group as a platform, a way of gaining
confidence before moving on to open employment, or
a paid work scheme. Employment is such a big area
of concern that staff see part of their effort as
one of linking up with borough-wide initiatives in
this field.

LEAVERS' GROUP

Some people leave us with ease. They go back
to work or find some valued activity. For instance
some people have worked in Oxfam shops or found so
much opportunity for voluntary work that they
really had their hands full. But there are others
who have used the day centre very appropriately but
find leaving much more difficult. It is not
obvious where they are going to go or what they are
going to do. At certain stages the Project has set
up a Leavers' group for people in this situation,
though it is not a permanent institution. At one
stage the Leavers' group worked like this. The
group didn't meet in the day centre. It met in
somebody's flat. It met in somebody's flat because
we felt that we wanted to detach that group from
the centre. Its members felt this would be
appropriate as well. Now the idea is that people
begin to address two things really. First the
whole grief process of actually leaving a place
which is very supportive. Secondly there is the
task of finding resources and opportunities within
the community and being able to transfer some of
their confidence into settings other than the day
centre setting. An example of that would be
someone doing some sort of craft work at the day
centre who gets a tremendous amount of confidence
and esteem from doing this. There's no actual
reason, if that sort of activity is their main

involvement, why they shouldn't do that outside, if that resource exists. So, for instance, some people in that group joined a couple of groups in local community centres and actually did very similar things to what they did in the day centre, but no longer in a mental health setting. And I think the message which is becoming clear to us is that quite a number of things which happen in community centres or various other places can replace certain activities in mental health day centres. Very often, if someone reaches a certain level of competence and belief in themselves and any obvious symptoms of mental illness have declined, there is no reason why they should have to come to a mental health day centre to get those opportunities.

ADULT EDUCATION CLASSES

We had a long debate about whether to have tutors to come in to hold these in the centre. But in line with the thinking mentioned above, we make a priority of encouraging people to use such classes outside the centre. We aim to build links with adult education, to spread information and to work with individuals to encourage them and support them. We try to pick up problems over literacy or numeracy which some members experience but we don't work on these inside the centre. We aim, instead, to channel them towards specialised help from teachers in community facilities. Some classes have proved particularly useful to us - notably classes at local community centres on yoga and sewing and at an AE Institute on typing, welding, literacy and numeracy.

While emphasising classes outside the centre, we have given some individuals opportunities to engage in craft or practical skills within the centre so as to gain confidence and a head start over classmates on particular courses they were hoping to take up outside. That is something that is very important on the Project - that every activity should lead somewhere, should be a stepping-stone towards the goals of the individual doing it. We hope that nothing gets done just as part of some time-honoured day centre programme.

'COOKING, DECORATING, CLEANING, SHOPPING, GARDENING'

Here are those famous day centre staple diets

93

- cooking, decorating, cleaning, shopping, all
those things which so many day centres have people
spending so much time on. Increasingly we have
been asking ourselves "Where ought all that to
happen? In what situations does it really matter
that someone has sufficient confidence to shop for
food and then cook for themselves or others? What
sort of gardening or decorating should a person be
able to do?" It dawned on us after about a year
that the best place for it to happen was not in the
day centre at all. It could happen in the day
centre but more importantly it ought to happen
where people are living. These are things people
need to be doing in their own lives, in their own
homes. The cooking or decorating that matters is
what you are able to do at home with whatever
resources are available to you there. Just because
you cook or decorate with a day centre team doesn't
mean that activity has become part of your own life
or even that you can do it on your own at home.
Our concern is always to build up what people have
or can do in their own lives. So shopping and
cooking is for yourself or the people you live with
and in your own kitchen. Gardening is the
gardening you can do at home. One example would be
a man who had really been quite ill with a
diagnosis of manic-depressive illness. He had been
stabilised to some extent with lithium over the
last six months, nine months. He was very, very
slow and lacking confidence in himself at home.
His wife phoned up the GP every time he didn't get
out of bed. She tended to undermine him quite a
lot of the time. When I first met him he said,
"Look I've got all these rolls of wallpaper at home
and I've had them there for three years". We
thought that if we started getting this man into
the work groups at the day centre this wouldn't
address the real situation where he needed to
summon up energy and build up his confidence. So
what we did was to transfer a part of the work
group to his house. One of his first tasks in the
work group was actually to stick up those rolls of
paper that had been lying around his house for
three years. There were one or two other jobs
which he had similarly let slip through total lack
of confidence in himself and we got round to those,
too. In some cases people's needs are very
individual and sometimes are most appropriately met
not in the day centre but in people's homes, in
their families, in the life they stay with when the
centre is gone. I suppose the underlying question

is "Where does mental health matter?". Doesn't
mental health matter at least as much where people
are living as it does during the day in a day
centre?

FOOD CO-OP

This is a joint enterprise by the local
Tenants Association, a club for elderly people and
some members and workers from our Project. It buys
food cheap from bulk suppliers and sells it in
small quantities every Friday afternoon in a large
room in the centre building. Sizeable numbers of
local people use the co-op. Besides the selling,
there is quite a lot of work in buying the food,
weighing it and bagging it. The co-op offers
opportunity to mix and work with valued local
people and to play a role in this community. Bear
in mind that the Project covers a tight catchment
area and many of our members live on the same
estate which uses the food co-op. Another aspect
is that the co-op's use of the building promotes
acceptance of the Project as part of the local
community.
The co-op has become a busy and lively
occasion. Some centre members have gravitated to
working on it along with the other local voluntary
workers. It could become a long-term interest for
some of them.

SOCIAL CLUB

Like the food co-op, this takes place in the
centre building and brings in some non-members from
the local estate. It is an evening social club,
originally meeting once a week. All centre members
and ex-members, along with families and friends,
are invited to use it. We've worked on encouraging
the families and friends of centre members to come
to the club, including children. As a result there
can be quite a community atmosphere and at times
the club becomes a lively and rewarding place for
many others besides centre members. More recently
the format has changed, with club members meeting
on a monthly basis. The focus of the evening is a
meal, a special meal with candles and good food.
This supper club focus has heightened the status of
the evening with a direct spin-off on the
self-esteem of the participants.
Former centre members who have got jobs have
made particular use of the evening social club.

95

They continue to be invited to the supper club.

VALUED ACTIVITY OUTSIDE THE PROJECT

Here we are usually talking about some form of socially valued work and how one can build bridges for people to move on to this. Quite a number of people, in fact, have found open employment. Others to varying degrees have become involved in voluntary work in things like charity shops or visiting isolated elderly people.

Where open employment is concerned, we have a job seekers group which works on how its members can widen the range of real job opportunities coming their way and present themselves effectively to employers. A number of MSC funded schemes, some organised by local MIND groups, have proved very useful in maximising people's chances - in giving evidence of recent ability to work, recent references and so on. Keeping in touch with training courses and schemes is an important part of helping with realistic links to open employment. Even with unemployment as high as it is, we have found that many people who come to the project are highly job-motivated and want to keep trying. Even with current unemployment rates quite a number of our centre members, here in London, have actually managed to eventually find jobs. Real, practical help towards gaining employment has emerged as the principal desire for a fair proportion of project users.

Concerning voluntary work, all sorts of links with informal local community leaders have helped us learn of opportunities which might suit particular individuals. Much has come the way of centre members from local churches, for instance. A useful break came when a couple of ex-members got leading voluntary roles in charity shops in the area. They could open opportunities to others whenever these arose.

SUPPORT FOR THOSE BACK AT WORK

Starting a full-time job can often be difficult - particularly if it's your first time back after an episode of mental illness. We make a point of being available for support at this important time. This means that as well as offering the Social Club we must be available to see individuals in the evenings if they are finding being back at work very stressful - maybe feeling isolated, facing personality clashes or whatever and asking for support. People going back to work, in fact, can also use any other centre resources that their shift hours permit.

TENANTS ASSOCIATION

We cultivate links with the Tenants Association for a lot of reasons. A couple of centre members have taken structured voluntary jobs with them. Association activities are an opportunity for contact with local people and for participation in community affairs. Through the Tenants Association, the local youth club meets in our building, since they do not have anywhere else. We are aiming for other local groups to use our building like this. This can create informal meeting points between centre members and valued local people, in the same way as the food co-op. It reduces barriers between us and the local community so we're not seen as a local extension to hospital but more like part of a community centre. This is a way to work against stigma. Also, lending our building like this encourages reciprocal help from the local community organisations who can help us so much to help our users to integrate into networks in this community. These organisations are one direct route into the community. So a member of our staff meets regularly with the Tenants Association and local community workers.

Community organisations and well-connected individuals like community workers or clergymen can contribute so much to this sort of mental health work, particularly when they see it to be in their interest to do so. To plug into this sort of opportunity, though, I think your centre needs to be small and with a tight local catchment area based on what local people see as a distinct community. The Erconwald Project is lucky to be based round two small densely populated areas which have genuine local identity. You need to be helping people from just one or two particular communities so that you have the time to build real links with people and associations in these places. You need this local focus, too, because to get help from community organisations and community leaders they must perceive your service as something specifically for the people of their community, not belonging to an outside bureaucracy which helps people from all over the place. If they see you as

their resource, this means they readily help you
when you ask for it. But it also means that they
expect you to offer all sorts of impromptu help
regarding mental health on the terms on which local
people request it.

DROP-IN

On Wednesday afternoon the centre is closed to
members. We run a drop-in service which is
particularly intended to help people who are not
centre members. This is not a social drop-in.
Rather, it offers walk-in, anonymous one-to-one
counselling, support, advice - someone to talk to.
This service is advertised in places like local
shops, clubs, community health centres, the
out-patients department and places like that.
People can come on their own terms without a label
and talk about what they wish. Sometimes an
individual comes several times. Sometimes they go
on to attend particular groups based round the
centre or even to become involved as a full member.
But mostly people do not take it further - which is
how it was intended, to give an opportunity to meet
your mental health needs in a very simple, informal
way without having to become involved in any
programme.

WOMENS GROUP

This also occurs on the Wednesday afternoon
when centre members are not around. It is part of
the idea of limiting mental health responses to
just the form of support or help which a person
needs, without undermining or interfering with
areas of life where they have strengths. Some of
the women who come to this Wednesday afternoon
group have been identified through doctors and
social workers as depressed; others refer
themselves. Most have small children, so a creche
is available. In no way would they fit in with a
conventional day centre programme and they don't
need such a programme, they really don't. What
they do need is a group where they can start
supporting themselves through their difficulties,
investigate what resources there are for them in
the community and be able to talk about their
depression and feel understood by people in a
similar position and by the staff members
facilitating the group. We find that some of these
women just drop in during the week and have a cup

of tea, then go away again, as well as coming to
the Wednesday afternoon womens group.

WORKING WITH PEOPLE WHO HAVE AGORAPHOBIA

Initially the project set up a group for
people who found it difficult to get out of doors.
As we became more experienced we were able to take
referrals from people who suffered from
agoraphobia. In conjunction with a clinical
psychologist, a series of groups were held at the
centre, again meeting on Wednesday afternoons. The
project has now organised four such series, and is
in the process of preparing another.

FAMILY WORK

If we are concerned to help people who are
recovering from mental illness to get on and
support themselves after the centre, then we have
to do some family work. If people are living
long-term with other family members, then major
issues and problems in the family need attending
to. Sometimes a family issue may be at the heart
of a person's problems - for instance a man in his
fifties who has been made redundant and suddenly
experiences himself as having no role in relation
to his wife and children. Sometimes family tensions
can be a very specific aggravation to someone's
mental health difficulties - for instance in the
way that researchers at the MRC Social Psychiatry
Unit have been finding concerning people with
schizophrenia diagnoses. They have established that
people recovering from schizophrenia are much more
likely to relapse if they have a lot of contact
with family members who treat them in either an
over-protective or a critical way.

We do some work with centre members and their
families together in their own homes. Quite often
it's fairly low-key and aimed at defusing regular
tensions and helping family members to have more
space so they can live together more easily.
Again, this is generally in the direction
recommended by the MRC research - working to reduce
relatives' anxieties, intrusiveness or critical
attitudes and encouraging living arrangements which
give family members a break from each other.

We see much value in day centre staff doing
such family work. Not only does the day centre
worker understand a person better by seeing them
with their family, but family work can be guided

and clarified by knowing what the person is like away from their family, when they're at the centre. We've had some experiences which suggest that day centre workers not only need to do family work but have a specially useful vantage point for doing it.

RELATIVE SUPPORT GROUP

With similar intentions we have run a support group for the relatives of some centre members. Sometimes if a person has been ill for a long time and living with relatives, those relatives may be the primary carers who need to be supported. So you invite relatives to use a confidential group in the evening whereby they can better understand what is going on with their son, daughter, husband, wife or whoever. This is sometimes contentious because some people will say that perhaps the relative may be bound up in the identified patient's illness. But that is the sort of thing we stay aware of when we work with relatives in this group.

OTHER PATHWAYS TO HELP

We also encourage some members towards mainstream ways of getting help with certain problems instead of using our own project for all their difficulties. We don't think everything should be done through the day centre and that applies to some mental health problems as well as to practical ones. If a centre member suffers a bereavement, for instance, besides being generally supportive we would put him or her in touch with a local branch of Cruse or the Family Welfare Association. Likewise for people with, say, gambling or drinking problems we would suggest contact with one of the self-help organisations which work in such areas in addition to whatever help we were giving over their main reasons for coming to us. For a member troubled by a sexual dysfunction we would seek referral to one of the very effective specialist services which are now quite common in the sexual problems area. We would not see it appropriate to work on that along with everything else in a group session at the day centre.

There are many emotional problems and other problems in living which have nothing to do with serious mental illness. They affect people who have not suffered mental illness and they affect some of our centre members. People may be

illiterate but that is not a problem related to
mental illness. We want members to know how to get
relevant help through mainstream channels. This way
they get access to the most specialised help for a
particular problem, rather than having an amateur,
second-rate version of every service imaginable on
offer within the segregated setting of a
psychiatric day centre.
      The activities described illustrate a
philosophy of 'day care'. The examples used are
drawn from activities created at the Project over
five years. Not all the features described have
stayed exactly the same. Some have ceased entirely
for the time being, as needs change. However the
philosophy holds good and is leading to further
developments, particularly towards the Project
becoming a focal point in a resource network. The
intention is to open the building to more voluntary
and self-help groups at evenings and weekends and
to involve centre staff with other professionals in
tasks outside the Project itself. An example would
be the increasing liaison with the Housing
Department to create a flexible detached housing
support team with Project staff members available
on a sessional basis. The Project needs to become
the driving hub which not only helps people search
out valued alternatives in the community but also
enables professionals and self-help groups to link
together as part of a team in order to better
resource a particular neighbourhood.

PART TWO: THE ERCONWALD MENTAL HEALTH PROJECT TODAY

Christine Embleton

      Although only one member of the present staff
team was part of the founding team, the fundamental
philosophical premises and most of the original
aims and concerns of the Project have not been
abandoned. They have been extended or honed
according to experience and the perceived and
expressed needs and rights of the changing
membership.
      Cyclical mental illness and long-term
disability are sad facts of life and we find that
the original aim of moving everyone through the
Project sooner or later has to be modified. We
recognise that some people will regularly depend on
the Project for practical help, support and social

contact. We review each member's attendance with
them and, possibly, with other mental health
workers with whom they are in contact at least
every six months. Thus we recognise small changes
and gains or longer periods of remission. Whilst
encouraging and facilitating the use of other
resources and opportunities we do not withdraw the
life-line. We avoid a waiting list because we
still do manage to put a majority of members in
touch with valued organisations, pursuits and
employment opportunities which make the Project
redundant and by ensuring that people attend for
the days or sessions agreed only.

Recent Changes

An example of something we have ceased to
offer is the Relatives Support Group. The
established group of four knew each other very well
and wanted to off load their frustrations and share
their experiences. They were knowledgeable about
their relatives' conditions and did not feel
committed to becoming a pressure group or doing
more than having a social evening together. A
couple of theatre trips were arranged, meeting in
the building without staff was encouraged and the
group met on their own for some months. Although
they no longer do so, various combinations of the
four meet and telephone each other regularly. They
also know they can contact us if they need to. We
hope to start a new group in the next six months,
if a worker can be spared for enough time to do the
groundwork.

The work group as described earlier in the
chapter has also ceased. The most important reason
was that local MIND were offering MSC funded
training opportunities in painting and decorating,
horticulture and a handyperson scheme. The most
interested and skilled members of the work group
were successful applicants. We noticed the work
group becoming increasingly nerve-racking and
labour-intensive for the member of staff involved
who would be responsbile for paint-spattered
furniture and dripped-on carpets in people's homes.
Members wanted to work to their standard, not to
that imposed by the member of staff, who sometimes
felt obliged to re-do work or spend time neatening
and finishing it. The small renumeration was
increasingly resented, although it had become the
main reason for doing the work, and staff felt
sympathetic to this but helpless.

An important development has been a pilot
scheme (for six months) for an employment agency
specialising totally in placing people who, though
skilled, are hampered in the search for full-time
permanent employment by their mental health
problems or history. The initiative comes jointly
from the Munster Road Mental Health Project in the
south of the borough, who have seconded a worker
full-time for the duration of the pilot scheme, and
Erconwald Street who have likewise seconded a
worker half-time. Called LINK, the scheme is based
temporarily in an office in a community centre. It
recognises that the difficulties encountered by its
clients are often to do with adaptation to the
social mores of a workplace, appropriate dress, how
to spend lunch-times, or such things as the
presentation of a CV and accounting for time in
hospital or in a day centre. More so than to do
with the skills required by the employer, to do the
job efficiently and well. Accordingly the service
offers support and appropriate information about
mental health to the employer as well as preparing
the prospective employees for work.

LINK has established contact with a few local
employers large enough to feel able to take what
might be seen as a risk initially. Personnel Staff
have so far responded well, saying that if LINK
know someone who could fill a vacancy, they will be
considered. Three months into the pilot scheme,
this is about to be tested. The services offered
to employers who use LINK to fill a vacancy are
information about mental health, particularly
relating problems to life events, regular contact
with LINK in the form of visits to employer and
employee at the workplace, and a promise to respond
to any telephone messages concerning the employee
within two hours. There is also the re-assurance
that LINK staff have the necessary skill, knowledge
and contacts to obtain appropriate services for the
employee if things become difficult. The intention
is of course to spot and deal with small problems
before this becomes necessary, or before employer
or employee become dissatisfied with the whole
arrangement.

Prospective employees are considered
individually by LINK; so far none of the eight
serious candidates for employment have needed
exactly the same amount or type of work
preparation. The preparation includes choosing a
career, compiling a CV, (in which mental health
problems are not ignored, but are related to life

events), filling in application forms, interview experience (with experienced personnel from the local authority and from willing local employers), discussion of what being back at work involves, and some work experience, if this is relevant.

LINK staff have had considerable financial and moral support from both mental health projects, whose staff have been committed enough to spare them for six months. They hope to obtain funding for three new posts so that the service can continue to develop after the pilot scheme ends. If, though it seems unlikely, funding is not obtainable, the two Mental Health Projects will maintain LINK's service to employers and employees already matched by LINK, but we would not be in a position to extend it further.

FACTS AND FIGURES ABOUT THE PROJECT

Catchment Area

The catchment area of the Project is the north half of the London Borough of Hammersmith & Fulham, approximately five square miles in area and with an approximate population of 70,000 people. This includes a high rise estate, and the White City Estate; four-storey blocks of flats arranged in a grid pattern, housing some 10,000 people. Most people who live there want to be transferred elsewhere and many people with 'vulnerable' status are offered accommodation there. Project members live in rented council or housing association flats or bedsits and a smaller number share group homes or hostels run by voluntary agencies or Social Services. The geographical centre of our area is Shepherds Bush where 62% of our members live. The large number of bed and breakfast establishments, modest cafes and take away food shops testifies to the high level of homelessness and rootlessness in the area.

Our building is a house in a residential street on a small council estate in the North West corner of the Borough - although we are geographically isolated, cut off by the A40 to the South, and Wormwood Scrubs to our north, our advantage is that these very boundaries create a community with a distinct identity from which have sprung some well-supported and established organisations.

Erconwald Project

The Members

In 1985, 110 people were referred to the Project, 70 less than in the project's first year. This is explicable by the facts that there had previously been no day care service for people with mental health problems living in the area and that people whom we know well who re-refer themselves are not in our statistics. During a typical week between 80 and 90 people have some sort of contact with the Project. Nearly 60% of our referrals last year were in the 20-39 age group. The remaining 40% (representing 18-19, 40-49, 50-59, 60-69 and over 70 years) being spread fairly evenly. The two largest cultural groups, apart from British, are West Indian and Irish. Between them they account for around 30% of people referred in 1985. 30% of all the people referred to us that year had a diagnosis of schizophrenia on referral. The second largest diagnostic category was depression which accounted for 19%. We noticed that, apart from one West Indian young man whose diagnosis was drug-induced psychosis, all the young West Indian men are diagnosed schizophrenic.

We wonder about the influence of cultural factors in these diagnoses. It is difficult to draw major conclusions from these figures because this is the first year they have been kept in such detail. But we hope in the future to be able to correlate such factors as age, sex, ethnic origin, diagnosis on referral and use of the Project, and to use the information when considering service development.

The Staff Team

The staff team of three women and three men, have been appointed not so much for their qualifications as for their personal qualities and particular skills. Willingness and ability to make relationships and to share practical skills are valued as much as specific areas of professional competence. Some of us therefore have wide experience in spheres other than social work, in teaching and housing for example. Collectively we also have social work experience in a variety of residential and daycare settings with elderly, teenagers, children, and in mental health. One of us has a degree in psychology. One is a trained psychotherapist. Three are qualified social workers, and one of them is currently doing the

Erconwald Project

Approved Social Worker training.
    To enable us to develop a team aim and shared
approach from our different favourite perspectives,
theories and experiences, we have regular Planning
Days when we stop our usual work and focus on 'why?
where? who?' questions about our 'Core Mission',
what we are doing or could do.
    We have also benefitted greatly from two
series of sessions with a staff consultant from
'outside'. She has enabled us to look at some
aspects of our relationships with each other, how
these affect our work, the members and the whole
Project at a variety of levels.

Budget 1985/86

    The three main categories of expenditure are
Salaries, Premises and Establishment expenses.
    Salaries for the Manager, four centre workers,
one assistant centre worker and one part-time
clerical assistant totalled £74,884.
    Under the heading of Premises, £4,260 was
spent. This included gas, electricity, water,
cleaning materials, planned maintenance,
maintenance of plant and machinery and household
equipment. Extra costs totalling £250 were
incurred when the building was vandalised while it
was closed.
    Establishment expenses are administered by the
Manager of the Project. The budget headings
include staff travel, members' fares, provisions,
instructors' fees, laundry, medical and health and
safety equipment, furniture tools and equipment,
Christmas extras, stationery, postage, telephones
and publications. The total expenditure is £8,855.
    Some items deserve some further explanation.
For example, Instructors' fees, staff travel,
members' travel and provisions.
    The Instructor's fees budget is £500. We are
fortunate in having the services of two adult
education instructors who work on a sessional basis
and are paid by the local education authority. The
classes are therefore open to people living locally
as well as to project members. In practice, the
members use most of the places and only few people
who are not otherwise attending the Project use
the classes, which are in art and photography.
    We employ a number of sessional workers for
between six and ten sessions at a time to run
groups or activities. These have included drama
and relaxation sessions and 'Creative Writing'.

has several benefits. Members have more staff to
relate to and opportunities to show other aspects
of their personalities besides those they feel free
to reveal to full time permanent staff. The
sessional staff often have greater expertise and
experience than the permanent staff in particular
areas and they generally arrive fresh and are
unpressured by other commitments to the centre.
The extra time available to permanent staff is used
in focussed work with individuals and also allows
us more freedom to go out of the building - to
meetings, to home visits or to work elsewhere with
members. Lately we have involved members in the
selection of sessional staff. One of the most
consistently popular groups is Creative Writing for
which the members interviewed two prospective
leaders and chose one.

Members' bus fares are paid to and from the
centre on the agreed days of their attendance if
they do not live within walking distance. This
budget also covers the cost of local trips, such as
photography group outings, shopping trips to
purchase gardening or other equipment which cannot
be bought locally and fares to visit another member
in hospital or prison. The budget is £1,670 and we
used it all.

Staff fares currently have a budget of £565,
which we are likely to overspend this year (86/7).
Staff are entitled to claim the cost of the return
bus fares to home visits, meetings and conferences.
We are negotiating car allowances.

The Project manager has considerable autonomy
as long as the total budget is not overspent.
Money can be transferred by agreement with the
finance section, from one budget to another.
Without this flexibility, it would be difficult to
offer the service we do, to attempt to respond to
changing needs and circumstances.

DAY TO DAY LIFE IN THE PROJECT

To clarify how our 'Core and Cluster' approach
works in practice, here are details of how two
staff and two Project members spent a typical week,
July 7-11 1986. First the two staff members'
weeks, then explanation of what we mean by
'keywork', 'being around in the centre' and other
activities mentioned, then how two different
members spent their week.

Erconwald Project

A week in the working life of two staff

Activities in capitals denote that they take place outside the centre.

MONDAY
Worker A
am   Keywork
pm   'Being around the centre'
      Time with visitors

Worker B
am   ALLOTMENT
pm   Keywork
      'Around centre'

TUESDAY

Worker A
am   Interview prospective sessional worker
      Keywork
pm   SUPERVISON ... VISIT 2 NEW REFERRALS AT HOME

Worker B
am   Keywork - KEYWORK (outside centre)
pm   Finances ... 'Around centre'

WEDNESDAY
The centre is closed to members on Wednesdays. In
the mornings the staff have a meeting. In the
afternoons, we work outside the building

Worker A
am   Planning Morning - We review an aspect of our
      'core mission' statement. Have we succeeded
      in this particular aim? How? Where are we
      not succeeding? Where do we go from here?
pm   COURSE

Worker B
am   Planning Morning as above
pm   WHITE CITY CONTACT GROUP
6.30 TRANSPORT MEETING

THURSDAY
Worker A
am   MENTAL HEALTH SERVICES DEVELOPMENT GROUP
pm   Meeting with sessional worker planning for
      Autumn. 'Around' for half an hour.

Erconwald Project

Worker B
am   Gardening
pm   KEYWORK. MEETING WITH SOCIAL WORKERS AND MIND

FRIDAY

Worker A
am   WRITING STUDENTS' REPORT AND INFORMATION FOR
       CYRENIANS
       AREA 2 MENTAL HEALTH GROUP
pm   Keywork and 'around in centre'

Worker B
am   WARD ROUND AT HOSPITAL
pm   TIME OFF IN LIEU

Explanation of some features in the staffs' weeks

'Keywork'

Every member has a keyworker, someone who
takes a special interest in them and is available
to them regularly as well as in crisis. The
keyworker is responsible for drawing the attention
of the staff group to any changes in their key
persons' circumstances, for better or worse, to
liaise with other workers, such as psychiatrists,
CPNs etc.

We consider that housing, employment and
leisure are the three most important environmental
factors in mental health. The keyworker therefore
involves him or herself in these areas as
appropriate, as well as offering the opportunity to
explore internal realities and relationships. If
someone wanted individual psychotherapy or focussed
counselling on a particular issue, we usually
refer them on for this but continue to work with
them in other ways.

Keywork can mean going with someone to view a
new room or flat, accompanying them to the WRVS or
to buy clothes or furniture, to the Job Centre, to
enrol for adult education classes. It can be
advocating on their behalf to the DHSS, to the
Housing Department or Housing Association. It can
be visiting that person at home and cooking with
them in their own kitchen, encouraging them to
maintain the cleanliness of their flat, helping
with budgeting. It can be none of these things,
but listening to someone attentively and
empathetically and confronting appropriately.
Whatever the mode or task, the vehicle is the

relationship between the worker and the member and we are sometimes able to engage seemingly quite unmotivated people by being prepared to start from where someone is, with what is concerning them and by moving at their pace.

Some of us make regular appointments with our key people, others prefer a more casual ad hoc response. These differences in style are considered when allocating keyworkers. Members have to accept that staff are different from each other and offer different things. On average each of the staff team is keyworker to around twelve members at any one time.

Some Cluster features

The centre allotment, where worker B was on Monday morning, is 7 minutes walk away and is also available to members outside centre hours, in the evenings and at weekends.

The White City Contact group, where Worker B spent Wednesday afternoon is a group for anyone on the White City Estate and meets for a cup of tea and chat in a Church Hall on the Estate. But it has really ceased to be a drop-in. In fact most of the people know us and each other quite well and drift in and out of the group according to circumstances and interest.

The transport meeting is for representatives of the user groups of the community mini-bus who run, maintain and contribute to its finances. The bus, like the Project, is based on the Old Oak Estate and is used by local groups such as Under Fives, the youth club, the History Group, the summer playscheme, the food co-op and the Mental Health Project.

The importance of 'Being Around'

Some members attend the Project for a period of weeks, months or even a year or more before they want to join in activities or groups or initiate social contact with others. Members each have agreed times when they attend, but can drop in if they are having difficulty coping with a crisis. There is a small number of people whose behaviour and appearance is such that they are shunned in 'normal' social circumstances and who have very little in the way of stability or relationships in their lives. If they drop in, whatever the day or time, however short or long they stay, they are

welcome. We attempt to make agreements with them
as soon as we have established a relationship which
can tolerate that. Although other members show
care and tolerance, often to a surprising degree,
it is necessary and helpful to have a member of
staff around all the time.

The member of staff can also seize
opportunities to encourage someone who has not
engaged socially to do so, initially through
activities such as playing cards or pool. Much can
be observed through these simple activities about
how people are, the ways they relate, their
strategies for avoiding relating, effects of
medication etc, which is useful for us in assessing
what to offer.

'Being around' does not mean being glued to
every interaction or involved in every
conversation. It is being available whether
pottering in the art room or garden, playing pool
or chatting with people, rather than in a
one-to-one individual session, running a group, or
immersed in administration. At least one worker is
always available in this way.

Hospital Liaison

We invite psychiatrists who know some of our
members to visit us, to talk with staff every six
weeks or so. But the main contact comes through
our attendance at a ward round every Friday morning
in a hospital some five miles away. This task is
rotated, each worker undertaking it for three
months at a time.

About 50% of our referrals are obtained
through this contact. Often we can contribute
information or an opinion on circumstances leading
up to an admission or re-admission. Occasionally
we may even have facilitated it. Our contribution
may be in the form of an offer to discuss coming to
the Project with someone about to be discharged, or
if the Project is not suitable we may know of
another more appropriate service.

Meeting the psychiatrist and ward staff on
their own territory facilitates a fruitful exchange
of ideas, information and opinions across the
professional barriers. Hospital staff gain an
accurate impression of who we are and the service
we can and cannot offer, ensuring realistic
expectations and more appropriate referrals.

The other equally important benefit of the
hospital visit, is the opportunity to go onto the

wards after the ward round and chat with patients
from our area. The contact established over the
weeks can enable even a quite paranoid person to
feel confident enough to risk coming to see the
Project when they are discharged. This is
particularly true of black people, who are often
justifiably suspicious of the services they
receive.

Time off in lieu

We have a monthly social evening to which
members, ex-members and their guests are invited.
Staff who run this (in rotation) and staff who
attend other engagements, like community meetings,
out of our normal working hours have time off in
lieu by arrangement with the Manager and the rest
of the team. Commitments permitting, it is the
same day or the morning after.

Lunch times are always busy even if no members
have wanted to cook a meal. Accordingly we want to
be around with members. Staff take a short break
when they can in the morning or afternoon, but this
is no substitute for a meal break in the middle of
the day. We have a day off per calendar month in
lieu, an arrangement of our own choosing. New
staff should not be compelled to do likewise and
according to our trades union are at liberty to
take their meal break at a reasonable time
agreeable to the Manager if they so wish.

Liaison with other workers

We regularly meet psychiatrists from the other
hospital which serves our catchment area, although
this involves far fewer of our members.

Each month we meet hospital and area team
social workers, CPNs, and a housing association
representative who work in our catchment area.
This is not intended to be a substitute for day-to-
day contact by phone or letter.   The main focus of
the meeting is people - how we co-operate in work
with particular individuals. But we take the
opportunity to inform each other of changes and
developments in our services and sometimes act as a
pressure group of mental health workers to
influence our managers on planning and policy.
Similar meetings are convened in other parts of the
Borough, defined by area team boundaries, and we
attend where appropriate.

We are represented at various meetings and

committees considering specific new projects, such
as the idea of a community cafe, a safe transport
scheme for local women, a new group home staffed
and occupied by black people. Several voluntary
and statutory agencies may be involved. A
representative is there both to gather information
and to contribute to formulations of strategy and
policy.

Two members' weeks

Their involvement in the centre and activities
outside the building to which they were introduced
through us. Capital letters indicate activity
outside the building.

Anne comes to the centre on Mondays and Fridays.

Monday a.m.	ALLOTMENT	
p.m.	Creative Writing group	
	Keyworker meeting	
Tuesday p.m.	ADULT EDUCATION CLASS: TABLE TENNIS	
Wednesday a.m.	PSYCHOTHERAPY GROUP	
Thursday (all day)	OVER FIFTIES RAMBLERS GROUP	
Friday a.m.	Members' Planning Meeting	
	Gardening	
p.m.	Making tea and socialising at the Food Co-Op	

Desmond comes to the centre on Mondays and Tuesdays

Monday a.m.	Cooks lunch or social time
p.m.	Social time
Tuesday a.m.	Often cooks lunch or social time
p.m.	Keyworker and social time
Thursday	WOODWORK CLASS
Friday	WOODWORK CLASS

Changing patterns in individuals' contact with the
Project

Although some members want to be involved in
the Core of the project alone, ie.activities in the
centre, many do join some of the Cluster features
at some time or join them instead of the Core. The
amount and type of contact changes according to
circumstances and the members' expressed wishes. A
number of people who before using the Project were
regularly in and out of hospital now turn to the
Project for help or support in the early stages of
difficulties. They may attend every day through a

crisis, or be visited by staff regularly, and then
resume a looser contact, just the monthly social
for example, when life is back to normal. We
notice that few people formally leave the Project.
Those who have jobs or full-time courses to attend
can be said to have left. Certainly their names
are no longer on the attendance list. But they
have friends whom we know, we hear news of them and
they may come to parties or socials. Some people
just stop coming when things are going well. The
keyworker will establish that this is the reason
and acknowledge it with the member. If people say
they no longer wish to have anything to do with the
Project, whether staff view this as a positive or
negative decision, we respect it. We will,
however, inform other workers, particularly the
person who referred the member, that this is so.

Below are some examples of changing styles of
use of the Project over various periods.

1.   Andrew's use of the ESMHP over three years

a)   Four days a week, after discharge from
hospital after "a serious schizophrenic breakdown".
Andrew, who was 19, did not talk to anyone, avoided
answering questions and seemed to be in a world of
his own. After a few weeks he stopped coming. We
wrote to him and visited him at home. He resumed
attending, apparently unenthusiastically. He was
allowed to drop in whenever he wanted and not
pressed to join in anything. He began to talk to
people, at first only other young Black men. We
learned that he was skillful and knowledgeable in
music and sound systems.

b)   By around eight months later he progressed to
spending three days at the Project and one day at a
Community Centre making music.

c)   Andrew got a place on a MIND work-scheme which
offers training in working self-employed as a
painter and decorator. He used the social evening
and dropped in when he had a day off. He is now
working and rarely comes.

Ivy's use of the ESMHP over two years

a)   Three and a half days at the Project, having
been referred by her GP because of depression. Ivy
spent the rest of her time mothering and
home-caring but said she had "no interest in

anything, not even my housework."

b)   Two days a week + a sewing class at a community centre.

c)   One day (Women's Group) + sewing class + yoga + swimming

Since the birth of a grand daughter, Ivy no longer wants to attend the Project, although she occasionally phones "to let us know how she is".

Claire's use of the ESMHP over ten months

a)   Four afternoons a week + group psychotherapy at the hospital. Claire was referred from hospital after a psychotic breakdown.

b)   One day + one afternoon + individual psychotherapy (through local MIND) + two days voluntary work on schemes providing help with furniture or gardening to elderly or frail people.

c)   A half day + monthly social + voluntary work + Adult Education class

d)   Through the Project Claire heard about a job as an administrative assistant and her application was successful.

Occasionally we tell someone that their attendance here is conditional on participation in something outside the Project. For example, Pete, who had no self-confidence, could see little purpose in life and had no friends or interests outside the centre, seemed to be embedded in a narrowing and increasingly dependent rut. We felt he was too young to be in this position and that unless we were firm, we would actually assist him in a long-term career as a consumer of psychiatric services. The staff group decided that we would offer him a social time here and keyworker time on condition that he attend classes at the local college. After we explained our reasons, he continued to grumble about college, but his life changed. He started going to the pub and to football matches with a couple of friends. Two years later, he is working and drops in during his lunch break on Fridays.

The importance of staff being supportive cannot be over-emphasised. We have found that it is not enough to tell people about a facility. We have gone with them, perhaps more than once and had to be prepared to discuss anxieties about the journey, what to wear, how to respond to people, how to approach people, and so on, perhaps at great length.

Finally, I would like to mention some factors which help us maintain the flexibility necessary to offer this service.

It is important that the staff team has support and is enabled to support itself. I have mentioned the staff consultancy, which I feel provides a necessary opportunity to explore issues and feelings which may be inhibiting the growth and creativity of the staff team, or affecting relationships with members of other agencies. I do not believe, given the stresses and demands placed upon workers by the diverse aims of the agencies with which they may have to deal - let alone the variety of levels on which they have to relate to many needy and sometimes highly disturbed or manipulative people - that this is a luxury, or that it is expensive.

At Erconwald Street, the chosen method of supervison is peer group supervision, in which each worker, including the manager and any students on placement, has a regular time to discuss their work, and any issues related to it, with the whole group. The manager also has line management supervision. This is in keeping with our aim of working as democratically as possible and encourages a rich variety of suggestions, insight, response and perspective. To allow time for this, and to make sure that the group communicates efficiently, we meet without members at the beginning of every working day.

The staff also need time, without members around, to evaluate their work, reassess their aims and plan future developments and we feel this is important enough to close the centre to members for a day or two, at least twice a year (apart from the regular Wednesday closing).

If community contacts are to be initiated, established and developed, staff need a degree of financial autonomy. For example, the Project may want to provide tea and biscuits at less than cost price for a large number of people, or to buy items such as swimming costumes, wellingtons and dungarees for members to borrow. Although our catchment area is small each member of staff spent more than £125 in travel last year - if we want the community to use us, we must also go out towards it.

Members benefit from some staff autonomy in several ways. A staff group can only help members towards independence, responsibility and self-determination if they feel they can exercise these qualities themselves. Whatever the staff have can be passed on. At an obvious level, this is seen in membership decisions on decor, furniture, etc. and very lengthily considered decisions such as not to have a TV or a dishwasher in the building.

Although we wish we had more space for a kiln, for movement, computers, woodwork, etc, the size of the building is an asset. Staff and members alike are forced to go out to engage in activities requiring special equipment. Our building was once a large house and retains a familiar aspect. It does not look like a place to visit to have something done to you.

Chapter Six

COMMUNICATING A NEW EMPHASIS IN DAY SERVICES

Charles Patmore

Editorial Introduction

This chapter is addressed to any manager,
planner, or development worker who wishes
either to develop a new day service with a
focus on users' informal opportunities or to
encourage an existing service to move in this
direction. It urges keen attention to some
common ways in which services which start out
with such a brief risk going astray.
Suggestions are made for ways of orienting
staff to the intended mission of such a new
service and for monitoring its development.

In the last few years there has been widespread
interest in alternatives to conventional day
services among people planning community mental
health services. The idea that one should focus on
users' opportunities away from the service, as
discussed in previous chapters, has certainly
received attention. But this still figures notably
more prominently in planning documents
than in actual practice. Quite often a new day
service is launched amid talk of 'core and cluster'
principles, 'mental health resource centre' or
other terms which imply something different from a
conventional day unit - but rapidly materialises
along very familiar lines. On the one hand, such an
alternative approach to day services is, in fact,
practicable - Chapter Five gives one example and it
is an example which has endured. But, on the other,
it seems a direction which quite a number of new
services say they seek, yet somehow do not really
achieve.

This chapter considers how a service developer
can seek to forestall such a new service going
astray: some problems to watch out for and some
steps which may promote the desired direction.
Chapter Four described some broad influences which
obstruct innovations - a mixture of structures,
like catchment sizes, budgetting and monitoring
systems, and staff perceptions and attitudes. This

118

chapter looks closer at the latter, which planners can less readily tackle on the drawing board.

SEEKING A GENUINELY SHARED VISION

Crucial to the development of this sort of service are the vision, values and sense of direction of the staff team. By its very nature the 'cluster' side of the service must be evolved gradually by the staff themselves in response to the emerging needs of individuals who come to the service. It has to grow in a steady dialogue between the varying needs of its users and local resources and opportunities at the time. It would be contradictory to seek to give staff a blueprint for 'cluster' opportunities, copied from what proved useful to different people in a different locality. So the direction of the service has to depend on the day-to-day decisions of its staff and the vision and sense of direction which guides their decisions.

How can a service developer help staff to internalise the vision behind such a service if, say, they have never worked this way before? Suggestions are made at the end of the chapter for some simple codes for practice which should focus staff attention on those aspects of their clients' lives which often vividly convey the need for this sort of service. A starting point, though, must be that staff are attuned and basically sympathetic to a brief to work this way, even if they lack the experience. They must be willing to help in areas of life which professionals have often tended to see as outside their remit, as the responsibility of service users to sort out for themselves.

To be motivated this way, staff need to share three particular perceptions: the importance of their clients' needs for roles, goals, relationships and occupation in their everyday lives; the value of meeting such needs through mainstream, non-segregated channels; awareness of quite how difficult it can be to meet these needs unaided when a person has recently suffered an episode of mental illness. Such motivation is essential on account of the considerable hard work and commitment needed to build links outside a mental health facility on 'core and cluster' lines. This may require staff to develop skills which are rarely part of any conventional mental health training - knowledge of the local community and a community worker-like ability to liaise with local groups, for instance. Such effort only comes from staff who value opening opportunities after mental illness at least as much as any other part of their work.

Planners and development workers need to give this utmost attention because, paradoxically, outward-oriented approaches can also attract mental health workers who take an opposite view. Some people take up jobs in mental health day services from a primary interest in doing skilled therapeutic work, often psychotherapy and sometimes specifically in a very specialised approach like art therapy or psychodrama. In some day centres and day hospitals such staff may wish to devote a sizeable proportion of their time to such formal therapeutic work. They may find workshop or social host roles frustrating and lacking meaning for them. They may regret the presence of clients who are coming for the latter, seeing them perhaps as manifesting a dependency which should be discouraged. They may wish to reduce those parts of the centre's services which address ordinary needs for company and occupation. Sometimes such staff see outward-oriented models for day services as opportunity to shed this side of the work, since it can be deemed to take place more appropriately outside the unit. Outward-oriented models may be misunderstood as justifying the restriction of the service to time-limited therapeutic work on a sessional basis. The bleak opportunities and non-existent networks of some clients may be deemed taken care of by a few token outward links, job-finding or leisure guidance sessions. Bridge-building, outward links or leisure counselling which start from such motives will not be done successfully. They cannot get the time, attention and care which are needed. Nor can they be presented to clients in a way which will catch on. There are superficial, brusque, even rejecting versions of these ideas which betray an 'on your bike' spirit.

A point well worth noting is that since the early 'eighties many services have appeared which are, basically, a centre which offers fixed appointments for group or individual sessions in various psychotherapeutic and behavioural therapies, rather like a non-medical out-patient clinic. Some of these have started as conventional day hospitals or day centres but transformed themselves to such a 'sessional therapy centre' model, the occupational and social side of the service being abandoned. Others have been set up

with notions of an American-style Community Mental
Health Centre. Quite a lot of mental health workers
would, it seems, like to shape their services in
this direction. One reason is that such centres
make really very good sense for meeting certain
types of client need. But it is also true that they
offer attractive opportunities to practise the
range of specialised therapies which nowadays
figure in the repertoires of many nurses, OTs,
social workers or psychologists. It must be
emphasised that such sessional therapy centres are
different from the style of outward-oriented day
service being advanced in this book. Sometimes the
two get confused with each other because they both
oppose traditional, all week, socially segregated
day centre programmes. But really this is about all
they share in common. So often the former ends up
wholly concerned with providing formal therapies,
frequently for people with relatively minor
problems, and ignores users' informal social or
occupational needs away from the service. For the
latter, the whole reason for challenging building-
bound day care programmes is to concentrate
on social and occupational opportunities outside
the building. Quite often, though, sessional
therapy centres associate themselves with arguments
like those advanced in this book. The acid test is
whether a service with such rhetoric can point to
features which are actually addressing social and
occupational opportunities. It is quite likely that
the model of a centre based round sessional
therapies will be familiar and attractive to some
of the staff of any new day service. Planners and
development workers should note that if a clear
alternative vision is not communicated and
sustained by management, then the sessional therapy
centre is a likely direction in which a new day
service may drift.

There is another familiar process through which
mental health workers end up still playing only the
more traditional mental health roles and not
getting involved with their clients' practical
opportunities. Sometimes such a new service starts
with the staff deciding that they will concentrate
on developing therapeutic and rehabilitation
programmes within the building for the first year
or two, then shift their energies to developing
links to opportunities in the local community. The
likelihood is that, when the time comes, all staff
time will already be fully committed and the
'cluster' side of the service never materialises.

There is, too, an intrinsic flaw in seeking to develop the 'core' side of the service in isolation from the practical opportunities to which it might lead. The same applies to the notion that in a 'core and cluster' service one group of staff can be involved in fairly conventional mental health roles within the service building, while the 'cluster' work is done entirely by external specialists, like attached community workers, social workers, employment development workers or by other organisations. It is excellent to involve people with relevant specialist abilities in areas like housing and employment, and to forge links with generic services and voluntary sector resources. But this should not be done in ways which insulate mental health workers from awareness of their clients' practical aspirations and opportunities. The principle must be that mental health workers work on both sides of the day centre door and can thus ensure that all aspects of the service relate to each other and to users' realities.

It is not only the service's actual staff who need careful and sustained briefing if a genuinely new type of service is to develop. Senior management may initially sponsor a scheme out of exaggerated hopes for client turnover and these may subsequently plague the service. Some senior managers are dominated by concerns that mental health day centres must not 'silt up' with permanent users. They may perceive the 'core and cluster' concept as promising accelerated client turnover and hence reducing long-term costs. If pressures to demonstrate turnover dominate a developing day service, it may preclude the accepting, non-pressurising attitude to 'leaving' which often seems necessary for users to work positively on alternatives to the service. It may also discourage the service from taking on people with serious difficulties. To counter false hopes, whoever is developing the service needs to educate senior managers concerning realistic expectations of turnover, a balanced understanding of 'dependency' and the realities of cyclical use and very long-term or permanent part-time use by people with serious problems. There is a tell-tale sign of a would-be 'core and cluster' service which is preoccupied with client turnover or 'throughput'. It is that most of its declared 'cluster' resources will be other social welfare institutions like other day centres, hospital-based industrial units or Part Three homes. The service has not in fact been seeking links to valued activities or settings in mainstream life. It hasn't mattered so much what people moved on to, so long as they did move on.

Planners and development workers need to recognise the paradox that the same approach to day services can attract both people who strongly want to work with their clients' everyday opportunities and people who are seeking a progressive-sounding alibi for limiting the time and money which goes in this direction. In many places quite a coalition of voices are calling for change in mental health day services. But they may represent very different perceptions and interests. Where a service is being planned jointly, it is essential to clarify as early as possible what everyone who is committing time or money hopes will be gained from the enterprise. Nearly everyone may agree with a single-paragraph planning document summary of the arguments for an outward-looking service. But each person will have understood it in different ways, support it for different reasons, and see a different aspect of its practical implications. Such differences in understanding should be assumed until agreement can actually be demonstrated in discussion of operational goals and roles. Clarifying details of operational policy is a good way of opening up diverging aims. How does each team member envisage the new service affecting his or her own day-to-day roles or the operation of other local services? Is success to be measured through what individuals are known to be doing away from the service? Or is it seen simply as their absence from the building? Such discussions may clarify differences in understanding and, hopefully, resolve them.

REACHING THE RIGHT PEOPLE

There is another process which can divert a new day service from a special brief to help people overcome the serious loss of roles, networks and opportunities which can sometimes follow mental illness. Sometimes it ends up with very few clients who really need such help. One reason can be that selection criteria are, in fact, excluding sufferers from the psychotic illnesses which are particularly likely to have had socially dislocating effects. A well recognised problem in community based services is that some staff teams discriminate against people with serious or long-term problems, preferring clients who are relatively advantaged or who may make good progress through short-term psychotherapy. But a newer route in the same direction is as follows.

Many new community mental health facilities start with a shared staff vision that their service should be as different as possible from the atmosphere of a mental hospital. The staff may place high value on an image of 'normality' and rightly be on their guard against anything which they feel introduces hospital-style practices or confers the stigma of mental illness on users. Many aspects of a service's image really do require such scrutiny - the building and its location, the service's name, its 'entry' rituals and procedures, its relationship with medical services, and the terminology used by staff, for instance. But a grave problem arises if among those reminders of hospital which you exclude are former hospital patients themselves. This can happen if staff distaste for traditional psychiatric roles and language keeps them from the discussions and procedures often required in referrals from psychiatric wards, which are prime sources for contacting people with socially dislocating psychotic illnesses. A staff team may themselves be blacklisted by such potential referral sources if no common language can be found. Such a team may end up seeking clients outside the 'psychiatric system', which may mean devoting its resources to people with less experience of mental illness. Sometimes staff see the presence of users with minor mental health problems as an index that they have succeeded in avoiding a 'psychiatric' image - "See, ordinary people feel OK to come here". Sometimes they may be reluctant to take on individuals with conspicuously more serious problems lest that were to put off other users. Another issue is that new day services quite often seek to distance themselves from hospitals through fear of control by the hospital - a fear which may be well-founded in reality.

But, whatever the reasons, there is a serious contradiction if a service with an aftercare brief seeks its referrals through local community centres and GPs, but leaves out psychiatric wards. How can such a service reach the people who need it most? If a service is concerned to redress loss and dislocation following illness, it needs to make itself a bridge from psychiatric hospital, hostel or family home to valued opportunities and community networks. Its means for seeking users are part of this role: it will need to reach out to some settings which are strongly associated with mental illness or social alienation. Furthermore, it may need to reach out quite actively since people who have recently suffered serious episodes of illness often lack energy or initiative. If a service relies on self-initiated referrals, it may miss many such people who might come with a little encouragement or direct invitation. An example of a positive response to these issues would be the practice at the Erconwald Mental Health Project, described in Chapter Five, whereby Project staff make weekly hospital visits to contact psychiatric in-patients who are from the Project's catchment. Likewise for the Salford Community Mental Health Project, described in Chapter Two, where work is often actually started while someone is still in hospital. Of course hospitals are not the only place where outreach work can contact appropriately disadvantaged people - there are also wholly non-medical settings, like some single-homeless accommodation. But hospitals are one logical starting point for a service pledged to continuity of aftercare and help back to a valued way of life.

NO DAY CENTRE?

Contacting and engaging people who are recovering from serious, disruptive illnesses also means being able to welcome and work with some individuals who suffer such after-effects from their illness that initially they cannot cope with ordinary expectations and pressures. This creates a quandary for the view that progressive rehabilitation and aftercare services should not possess any 'sheltered' premises at all. Some advocates for social desegregation argue that the best way to ensure that a service links to mainstream opportunities is to have no building, no day centre of any sort, where service users can congregate - or be relegated. They see this as forcing staff to work on an individual level and to find mainstream opportunities relevant for even their most disabled clients. They warn against the labelling effects of any building-created social group based on common experience of mental illness. They suspect an inherent drift for mental health services to revert to building-bound forms of service, particularly in respect of their more disabled clients, whenever staff have the option of a social milieu within the building.

Many of the interventions described in
previous chapters did not require a building. But it
it is those involving people with serious
difficulties which require scrutiny. The case example
in Chapter Two would be pertinent. Here a
person, who at initial contact was seriously
impaired and withdrawn as a result of her illness,
was gradually helped all the way to a job and a
home of her own. This was done without any use of
day unit or hostel buildings. There was,
nevertheless, a crucial need for a sheltered,
supportive, 'stepping-stone' environment in the
early stages, but it proved possible for the family
itself to supply this environment, given extensive
support and advice from the workers. Chapter Five
includes a brief description of how the Erconwald
Project worked with a seriously withdrawn young
man who initially needed some sort of social
environment, but one which did not demand ordinary
social responses from him. There, appropriate
'sheltered' opportunities were supplied through
unpressured access to social life within the
Project's building until he became able to venture
elsewhere, eventually getting work. How could one
offer people like these an appropriate
'stepping-stone' environment if neither
a sheltered social milieu nor a supportive home
situation were available? Some people would offer
answers like, for instance, that one could work
with local people to develop special voluntary
'jobs' with expectations which were adjusted to
offer relevant individuals the right initial
environment. But can such solutions be arranged for
the required numbers, with reliability and with the
speed which is necessary to meet needs as they
arise? Probably they can in some places. But in
others it might prove extremely difficult.
Communities vary considerably in the numbers of
people with serious difficulties and in the
mainstream resources available for helping them.
Every aftercare service needs some means for
responding to the person who initially can cope
with very little, on lines which match local needs
and resources. In many inner cities some use of
a 'sheltered' base within a 'core and cluster' model
may be the most practicable way of making a service
genuinely available. Desegregation of mental health
services seems to require constant self-scrutiny
that help is not being put outside the reach of
those who need it most.

WHEN AN ESTABLISHED SERVICE SEEKS TO CHANGE

Some different issues arise when, rather than a new service, an established day centre is seeking fresh emphasis on opportunities away from the building. One prime issue is to recognise how the dynamics of the whole service affect and are affected by moves in this direction. Of course introducing 'cluster' activities or work on outside networks can only be done gradually, step by step at propitious moments. But gradual transition is not the same as partial transition. Introducing things like work activities away from the centre, work with an individual on a class at an AEI, or an evening family visit all take staff time away from providing activities in the building. They take user time away from attending such activities. Gradual routes in this particular direction seem to lead sooner or later to a turning point where staff have to consider major changes in how they allocate their time. Past a point it is not possible to run the two systems side by side, both in terms of contradictory demands on staff time and the inward pull of a structured, centre-based activity programme. A number of day centres which began developing more outward-oriented features have found that one could add on new features piecemeal up to a point. Then one had to consider subtracting existing ones. This can mean users and staff losing some valued roles and activities within the centre. It may be important for a centre to acknowledge this plainly. Some of the practices which get displaced in this transition are good and useful. The new arrangements, however, should offer greater overall benefits.

A turning point is forced, too, by the need to negotiate with senior management over yardsticks for monitoring output which promote the new directions rather than hinder them. If being effective means that your clients are developing sustaining involvements away from the centre building, then daily average numbers attending inside it are a wholly inappropriate means for assessing workload, effectiveness and desirable staffing levels. It may be necessary to negotiate, too, concerning staff roles and training and budgetting arrangements which permit the sort of occasional payments and travelling expenses which this sort of service needs. Redefining catchment boundaries and referral criteria may be necessary to work within users' home localities.

Negotiations here are more complex, since to change
one unit's boundaries is to change those of others.
Quite soon one is discussing policy changes across
an Authority.

MAKING SPACE FOR WORK WITH INDIVIDUALS

Revising a service like this is difficult. It
requires discrimination between those compromises
which are necessary for the time being to keep the
support of staff, users and senior management and
those compromises which so water down new ways of
working that they render them ineffective. A
crucial step in many centres is to free some staff
time from commitments to working with users in
groups. Achieving this overcomes a major practical
obstacle to one-to-one work, working outside the
centre or outside centre hours. A compromise which
is never worth making is to go along with pressures
to always use groups, rather than individual work.
Quite often when a day centre team do take up
users' resources and opportunities outside the
centre, they do so wholly through group activities
- groups to investigate community facilities,
groups to seek out local work opportunities, groups
to study welfare benefits. While often such group
approaches can be very helpful and productive,
there are also common situations where they are
wholly inappropriate, self-defeating even, for
these particular purposes. Perhaps the single most
common flaw in day centre initiatives intended to
enhance clients' opportunities away from the centre
is blanket reliance on groups, to the exclusion of
one-to-one work.

Sometimes there are strong pressures on day
centre staff to do everything through groups. Some
day units are really grossly understaffed. Staff
may find working in groups the only practicable way
to share out attention or to fit in rehabilitation
roles alongside making users feel welcome and
seeing that all goes well. But there can also be
pressures at centres where staffing is adequate.
For instance there are those day units which are
structured so that each user has a daily timetable
of a sequence of small groups, often a mixture of
therapy groups and craft activities. Staff play an
active, leader role in these groups and this may
take up most staff time. Should a staff member seek
to withdraw from leading some groups in order to
work with individuals, then the question arises as
to how the clients in those groups would now spend

the time. If they join other staff members' groups,
the numbers in these will rise, which may threaten
the way these groups can be run and the job-
satisfaction of the staff concerned. If they simply
sit around drinking tea, this may be seen by quite
a few staff teams as undermining a desirable day
centre ethos, whereby everyone appears engaged in
some sort of programme. Rather than challenge
colleagues' values and work practices, a staff
member, who wants to address opportunities outside
the centre, may agree to provide a group activity
at his or her slot on the timetable and then seek
to focus it outside the centre.

Besides these pressures there are also obvious
positive aspects to adopting a group approach. As
Chapters Seven and Fifteen make clear, collective
projects outside the centre can have much to offer
- people being able to support each other, becoming
friends or sharing each other's interests or
resources. It is not surprising therefore that day
centre workers quite often take a group approach
without second thoughts. Those chapters just
mentioned convey adequately the positive aspects of
working with people in groups on opportunities away
from the service. Here we focus on its
shortcomings. It is worth asking the following four
questions about any approach for helping people
develop opportunities away from a day centre.

Can this enable individuals to cope on their own?

People should have the opportunity to pursue their
own private directions, should they so wish. A
notable problem is programmes which, because they
always involve people doing things together, do not
address major challenges which face an individual
on their own. Such group ventures often bypass
issues like handling social interchange and
transport on one's own, taking initiatives and
keeping appointments oneself, and finding
activities which really interest you rather than
those where you are simply prepared to accompany
others. It is quite easy to underestimate how many
obstacles get bypassed for individuals when they
are doing something as part of a group.

What staff presence is needed for this to last?

Some centres seek to work through groups precisely
because groups do bypass so many obstacles and
enable their members to do things they cannot

do on their own. This is no problem if staff
acknowledge that, say, a weekly pub outing may
always need their presence. But sometimes staff
hope that staff-led group outings to mainstream
facilities, like sports-centres or pubs for
instance, will turn into regular social events for
that group of people, who will keep on going
together if the paid workers withdraw. But for this
to succeed requires that the group evolves the
same sort of relationships, dynamics and decision-
making as you find in any situation where
people choose to go an outing together. If such
natural companionship does not evolve, then the
staff involved may find that a well-attended
activity, which they have been organising, ceases
the moment they withdraw. If you go somewhere in
the company of others, you are affirming a
relationship with at least one of your companions.
Sometimes members of such a group may start off by
seeing themselves as accompanying the paid worker,
but accepting no special link with each other.
If the staff member pulls out and you continue with
the outing, you are defining at least some of your
companions as your chosen friends, supporters, or
as kindred spirits because there is now no other
reason for you to be with them. If people cannot
identify with such implied relationships, they may
discontinue something in which they were actually
quite interested. Besides this question of how
real friendships form in artificially created
social groups, staff-provided transport and money
can also influence whether such ventures continue.

Can this address the needs, interests and
resources of service users as individuals?

A group-based programme can risk glossing over the
talents, interests, resources and opportunities of
individuals if it needs 'common denominator'
activities in which all can take interest. This is
perilous if one hopes to help people to develop
activities and social connections which might
become major, lasting resources. So much of what a
person needs to build on is highly individual -
long-standing ambitions, past interests and skills,
reviving old acquaintances, opportunities which
come your way through family or friends. If a
service helps people explore opportunities for
valued activities only through shared ventures, it
risks ignoring those highly individual seeds for
activities and relationships which can have meaning

for just one individual.

Can this address opportunities for major
involvements?

An inter-related issue is attention to the sorts of
of involvements which can offer someone a major
source of sustenance, interest, or sense of
identity or purpose - as contrasted with occasional,
'one-off' entertainment activities, which are
pleasurable when one is feeling like it but rarely
the sort of thing round which you can base your
life. Many services nowadays are accomplished at
introducing people to the latter, often through
group visits to facilities like leisure centres,
libraries, swimming pools, pubs or museums. But
opportunities for major involvements usually prove
much harder and often involve sources which can
only be addressed on an individual level. For
instance, for much of the population it is paid
employment, intimate relationships and family
roles which are the main sources. Notably, many
long-term sufferers from mental illness lack all
three. There are fairly few common other sources.
Roles in community organisations, clubs and
societies, church and political organisations are
one direction. Voluntary work is another, sometimes
with a special level of meaning like the political
or religious motivations which Fryer and Payne
noted in their study of people who coped well with
unemployment (1). Leisure activities which supply a
major focus in life often involve long-term goals,
like serious hobbies or mastering a skill, or a
social context, like competitive sports and hobbies
or activities which require commitment to
membership of teams, societies or classes. Or they
may offer regular social links or an identity
which is valued locally. Such sources for major
roles tend so often to be things which can only be
approached on an individual level, precisely
because they need a type of interest, commitment or
skill which is usually highly individual. If a day
centre approaches its outward-oriented work solely
through groups, it risks having to ignore such
opportunities for major involvements. Instead it is
likely to focus on occasional entertainment or
leisure activities since in our society these are
customarily approached in couples or groups and
thus readily fit a collective framework. But to
make this point is in no way to belittle the value
of helping people who suffer social fears to feel

131

comfortable about venturing into public leisure facilities.

It is worth noting that Chapter Fifteen, for instance, includes examples of collective arrangements where the answer to all four questions would be 'yes'. Likewise for Chapter Seven which describes some voluntary work projects successfully organised on a group basis, as well as those negotiated for individuals. Nevertheless the problems just listed are commonplace. No day centre should be staffed or organised in a way which rules out significant one-to-one work.

POSITIVE STEPS TO PROMOTE FOCUS ON EVERYDAY OPPORTUNITIES AND RESOURCES

Suggestions have been made concerning obstacles to watch out for, when starting a new service or re-orienting an established one. But what positive steps can a planner or development worker take to communicate the vision behind plans for a service which addresses opportunities in users' everyday lives?

Previous chapters indicate how basic parameters need adjusting to assist an outward-looking approach: location, catchment size, job description and staff ratios, flexible budgetting, freedom to recruit sessional workers, and management attitudes to building occupancy. One more can be mentioned - a building which is not too capacious. For instance the planner behind one successful service consciously picked a building so under-sized for the scheduled caseload that the staff would have to partly work outside it.

But these are all things which facilitate. They cannot on their own fill new staff with the spirit in which a service is intended. Much simply has to depend on the vision and skills of the staff who launch the new service. But perhaps there are a couple of steps a planner can take to set them looking in the desired direction.

Without seeking absurd degrees of long-range control, it should be practicable to prescribe some basic structures which encourage staff to notice certain aspects of their clients' lives. It could be required, for instance, that every client receive a home visit early on, which may give staff a fuller initial picture of each individual's life. It could be required at the outset that staff discuss with each new client their practical

132

situation and aspirations, using some structured formula which ensures that a broad picture is grasped and which provides a written record usable for case-reviews and service monitoring. Such a procedure could draw, for instance, from the eight areas of life investigated in the survey of service users' views of 'quality of life' by Lehman and his colleagues, which is summarised in Chapter One : family contacts, home situation, friends, work, income/ poverty, leisure activities, general health, and safety from crime (2). Staff could be required to record each new client's circumstances and wishes in these areas. One could also use a goal-setting exercise, like that described in Chapter Two, to identify areas of life where a person wishes to rectify losses they have suffered as a result of their mental illness. Lipton's study of losses of relationships following schizophrenia, summarised in Chapter One, may add ideas for how to record changes in a person's social world (3). Chapter Two's case-example also illustrates how a person's strengths and potential resources can be used to suggest directions to work in. Chapter Three offers the idea of using a week's diary as a guide to self-perceived resources and gaps in a person's everyday life. Such approaches can have a multiple function of increasing staff awareness, giving clients a framework for deciding what help they want, and monitoring objectively what changes are being achieved. Another resource for orienting staff this way would be the model for contractual work on client-selected goals described in Falloon and Talbot's 1982 paper, 'Achieving the Goals of Day Treatment' (4).

The above procedures do depend on the service working with appropriate people, since it is really developing the service round its initial users. Here too a planner can supply advance assistance. Positive operational criteria for the people whom the service is particularly concerned to reach can be drawn up, rather than simply categories who are excluded. These criteria might emphasise lack of friends, occupation, home, money and other resources for recovery. Here too it should be possible to monitor and review whether the service is operating as intended. It would be possible, too, to prescribe some sort of regular liaison arrangement with the local hospital.

Another benefit to a new service would be

support, liaison and review from an outside group
or committee with enough involvement in its
planning to value the service and the hopes behind
it. Such a body might helpfully co-ordinate
periodic monitoring and review. It is in the early
stages that such elements are most important. Once
established, the sense of tangible, demonstrable
results, which this orientation should offer,
should provide ample encouragement to continue.

NOTES

1. D.Fryer and R.L.Payne, 'Towards
understanding proactivity in unemployment',
1982a, Memo 540 MRC/ SSRC Social and Applied
Psychology Unit, University of Sheffield

2. Anthony Lehman, Nancy Ward and Lawrence
Linn, 'Chronic mental patients: the quality of life
issue', American Journal of Psychiatry, Volume 139,
1982, pp. 1271-1275

3. Frank Lipton, Carl Cohen, Elizabeth Fischer,
Stephen Katz, 'Schizophrenia: a network crisis',
Schizophrenia Bulletin, Volume 7, 1981, Issue No.1

4. Ian Falloon and Ralph Talbot, 'Achieving the
goals of day treatment', Journal of Nervous and
Mental Disease, Volume 170, 1982, pp. 279-285

Chapter Seven

VOLUNTARY WORK AND ADULT EDUCATION: ONE DAY
CENTRE'S EXPERIENCE

Jan Marsden

Editorial Introduction

Harpurhey Centre is a Social Services mental
health day centre in Manchester. Together
with Victoria Park, another Manchester day
centre, it is part of a local service network
with a long tradition of helping users get
voluntary work. Here Jan Marsden, Group
Therapist in Charge at Harpurhey Centre,
describes different ways in which the centre
has used voluntary work, examples of
individual-based and group-based approaches to
getting a voluntary work project started, and
practical aspects of encouraging centre users
in voluntary work and responding to
difficulties and apprehensions. The chapter
also describes Harpurhey Centre's use of a
local Adult Education scheme which offers
opportunity to study for formal educational
credits. These are available across a range
of standards, so that individuals can try and
succeed at whatever level matches their
current ability.

PRE-CONDITIONS FOR ENCOURAGING CLIENTS TO MOVE ON
TO VOLUNTARY WORK

The type of centre and the 'ethos' has a direct
relationship with how the clients see themselves.
This in turn creates pre-conditions for people
wanting to and being able to move from the centre
to the 'community'. Here are factors which we feel
contribute to the readiness to go out to voluntary
work at Harpurhey:

*   Only a minority of members are expected to stay
    for a very long period of time. Needs and
    especially the potential of an individual are
    assessed at initial interview and reviewed at
    regular intervals (which of course include the
    client).

*   The emphasis in the centre is on a person's
    positive qualities, not on illness and
    dependence on hospital. Members are told that
    although s/he may have had a breakdown or
    whatever in the past (and may possibly be
    admitted to hospital in the future), now s/he
    is out of hospital. Although s/he may still
    have problems, s/he is now expected to develop
    goals which are directed towards living or
    working in the wider community.

*   In addition to the built-in expectation that a
    member will make 'progress' (which of course
    can only be defined individually), the emphasis
    in the centre is on self-help and mutual
    support. Members are discouraged from seeing
    themselves as recipients of treatment. Instead
    they are encouraged to see themselves more and
    more as people who are in the position to give
    support to others and have personal qualities
    and skills to contribute to the general well
    being. One consequence is that when members
    take on duties or carry out tasks which they
    have never tackled before, support and
    encouragement comes from other members as well
    as staff. Thus centre members respond to
    someone contemplating starting voluntary work
    with encouragement and support.

*   There is a 'tradition' of people moving on to
    voluntary work and having found this a positive
    experience. By word of mouth voluntary work is
    known as a positive option. For the last ten
    years or so, members from Victoria Park centre
    and later Harpurhey have been taking part in
    voluntary work projects.

*   There is a general emphasis on outside
    activities in our time-table - such as sport,
    outings to museums and exhibitions, trips to
    the seaside, evening drives to pubs, etc. In
    this way members can become accustomed to using
    buses, and generally finding their way round
    strange places. This also gives opportunities
    to practice techniques learned through social
    skills training in realistic settings but with
    support available. Different members go on
    errands for the centre - to local shops,
    delivering letters, to town for shopping.

We have used voluntary work in all sorts of
ways and for all sorts of purposes. Some people
have used it as a stepping-stone to employment.
Some have sought it as a long-term end in itself,
after leaving the centre. For some it has offered a
short period of change or experimentation away from
the centre, a chance to test out something
different. Many different arrangements are
possible. Sometimes people do voluntary work a
couple of days a week, while retaining the support
of the centre on others. We have worked with
individuals on many single-person voluntary work
placements. But we have sometimes done it with
groups too, where more capable centre members
support others. Sometimes a couple of centre
members have supported each other. We have used,
too, a wide range of settings and services where
voluntary work is needed.

Voluntary work first became important over ten
years ago when it was introduced to Daisy Bank, one
of the other Manchester centres, then to Harpurhey.
In those days it was chiefly used as a full-time
permanent outlet for an individual after leaving
the centre. Close links were formed between the
centre and Community Transport, an organisation
which gathers together cast-off furniture and
supplies it at low cost to people in need. They
also operate a reasonably priced removal service
and hire out minibuses. About ten volunteers are
needed to load and unload the vans and to accompany
the drivers. In past years, when employment was not
quite so scarce, working a couple of months with
Community Transport made it easier to get a job
because it was more impressive to tell an employer
one was doing voluntary work than attending a day
centre. Then, most people who worked at Community
Transport later got and kept jobs. Most people who
use this particular voluntary work opportunity have
been employment oriented and ready for work. They
have accepted voluntary work as a stop gap measure.
Of course, it is much more difficult to get a job
now. But some centre members go on to work for CT.
(Less now that CT accepts volunteers from MSC
schemes). Three of them have in fact been given
paid employment as drivers by CT, resulting from
their voluntary efforts. We developed close
contact with the management of Community Transport,
who were very helpful. Because so many placements
were successful, it became relatively easy for our
people to be accepted. Occasionally we have been
able to ask CT to try someone whom we anticipate

137

may cause problems, like sometimes not turning up or being withdrawn. The style and organisation of CT has facilitated acceptance - it is an informal, democratic organisation involving many students.

Community Transport has, in general, offered full-time, quite demanding work to men who were now fit and capable and recovered from their illness. But we have also promoted part-time or temporary voluntary work for people with different needs, often more vulnerable. This is especially appropriate for someone who wants to try something new and more challenging but would like to keep their place at the centre and would perhaps not venture out without the safety-net of the centre. If someone spends two or three days a week at voluntary work and two or three days in the centre, problems can be recognised and hopefully sorted out. Here is an example of how the centre set up a two day a week voluntary work placement, helping to decorate a community centre, for one young man, then worked with him on problems he faced in completing the project successfully.

> Joe, then aged 28, had been receiving help from mental health services, on and off, over the previous ten years before he came to Harpurhey. He got on quite well at the centre. However after a few months Joe and the staff came to the conclusion that it would be a positive move for him to do something outside the centre, as a preparation for possible future employment. This was despite Joe's fears of facing a new situation and new people.

> So a voluntary work project was set up. Beforehand the ground was prepared. The organiser of the community centre came up to Harpurhey and was shown around, told all about the centre and our aims. We exchanged ideas for involving some of our members in helping at their centre, eg. decorating, making tea, teaching dancing, teaching handicrafts. Our staff outlined the sort of problems that could arise generally and assured the organiser that we would be on hand with support if they did arise.

> Joe was accompanied on the initial visit by a staff member. Although the community centre organiser knew that Joe had had psychiatric

138

problems, the other workers were not told
this. In fact he told them himself later on.
It was arranged that Joe should go to the
community centre two days a week. This was
two days mid-week so we could give support
before and after. However at first this did
not work out. Joe sometimes did not attend or
he would leave for lunch and not go back. We
discussed this with Joe. He felt he was
unsure of what exactly he was supposed to do
and was too shy to ask. He also felt lonely
when he was working, although he felt he had a
good relationship with the caretaker and the
kitchen staff. Eventually the problem was
sorted out by another member of the centre,
Paul, going to this project and working with
Joe. Paul did not particularly want to do
voluntary work. But he was an easy going
person who accepted the opportunity to try a
different job. He was in fact an electrician
who hoped to eventually return to his trade.
The two men completed the project
successfully. Paul went on to do electrical
jobs in Social Services minimum support homes
on a voluntary basis.

There is another aspect to involving people
who are still quite troubled in voluntary work.
Some people find that a role in a 'normal' social
setting helps them control their behaviour. One
woman went from Harpurhey to a community centre
every lunch time to help serve meals at the
luncheon club. She was in fact quite an unstable
person with a long history of overdoses and abuse
of alcohol and medication. Both she and the centre
staff felt that this work role contributed to her
having a relatively long period of being on an even
keel.

VOLUNTARY WORK PROJECT ON A GROUP BASIS

So we give this sort of individual-focussed
support for voluntary work as part of a person's
individual rehabilitation programme. Sometimes it
is towards voluntary work as someone moves away
from the centre. Sometimes, like the example just
given, it is temporary or part-time. We also
sometimes set up projects where groups of centre
members engage in voluntary work. An especially
useful feature is how more capable members can
support those who are less so. Here is an example:

At Victoria Park centre we got in touch with
the specialist social worker for three
residential units for mentally handicapped
children. These units had practical needs
which our social worker felt our members could
perhaps help with. The social worker for the
mentally handicapped children came to the
centre, was shown round, met members and staff
and later spoke at a business meeting asking
the community for assistance. This resulted
in a group of 15 people volunteering an
interest in helping. Staff divided these into
three groups each with a balanced range of
capabilities.

Each group 'adopted' a unit and went there as
a group to meet the officer in charge, look
around and meet the children. They came back
with a list of needs. Most of their
requirements were articles we were able to
make, eg. floor cushions and aprons,
disposable Mr Men posters. When the goods
were completed, the group took them up to the
unit.

This was the end of the group project. But it
had longer term consequences for a couple of
individuals, besides the experience of
tackling and achieving this task. It led in
fact to one member spending one day a week in
a handicapped children's school on a voluntary
basis and eventually going on a teacher
training course which specialised in the needs
of handicapped children. Another member took
a couple of days off from the centre each week
to go to one of the units and play records for
the kids. This proved a great attraction for
them!

Another group project was initiated when a
local community worker came to the business meeting
at Daisy Bank to talk about needs in the local
community. This led to centre members setting up a
service for pensioners to have their hair shampooed
and set in their homes. Information about this
service was circulated by the community worker and
a regular clientele built up. Members who
volunteered to give this service discussed it
beforehand, especially concerning any problems they
might anticipate. As a general rule at least one

experienced member would accompany what was usually
two or three people on each occasion from the
'pool' of volunteers. Staff participated at first,
especially to make sure the scheme was running
smoothly. They gradually dropped out as the
members felt confident and proved their competence.
Two of the women who were particularly active in
this group left the centre to do hospital visiting
and escorting patients.

Another group voluntary work project which has
operated at Harpurhey has involved members
repairing and constructing toys for Social Services
Day Nurseries. This would entail a couple of
members going to each nursery with a Social
Services driver and van. They would deliver and
pick up items, discuss requirements and collect
payment.

ISSUES TO CONSIDER WHEN PLANNING A VOLUNTARY WORK
PLACEMENT

Careful and accurate assessment of an
individual is vital to successful placement.
Because much of our work in the centre is based on
our relationship with the client, the centre staff
have confidence that our assessment is accurate.
However we also learn from our mistakes. We must
bear in mind that there may be unexpected aspects
to the situation where the client will be working,
which our assessment has not taken into account.
So obviously as much information as possible about
the voluntary work agency is helpful, especially a
visit or some first hand experience by staff. We
have used, in fact, a wide variety of opportunities
for voluntary work. For instance:

* Social Services establishments, both those with
  a mental health remit like group homes and
  others, like nurseries and old people's homes.

* Community centres, and clubs, also community
  workers.

* Independent voluntary organisations eg.
  Community Transport.

* In Manchester there are volunteer organisers
  attached to some Area Social Services offices.

With respect to the client, we need to assess their abilities from the skills and qualities they have shown in the centre. Some clients are ready for a working situation and would obviously prefer full-time permanent opportunities. At the other end of the spectrum a person may have limited abilities and a low level of concentration but feel that he or she would like a change. For this person, staff need to assess how much support a person will need and whether they can realistically offer this. Here are some questions worth asking:

Does the person have whatever skills and knowledge, whatever physical strength and mobility this job requires?

Can this person cope with any stressful features of this work? What might these be? Are there deadlines to be met? How much contact with other people will be required? Are they likely to be difficult to cope with? How would this person cope with these stresses?

Do practical considerations add up - distance from home, access to transport, a place to eat lunch? These mundane points can make or break a project.

Are situations likely, which this individual fears could tempt them to act unwisely - to dishonesty, for instance?

Is this person sufficiently in control of symptoms to manage socially in the placement in question? Do they have the insight to withdraw and rapidly seek help, if symptoms suddenly get worse?

Here are a couple of points worth bearing in mind with respect to the sort of work opportunities which different individuals seemed to find rewarding.

Shy and unconfident people often relate more easily to children and possibly also to older people, rather than people of their own age. Many people respond to being given a caring role and responsibility for other people. Sometimes we found that a person who was not particularly co-operative in the role of recipient of 'treatment' would react quite differently when in

142

the role of someone who is giving.

When we are hoping that a particular agency might offer voluntary work to one of our members, the staff from the centre make the initial overtures. Although we feel that clients should be involved as much as possible in deciding their future, agencies do not respond as readily if the client makes the approach. Refusal is more likely and resulting disappointment and loss to confidence. We would usually ask key people from a 'customer' organisation to visit the centre. We would explain the work we are doing and convey the differing needs of different individuals. We would assure our support and aim to inspire the other agency with the feeling that our judgement could be trusted. Of course no-one can give a cast-iron guarantee that a placement will be successful. But we would explain our assessment procedure and also find out from the organisation exactly what they would expect from a volunteer. Our experience has shown that direct contact is most effective and likely to achieve results. We have found, too, that successful voluntary work placements at one agency lead to word of mouth reputation and approaches from other agencies.

FEARS AND RELUCTANCES ABOUT ENGAGING IN VOLUNTARY WORK

These are much the same as one would encounter in any situation where someone is contemplating a change in way of life, like beginning a job or moving home. Mainly it is lack of confidence. If so it is helpful to discuss exactly what situations that s/he fears will be hard to cope with. For example, many clients feel alarmed at the prospect of meeting new people and feel that they will not have the know-how to start conversations. We would perhaps discuss how s/he felt when s/he first started at the centre, and thereby point out how they had successfully coped with that situation. We might recap on conversation-centred groups which they attended in the centre. We might possibly have an impromptu role-playing session. We have found it is important to reassure people that our support is still available even if they leave the centre to do voluntary work. We stress that they should get in touch, if problems arise, even to the extent of phoning a staff member at home. If necessary, we allocate time at regular intervals for staff and client to discuss the progress of

voluntary work, especially the part-time variety.
We emphasise to clients going out that their
performance will affect the future for other
ex-mentally ill people from day centres. If a
voluntary work agency has a positive experience
with someone from the centre, they are more likely
to accept others in the future.

ASSESSMENT OF THE SUCCESS OF VOLUNTARY WORK

Many voluntary work positions are not
particularly long term. Often the task is
completed, therefore terminating the arrangement.
Sometimes the work changes in character. The
volunteer can feel that s/he wishes to give up the
work for a variety of reasons, eg. to move on to
paid employment. People's feelings about a period
of voluntary work can be used as an indicator of
its success. Usually we have found that a period
of voluntary work has made a person more confident,
more able to cope with new situations and notably
willing to tackle something similar in the future.

ADULT EDUCATION

A more recent venture at Harpurhey Day Centre
is that of involvement with Education in the centre
and in local colleges. Day time basic education
and evening classes have always been an option for
centre members, but have not been used much in the
past. Younger people seemed generally more
amenable to continuing education, however for many
older people and some younger ones the experience
of school had been negative or even traumatic. The
feedback from centre members indicates that often
they had been in large classes where the teaching
methods may not have fitted their individual needs,
people had been ridiculed for making mistakes or
being slow learners, teachers were seen as
unapproachable and physical punishment administered
frequently. Some members missed school through ill
health. Some older people were particularly
conscious of having had a 'poor' education. Added
to this was lack of self-confidence, feeling
stigmatised, and reluctance to try new ventures.
All these factors created anxiety about education
and courses.
The first venture into providing for the
educational needs of members took place about seven
years ago; we observed that a number of our members
had difficulties regarding reading and writing.

Consequently, centre staff undertook training in literacy teaching techniques and worked with individuals in the centre. Later we were able to obtain literacy tutors in the centre as part of a general realisation at that time that many adults in the community at large had literacy needs. This class continues at present.

However, the first major breakthrough occurred when the Community Liaison Officer at Manchester Polytechnic put us in touch with a project called Manchester Open College Federation. The Open College scheme enables people to gain 'credits' for the work that they undertake, these credits being awarded at four levels, level 1 being quite basic and level 4 being O/A level standard. A predetermined but flexible syllabus is established, units of credit are evaluated based on this and based on the number of hours' work which would usually be required to attain credits. We felt this scheme would be most appropriate to members' needs for several reasons: credits could be given at all levels of ability, there were no stressful exams or tests, work did not have to be college based but could take place in the centre, also we felt that a positive experience of learning in the centre would boost confidence and perhaps even lead to more members taking up college courses. We therefore became the first pilot outreach scheme for Open College.

Several meetings took place at which many members showed interest in this project and the most popular subjects for study were chosen, these were Maths, English and Art. The Education Department agreed to fund teachers for three two-hour sessions each week.

Straightaway we found that members who would not contemplate courses out of the centre were willing to try out these sessions within the secure environment of the centre and because members had chosen the subjects themselves, greater commitment was evident. Members were pleasantly surprised that they were being treated as adults, and that the competitiveness of school had been replaced by either group projects based on co-operation or individual programmes and one-to-one teaching.

At first the teachers were based in the centre, but as changes took place in the provision of outreach education, teachers came from local colleges. Often the same teachers taught in both places which was very reassuring for members who ventured into colleges. Day centre staff were able

to discuss the general issues and needs of day
centre members with teachers and thereby develop a
deeper understanding in colleges of the
difficulties which many centre members face.

At this point it would be useful to illustrate
how different members have used the education
classes in the centre to meet their own particular
needs and how they feel about this experience; some
people have put this in their own words.

John is a man in his late thirties who,
despite numerous admissions to hospital, has worked
for periods of time and hopes eventually to return
to paid employment. He lives in his own home with
his wife and two young children. This is what he
says:

> "Education at the Day Centre has been very
> beneficial to me and other members of the Day
> Centre. I had a very poor education at
> school, which probably contributed to the
> illness that I've been suffering from. My
> Maths and English have improved. I have
> gained level 2 credit for writing workshop and
> brought my Maths up to standard to take an O
> level Mathematics course.
>
> This kind of education helps me with day-to-
> day problems, working out my DHSS
> entitlements, reading DHSS and Housing
> letters, form filling, etc. and obviously
> increases my chances of employment. Practical
> subjects such as woodwork and pottery, well
> woodwork has been extremely beneficial to me.
> I'm doing jobs at home which I thought were
> well beyond my ability, which is quite useful
> and saves money. I think woodwork does not
> only increase chances of employment but also
> self-employment! The education courses at the
> centre have given me confidence and
> motivation, lifting my depression which is
> part of the illness that I suffer from.
> Learned men of thousands of years ago came to
> this conclusion - 'One who does not increase
> his knowledge decreases it.'"

Eric is a man in his late fifties who was
referred to the centre to alleviate the stress of
him caring for his sick wife. He was persuaded to
try out the English class: this contributed to him
being transformed from being withdrawn and
uncommunicative to an outgoing man who enjoys

writing so much now that he writes for the local
paper and composes fund-raising appeals. Despite
the death of his wife, he has maintained his
interest and thoroughly appreciates the
opportunities offered in the centre.
       Joan is a West Indian woman in her early
sixties, who has suffered from severe depression
for a number of years following the death of her
husband. Joan had missed out on her basic
education as a child and had problems with both
reading and writing. At first because Joan felt
quite ashamed of her difficulties she was reluctant
to involve herself in the literacy classes and she
would attend intermittently with limited success.
However, at the time the Open College classes
started, she expressed an interest in the Maths
class and it was discovered that she has an innate
ability with numbers. Joan's confidence and self-
esteem increased and she gained a number of
credits. Following this Joan became involved in
administrative work in the centre, working with
money. This gave her an incentive to improve her
literacy skills and she rejoined the literacy
class. She has recently made vast improvements in
reading and writing and is considering joining an
outside class in literacy so that she can devote
more time to this.
       Vincent is a man aged 40 who was in a long
stay institution for 20 years before coming to the
centre. He moved back to Manchester into a
rehabilitation hostel four years ago and now lives
in a Social Services group home. He had much
learning to do, particularly coping with everyday
life, an important part of this being use of basic
literacy and numeracy skills. Vincent undertook
this work in the centre and this year has taken the
plunge and enrolled in college classes.
       At present there are 40 people on the register
at the centre, of these 39 people take part in one
or more classes in the centre. 13 people attend a
variety of classes in local colleges. There has
been a steady progression of people gaining Open
College credits. In 1984/85, 25 members gained
credits in one or more subjects. Sets of credit
per subject were 14 for English and 13 for Art.
Also this year some members moved up to level 3
work.
       In conclusion the introduction of education
into the centre has been highly successful in many
ways. Members have a strong sense of pride in
their achievements, the awarding of credits being

viewed as a valuable acknowledgement of this.
Knowledge gained relates to other activities in the
centre and to the 'real world', some examples of
this having already been quoted. Members' horizons
have been broadened from seeing education in a
narrow academic sense to all sorts of suggestions
for future courses. Expectations of what they can
participate in are much more imaginative than a few
years ago. Members are more willing to take risks
and face the world with confidence. Thus
attendance at a day centre has become for many a
gateway to stimulation, new interests and new
opportunities.

Chapter Eight

STRATEGIES TO COUNTER POVERTY

Charles Patmore

Editorial Introduction

This chapter discusses reasons why action
concerning poverty can be essential to helping
people re-establish themselves following
mental illness. It lists some practical
responses which are illustrated in subsequent
chapters. Notably, it describes the DHSS
regulations relevant to running an amenity
fund financed through voluntary work, a little
used possibility with wide potential
application. Practical examples of such funds
are described in chapters 10 and 11. Please
note that most actual figures involved in
welfare benefit payments are regularly changed
and those mentioned in this book should be
assumed to have altered unless enquiry reveals
otherwise.

Today's great shortage of jobs means that for many
people life after mental illness means years
without end on low Supplementary Benefit incomes.
Living on very low incomes can have major effects
on social opportunities, morale and mental health.
Low incomes hit home particularly hard if you lack
any savings to handle emergencies or to take up
opportunities for small treats, or if you cannot
get loans or gifts from relatives or friends for
such purposes. Hardship is compounded, too, if you
lack possessions from past days of plenty, be it a
nice flat or house, clothes, television, records,
books, equipment for hobbies - any of the
possessions or resources which many people build up
in the course of their lives. Such poverty has an
extra impact if it seems your unending lot, when
after running out of all your reserves you can see
no prospect of ever having more to live on.
     People recovering from mental illness are
significantly more likely than other Supplementary
Benefit claimants to suffer these aggravations to
poverty. They are disadvantaged from employment by
virtue of their psychiatric record. They thus have

less chance of ever escaping to a higher income
through a job. They are more likely to lack
friends or relatives who will help financially, in
view of the loss of social contacts which quite
often accompanies mental illness. Furthermore
their chances of being low on possessions are
greater as well. Someone who experiences repeated
hospital admissions may sooner or later lose their
home and any possessions beyond what he or she can
carry or which can be stored. Then there is the
likelihood that people recovering from mental
illness will fail to press a full benefit claim,
something which surveys have demonstrated.

Of course, this does not apply to everyone.
Some sufferers from mental illness do not have
money problems, owing to combinations of invalidity
and disablement pensions, well-off spouses or
relatives, and personal reserves. But others
experience their lives as dominated by a poverty
which chokes their most basic opportunities.
Mental health workers need to absorb the various
ways that poverty can affect their clients' lives.
They need to assess for whom poverty is a major
issue, when a person's resources are viewed in
total - income, savings, possessions, resources
available from relatives, co-residents or friends.
They need, as a priority, to develop some basic
practical strategies which can help.

One way in which poverty affects mental health
is the unending austerity and self-restriction if a
Supplementary Benefit income really has to cover
everything. Ann Davis is a Social Work Lecturer at
Birmingham University who has worked to publicise
the financial problems of psychiatric service
users. She describes it like this:

"Living on social security means counting
every penny, it means trying to understand and
communicate with a large, confusing and
understaffed government organisation - the
DHSS. It means hours of your life are spent
waiting and queueing, it means frustration,
anger, anxiety and depression for millions of
claimants and their families. When you are a
claimant you confront poverty every day. The
problems of managing on your income are
formidable. At the moment a single person
with their own home to run is entitled to
£26.80 a week Supplementary Benefit to cover
all their basic living expenses which include
(according to law) food; fuel; buying,

cleaning, repairing and replacing clothing and shoes; travel; laundry costs; toilet articles; cleaning materials; replacement of small household goods like bulbs, crockery; leisure and amenity items such as TV licence and rental; newspapers, tobacco and sweets.

Do you think it is possible to meet these items on that sum of money? Just think of the increases we have all experienced over recent years in gas and electricity prices. More people than ever this winter will be choosing between fuel and food - because a regular intake of both is a luxury in cold weather if you are a claimant. For claimants, confronting poverty means endless stress in managing a small sum of money, watching every penny. It means that a gas oven that needs repair, a pair of shoes that need replacing, become major disasters - because there is no spare cash available to cope and finding out if you can get extra help is not easy. It means that you rarely go out and mix with others because entertainment and meeting people costs money. And many people who have suffered and are suffering from mental illness are in this position, alone or with their families, because their chance of having to depend on state benefits for lengthy periods of their lives in a society with these current levels of unemployment are higher than other groups within the community".(1)

The poverty which makes it difficult just to stay where you are also stops people who are recovering from mental illness from moving forwards. Practically every positive step you care to name involves some expense and this may be critical for someone on Supplementary Benefit. Almost any mainstream social role involves some money, be it a bus fare to an Adult Education class, the cost of drinks with a friend, Christmas presents to family members, equipment for a sport or hobby or the cost of going to a family wedding. For those many people who cannot dip into savings quite small sums of money can seriously limit their opportunities to re-establish themselves socially - and in so many, wide-ranging ways. Here is the experience of a woman at a London day centre who had taken on many new activities in the years following her mental illness:

"Shortage of money can even spoil my Ramblers Club outings. For instance they go in for cups of coffee and tea. Most of them have money. They'll stop off a couple of times for cups of coffee when we do outings. I've told them, 'No, I don't want to come into the restaurant. I'll just have a look round the shops'. It isn't really true. I mean I didn't need the cup of coffee but it would have been nice to have been together with the people. And another thing is that one of the Club members died and then they came round collecting for a wreath and I gave my fair share. But I thought, 'Well, I don't know, my daughter and I will be going without supper tonight because of this'. When my birthday comes, they'll expect me to produce some kind of feast because that's what they do. On anybody's birthday they have a meal with a couple of bottles of wine which that person is supposed to host ... All I would like is the right to earn the little bit of money which I could be earning right now. So I don't have this sort of trouble with the things I've managed to get doing since my illness. So I am not waiting for days without any money at all because my Giro hasn't arrived, like I am at the moment, six days now....I could be earning money from the voluntary work I am doing now. There is the odd jobs I do for the old lady I visit. I know she would like to pay me something. And also there are the children I collect from school, whom I told you about. But there's the problem about how much I can earn because of being on Supplementary Benefit ..."

The manager of the same centre offers another example:

"One of our members tried going to a singles club. He described to us how he met a lot of people in the bar of a hotel. The evening progressed in a fairly sociable manner, if a little bit frantic. Then, at a certain point, some sort of organiser got up, hushed everyone up, and demanded quite a lot of money. And this man experienced a lot of shame and discomfort because there he was, on Supplementary Benefit, and there was everyone

152

else just getting out their cheque-books. He
felt put off trying anything like that ever
again. He found it a very humiliating
experience. It made him feel very hopeless
about his prospects for meeting people in
general. We're lucky in this part of London
because there are a couple of clubs where
people can go along without paying any charge.
I think there aren't enough such
opportunities. It is hard, after all, for any
of us to get to meet new people, whoever we
are. But if you have no money and very little
confidence and your home isn't a place where
you're able to invite people back or where you
can feel comfortable about doing so, then your
social life is going to be very constricted."

Very low incomes, then, can make it hard to move
forward or even stand still. They can, though,
sometimes mean dramatic moves backwards. An issue
for some people who are living on Supplementary
Benefit are the disasters and fears of disaster
which can arise when struggling to manage on a very
low income and lacking reserves. An unexpected
extra cost, a small budgetting mistake, or a Giro
which fails to arrive can leave a person stranded
without any money whatsoever for days - or
borrowing into a dangerous cycle of debts to pay
other debts. A level of debt which is impossible to
pay off can be reached quite rapidly. Default can
mean disasters like electricity disconnection or
eviction, disasters utterly removed from the
experience of most mental health workers. Eviction
for default on rent can sometimes bring to an end a
person's whole way of life. It can mean being
tipped into the world of temporary boarding house
accommodation from which it is so hard to escape.
That, the penultimate stage of poverty, can mean
ending up in a dormitory and spending the day on
the streets or in the library newspaper room if
your hostel requires you out from breakfast to tea.
People living on Supplementary Benefit and failing
to cope financially may authentically feel a deep
insecurity since they really can pass over a
precipice which may occasion huge changes in their
status, opportunities and future.
    But mental health workers can be slow to
absorb the financial realities which face their
clients. Ann Davis comments:

"It seems to me that living in Britain in 1984

it should be impossible to miss the effects of
increasing poverty on some people's lives.
And yet many people working as mental health
professionals appear to be able to avoid
confronting this issue. A depressed woman in
her early twenties with two young children, an
unemployed husband and rent and fuel debts,
was advised by the psychiatrist whom she has
been seeing in an outpatients' clinic that
what she needs is a couple of nights in a
hotel, away from the family, to get some sleep
and look after herself. A group of people in
their thirties in a day hospital, all
suffering from schizophrenia and drawing state
benefits, are regularly told by their doctor
and the nursing staff that they are too
isolated and lack social contact and to combat
this they must get out more, go to the pub,
the cinema, have a meal together in a
restaurant. Community Nurses telling the
people they regularly visit in boarding houses
in the community that they have poor personal
hygiene and need to improve their diets - as
if it is a personal failure rather than the
fact that hot water and soap and nourishing
food are not readily available.

A worrying aspect of this professional
blindness to the facts of poverty is that the
messages that are conveyed to 'clients' or
'patients' or 'residents' is that it is their
own inadequacy, ignorance or pathology that is
the major problem and not the social
circumstances in which they are often
trapped."(1)

Maybe this blindness has something to do with
feeling incapacitated by the problem, not wishing
to see something which seems to defeat every single
positive move a mental health worker would wish to
encourage. But mental health workers can sometimes
reduce the stress imposed by poverty and its severe
long-term restriction of so many opportunities.
Here are three types of response:

- Helping people make full and effective benefit
  claims
- Setting up a fund which can make grants and
  gifts, maybe financed by voluntary work
  contributed by potential beneficiaries
- Helping people work part-time on a

154

self-employed basis within DHSS rules

WELFARE BENEFIT ADVOCACY

Mental health workers can ensure that their clients are getting the full welfare benefits to which they are entitled. They can check this themselves, if they can acquire the expertise, or fix up a firm and certain connection with a welfare rights specialist who can work with people who may have difficulties in presenting their case effectively themselves. Income surveys of people suffering from mental illness show they are particularly likely to be getting less than their official entitlement. For instance, Birmingham Tribunal Unit and Birmingham University ran a programme to help staff at Rubery Hill psychiatric hospital to enable patients claim full benefit entitlements. On one admission ward the staff were successful in claiming £2,800 for 39 patients in lump sum payments which had been missed. They also increased the overall weekly income of these patients by £200 a week. At the day hospital 46 patients were assessed, 22 ended up with benefits to which they had been entitled but had not previously claimed. For many of them it was bus fares, a sizeable addition to a Supplementary Benefit income. On a rehabilitation ward, where staff assessed 22 patients, 23 instances of unclaimed benefits were discovered.[2]

So checking benefit against entitlement is one way mental health workers can help clients get more money in their pockets. Sometimes simply information on full entitlements may be all that is needed. Sometimes contact with an expert on benefits may be necessary, say, for an appeal on a complex issue. Sometimes help may be required concerning the difficulties a vulnerable person experiences in dealing with any sort of bureaucracy. Some people lack the confidence or social skills even to refer themselves to mental health services, let alone make an effective benefit claim.

In Chapter Nine Teresa Leo, who has specialised in welfare rights in mental health settings, describes some ways that mental health workers can liaise with benefit specialists, check their client's entitlements and help them pursue claims effectively. This response to poverty can bring sizeable extra payments to some people. A much larger number, too, will gain smaller sums

through this process. We should recognise, of
course, how proportionately large is an increase of
a couple of pounds to someone on Supplementary
Benefit.

A GRANT-GIVING RESOURCE FUND - AND WORK-SCHEMES TO
FINANCE THE FUND

     This response to poverty is relatively rare
and little considered. Yet so many people could
benefit substantially if more projects set up
schemes like the one described in Chapter Ten.
     Everyone has heard how people on Supplementary
Benefit may not earn more than £4 a week without
deductions being made from their benefit. But this
applies to earnings. There are other means whereby
people on SB can be legitimately helped over some
of the obstacles of poverty. Grants can be made to
claimants of cash or goods or cash ear-marked for
particular purposes which Supplementary Benefit is
not intended to cover. There are important DHSS
rules which reduce or suspend SB if private gifts
are being made towards the very same items for
which SB is being claimed - eg. food, electricity,
rent. But, broadly speaking, grants towards
'non-essentials' like luxury goods or social
opportunities tend to be well clear of the risk of
duplicating SB payments. A long-standing feature
of voluntary sector activity in Britain, in fact,
are many small charitable trusts or grant-giving
bodies, which make grants to needy individuals for
expenses which the DHSS will not cover. An
incidental example would be the long-established
Queen Adelaide Fund, administered by MIND, which
offers grants for holidays, telephones, TVs and
other adjuncts to quality of life for people
recovering from mental illness in London and
Middlesex. DHSS rules on grants and earnings will
shortly be described in detail. But, generally
speaking, it is entirely legitimate for a mental
health project to set up a grant-giving fund to
broaden the social opportunities and general
quality of life of its users. There is an obvious
practical issue facing any small, grass-roots
projects wishing to establish such a fund. How do
you get the money for such grants? The most
interesting proposition is to raise it through
commercial crafts or services performed by
volunteers who contribute their labour on behalf of
the fund. Many people recovering from mental
illness are themselves able and willing to

contribute to voluntary work of this sort.   They,
after all, understand better than anyone else why
such a fund is worth supporting, for they are
themselves potential beneficiaries.

One example is the furniture repair business,
described in Chapter Ten, which is run by the Peter
Bedford Trust in Islington, London.   This finances
a grant-giving fund operated by the Trust.   All
work is done by people who are Trust beneficiaries,
working on a voluntary basis.   They include many
former long-stay patients from psychiatric
hospitals.   Grants are kept within DHSS approved
arrangements for people on Supplementary Benefit.
Indeed the whole scheme has been approved by the
local DHSS Office.   Started with minimal capital
outlay, this fund-raising workscheme now brings in
a sizeable income which is distributed in grants.
These grants have made a substantial difference to
quality of life for the voluntary workers, enabling
them, for instance, to fix themselves up with their
first proper holidays for years or to acquire
consumer goods like colour TVs.   Besides money, in
fact, this scheme places strong emphasis on the
value of work activities in their own right.

This scheme is now sizeable.   But a similar
basic formula of financing a fund through voluntary
work could put a grant-giving fund within the reach
of many mental health projects.   There are few
people, in fact, who do not have some sort of
money-making power, given appropriate opportunity,
even if nothing like enough for self-support.
Besides raising money such work can also give
someone a role as a productive person, who can
contribute something useful to others.   It can give
a sense of control through effecting a change in
your circumstances through your own efforts, if you
are helping generate the money for a system which
is going to make possible a positive change in your
life.   Depending how it is organised, it can also
give social contacts, a routine, somewhere to go
outside the home and other such elements which
unemployed former patients often name as important
to them.

A project like this must keep within two sets
of DHSS rules, those concerning doing work or
voluntary work while on benefit and those
concerning gifts.   There are these two distinct,
unrelated roles involved - that of worker and that
of recipient of a grant or gift.   Let us consider
the various DHSS rules involved.   DHSS Headquarters
have kindly advised on the preparation of the

following section. First the rules concerning working while claiming welfare benefits and what direct earnings are permitted on different benefits. Then the principles governing gifts or grants to claimants.

BENEFITS: GENERAL CONSIDERATIONS

As with a lot of the laws that closely affect people's lives, Social Security law is by no means easy to find your way around unless you have had training or experience. If in doubt, go to the experts inside or outside the DHSS and explain exactly the position you are trying to cover. You may not be able to guess at the intricacies of the law; the experts can't be expected to guess the particular situation you are working with. It pays to see the Acts and Regulations which govern entitlement as Parliament's means of deciding who gets the money, rather than the means of deciding who doesn't. Don't be put off by campaigns against fraud and abuse: pretending that things are other than they are, or concealing vital information, is cheating; helping people who are sick or unemployed to help themselves a little, within the benefit rules, is perfectly legitimate. If you are planning a new 'work' scheme:

(i) Try to establish whether anyone else has already launched such a scheme which will give you benefit precedents to quote;

(ii) If the situation doesn't seem clearcut, talk it through with any welfare rights specialists in your area;

(iii) Contact your local DHSS office - a letter to the Manager explaining broadly what you want to talk about and what you already know is a good start. Then talk the matter through with the Manager or whoever he nominates. Follow up with a letter to confirm your understanding, and ask for written confirmation. Expect a certain amount of caution: decisions on individual entitlement are taken by independent adjudication officers in individual cases and subject to appeal rights.

(iv) If you are planning a scheme affecting
people on more than one local office patch,
ask the manager you make contact with
whether he minds you copying the
correspondence to his neighbours to check
that they have the same position. If there
seem to be problems about getting advice
locally, ask the manager who to contact at
Region or HQ - unless he is willing to do
this for you.

DIFFERENT SITUATIONS: DIFFERENT RULES

Social security tends to work on the basis of
fitting people into categories and then relating
the rules to that category. Very often, this works
quite well, because you can categorise your own
position in the same way: retired, unemployed, etc.
But the lines are not always clear, as anyone knows
who has discussed with their doctor whether they
are fit to go back to work. In thinking about
schemes involving people who still have symptoms of
mental illness or who are still getting over the
residual problems left by mental illness, it is
quite important to decide whether you are dealing
with people who are by now fit for work and looking
for work; or with people who aren't likely to get
an employer to take them on, even with good job
prospects locally; or with both groups. It might be
important, for instance, in any discussions with
local DHSS to be able to say which category applies
to each individual using the scheme. It is true
that for many purposes Supplementary Benefit rules
apply across the board, whether you are sick or
unemployed. But even with Supplementary Benefit
the distinction is an important one.
    In benefit terms the advice must be that if
your doctor thinks you shouldn't be working just
yet, and you agree with him, stay with 'incapacity
for work' and do what you can to help yourself
under that label, until you are ready to launch
yourself on the employment market. There is
nothing to stop someone who is 'off sick' or
'incapable of work' from finding a small job which
his or her doctor agrees would suit his or her
health or well-being. But by keeping the 'sick'
label you lose the ability to get very far into the
network of employment and training service
provisions.
    These notes don't go into sick pay from an
employer. Often this will be paid to someone who

has a job to go back to. If supplementary benefit
is being paid on top of sick pay, the same
supplementary benefit rules apply as with
supplementary benefit plus DHSS sickness benefit.

WORKING WHILE UNEMPLOYED

Unemployment benefit is for people who want a
job, could do a job if one were available, and
haven't put unreasonable restrictions in their own
way by the commitments they have taken on or the
conditions they have imposed. So anyone who has
taken on 'work' while unemployed has to be able to
drop it when the chance of a job comes along. This
is the position even if the 'work' produces no
income at all. Broadly the same rules apply to
supplementary benefit for people who are
unemployed. There are some easements for
'voluntary work', and it is worth looking at DHSS
leaflet NI 240.
A scheme which doesn't tie people down, but is
designed to help people look forward to and prepare
for a 'proper job', and encourages them to take
opportunities, is not likely to fall foul of the
basic benefit rules.
If the work being done produces some income,
the first step is to check on how far gross
'earnings' differ from net earnings: it is net
earnings that affect most benefits. The most
important deduction is working expenses; but check
with your local office what can be allowed and what
can't. Any detailed information given here could
rapidly become out of date. Check! Note that more
generous supplementary benefit rules apply to
single parents, who aren't required to be available
for work to get benefit while unemployed.
At the time of writing, the earning rule for
unemployment benefit allows up to £2 a day; while
the supplementary benefit rule is that benefit
starts being reduced once earnings go over £4 a
week. Note that these two rules work in very
different ways. UB for that day will be lost if
'earnings' go over £2; while earnings at any time
during the week affect the amount of supplementary
benefit for that week. For anyone getting both
supplementary benefit and unemployment benefit, the
supplementary benefit rule is the one to watch.

WORKING WHILE 'OFF SICK'

Rules allowing someone, who is getting benefit because they are incapable of work, to do some work and get paid for it were first introduced with patients in the large mental hospitals in mind; though this has long applied to people living in the community too. Since it wouldn't need very high disregarded earnings, combined with untaxed benefit, to put the part-time earner on benefit well ahead of the full-time earner in sheltered employment, it is understandable that the rules are fairly tight and tend to be cautiously applied.

The basic rule for sickness benefit, invalidity benefit and the non-contributory Severe Disablement Allowance (formerly Non-Contributory Invalidity Pension) is the therapeutic earnings limit. This means that your doctor has approved the work as being OK for your condition and the DHSS adjudication officer has decided that the work is not inconsistent with your being held incapable of doing a full- or part-time job for which an employer would pay you. So you may need to explain why you can do that amount or sort of work and no more, especially if the 'work' takes up quite a lot of time or involves quite a lot of effort for a short time. (Often 'therapeutic' work allows people to work at a pace that would make employment or self-employment uneconomic.) 'Therapeutic' doesn't mean that the work has to make you better; but it mustn't be such as to make you worse.

At the time of writing, the therapeutic earnings limit is £25.50 a week, net of working expenses. The figure has been going up at each uprating. The figure is the same for each of the three benefits: SB, IVB, SDA.

Supplementary benefit for people who are incapable of work has the same earnings rule as Supplementary Benefit for people who are unemployed: over £4 a week, benefit is reduced. So those getting another incapacity benefit plus Supplementary Benefit need in the main to look to the Supplementary Benefit rule. However, it is worth bearing in mind that if Supplementary Benefit is fairly low, you can earn your way off it and just have your invalidity benefit and 'therapeutic earnings'. This possibility is worth thinking about for anyone well on their way back to being fit for ordinary work.

161

GIFTS, GRANTS, AND FUND-RAISING BY VOLUNTARY WORK

This section deals with income which isn't earnings in any normal sense of the term, and which may go to people who are either sick or unemployed. But the basic benefit rules have to be kept in mind; and the regulations can bite on concealed earnings as though they were real earnings. This underlines the importance of talking any scheme through with advisers and with the local office at the planning stage. Don't build your scheme on the sand of half-knowledge and wishful thinking. The viable schemes now in operation have been very carefully prepared, and those who run them keep a weather eye on benefit changes.

The starting point is with broad principles. Gifts of money or goods are acceptable within limits, but it would obviously be inconsistent with the rationale for supplementary benefit if someone received substantial regular weekly gifts of food or money while getting supplementary benefit payments on the basis that they lacked any such means for support. Regular gifts towards ordinary living expenses, which benefit is intended to cover, are suspect whether paid in kind (eg. someone paying your milk bill every week) or as regular gifts of cash for such a purpose. Gifts of amenity or luxury items, which SB is not intended to cover, or money towards their costs, are not likely to cause problems. The other major limitation on gifts or grants is that they should not become regular. That way they lose the sporadic character of genuine gifts and effectively become income and thus affect benefit calculations.

An Example
(this has been discussed with DHSS Headquarters):

Consider a general amenity or benevolent fund, possibly financed by donations, jumble sales, or work done by volunteers including people who would benefit from the fund. This fund makes gifts to certain individuals receiving supplementary benefit. Occasional sums of up to £100, for example at Christmas or birthdays, would be ignored in the calculating of benefits. This applies to all occasional payments of up to £100. Regular charitable payments of up to £4 a week can be ignored. In addition, gifts (cash or kind) to individuals or a group are permissible for a

wide range of amenity or leisure items and
activities for which benefit isn't payable.
Items might include, for instance, a
television set, money for a holiday, cinema
tickets, and craft or hobby materials or money
to pay for them. Other items likely to be
permissible are money earmarked to cover
expenses involved in going to a family
member's wedding; or a grant of money for an
educational course; or tools for either
employment or leisure purposes - though of
course a beneficiary of such help would not be
able to also claim any special supplementary
payment for a tool kit. A gift of money to
provide a down-payment for a mortgage or a
deposit for a private flat or bed-sit would be
also permissible.

A WORD OF CAUTION

Any substantial addition to capital or income
should be declared and its nature explained to the
local office. This keeps the record straight and
so avoids any subsequent difficulty; and clearly
supplementary benefit shouldn't be expected to meet
a cost which has already been met in another way.
Note that, in certain circumstances, single
payments of supplementary benefit may be made for
such items as: returnable deposits on taking up a
tenancy, furniture, or tools for starting work.
Such payments can only be made, however, where
there is a 'need' for the item or expense at the
date when the claim for it is made. There would be
no 'need', and hence no payments if the item was
paid for - whether by way of a gift or a loan -
before the claim was made. So it would not be
possible for a claimant to buy such an item through
a loan from a charitable fund, then seek to claim
supplementary benefit payment to repay this loan.
Supplementary benefit cannot be increased to cover
repayment on loans except in the special
circumstances of loans connected with buying your
home, home repairs or improvements, or certain HP
agreements for essential household items which
began prior to receipt of supplementary benefit.

SINGLE PAYMENTS AND CAPITAL

There is another way gifts of money to
claimants can affect general entitlement to single
payments. Single payments can only be made if a

claimant's capital is currently £500 or less; any
capital or savings over £500 is expected to be put
towards items needed. Should any gift of money
take a claimant's capital past £500, that person
would no longer be eligible for a single payment.
Entitlement to weekly Supplementary Benefit would
be affected if a gift brought a claimant's capital
over £3,000. A once and for all charitable
payment, whether or not intended for a specific
purpose, is usually treated as capital, not as
income. Thus it will not affect benefit - unless
it brings a person's total capital to more than
£3,000.

BORDERLINE BETWEEN EARNINGS AND GIFTS

Such is the general position on gifts or
grants, though obviously decisions are taken by
local adjudicating officers with regard to
individual circumstances. What of a situation
where a fund making such grants is being supported
by voluntary work by people who may themselves
benefit from the fund? Say the fund wishes to pay
the voluntary workers the £4 weekly 'earnings' net
of working expenses, (which will not affect
calculation of benefit) and then eventually
distribute the remaining proceeds from the work in
grants or gifts. The general principles regarding
availability for work or incapacity at work would
apply, and the general principles regarding gifts.
There are one or two extra points to watch.

Earnings over and above the disregarded
amount, whether cash earnings or benefits in kind,
should not be substantial. Nor should they fall
into that category where in effect somebody is
earning a full wage but is getting part of it in an
orthodox form and the rest in an unorthodox form on
a regular basis. The closer the arrangements get
to an artificial syphoning off of regular earnings
for the worker's future benefit, the greater the
risk of falling foul of the rules. The more
marginally commercial the enterprise and the less
akin to normal employment the individual's input
and entitlement, the smaller the risk of problems.

It is for local adjudicating officers to
assess the implications of such schemes according
to individual circumstances. Remember that the
adjudicating officer has power to assume 'notional
earnings' if the work is remunerated at less than
the market rate; to assume income where it is due
to be paid; or to treat as possessed by the

claimant any earnings of which he has deprived
himself. But the rules were not designed to
forestall schemes of this sort financed by
voluntary work and the Department should be
approached on this basis. The Department's own
Mental Health Division has made it clear that it
welcomes schemes designed in consultation with the
Department, and within the ambit of the benefit
rules, which extend the opportunities open to
people recovering from mental illness and may
improve their long-term prospects as well as their
short-term welfare. Should a local DHSS Office
wish clarification concerning issues discussed
here, they should refer to Policy Division at DHSS
Headquarters.

GENERAL APPLICATIONS

    Chapters Ten and Eleven describe different
models for a workscheme which finances a
grant-giving fund. There are many possible
variations on this theme. The Peter Bedford Trust
scheme grew out of a philosophy which particularly
values work and the scheme, accordingly, takes
great interest in making its work activities
rewarding and engaging in their own right - in fact
the workscheme came first and the fund was a
subsequent development. There are many situations
throughout welfare services where the approach
would be helpful, whether along the Peter Bedford
Trust model or in some other form which suits a
different set of aims or circumstance. The idea
could be used, for instance, on a very small scale.
A case can be made that every rehabilitation or
support service nowadays needs access to a
grant-giving fund if certain of its users are ever
again to participate in the sort of roles and
activities which are valued in mainstream society.
    Almost any day centre, for instance, could
launch such a venture quite easily, at least on a
small scale. They have a potential workforce
assembled on their premises. Often, too, they
already have centre amenity funds, sometimes
several funds. These funds quite often already
receive finance from activities like jumble sales
or sales of handicrafts, where centre users do most
of the work. But it is rare that these give grants
to individuals. Sometimes staff assume incorrectly
that DHSS rules forbid amenity grants to
individuals and that the funds may finance only
collective activities, like group outings to

cinemas or restaurants or group holidays.
Sometimes, too, staff fear that to start funding
individuals would arouse envy and a wave of demands
among other users and complicate staff-user
relationships by placing staff in the role of
financial benefactor. There is, of course, a very
real issue here. There needs to be a clearly
defined rationale for why grants are made and an
open, agreed procedure for allocating them. It
cannot be left to appear a matter of staff whim.
Both for this reason and to satisfy the DHSS and
senior management, it is advisable that such funds
have written constitutions which define criteria by
which people are eligible for grants, when, how and
by whom decisions on grants are reached, and
procedures for various contingencies, like amending
the rules or dissolving the fund. An example of a
written constitution for a slightly different fund
can be found in Chapter Fifteen. There could be
many advantages if a fund's constitution required
service users to be represented in decision-making
on the fund's administration.

Another brake on the development of such
opportunities for work and making money can be
staff feeling about the proper place of work in day
units. The 1976 National Day Care Project noted a
trend for mental health day unit staff to wish to
remove work activities from their programme. Quite
often, nowadays, where there are staff/client
disagreements about the presence of work, it is the
clients who are wishing to keep work in the centre
and the staff who do not. As their clients' future
employment prospects have dwindled, some staff will
say, work has become meaningless since it leads
neither to money in the present nor money through a
job in the future. But to introduce a benevolent
or grant-giving fund as a focus for work adds
meaning and motivation to the other positive
features of work. One can argue that the decline
of employment makes opportunity to work all the
more important. Clearly, though, we are not talking
about boring, insulting or alienating tasks of the
sort sometimes organised in psychiatric settings.
These have understandably angered progressive
mental health workers.

A centre can be a good base from which to
start a project aimed at financing a benevolent
fund or similar arrangement. Potential voluntary
workers are there. Potential beneficiaries are
there. But there are sound grounds for placing
some sort of administrative barrier between the

centre on the one hand and the fund and the
workscheme which finances it on the other. Many
people are likely to need both opportunities to do
voluntary work and to draw on the fund's resources
for a long time after they have substantially
recovered from their episode of mental illness.
These opportunities are resources for positive
mental health in the same sense as is a social
club. They need to be available long-term in
settings which do not define a person as currently
suffering from mental illness. If either work or
fund are formally part of the day centre, they risk
acting as a magnet which ties people to the day
centre, if the price of leaving is loss of such
valuable opportunities as these. So it is
important that such opportunities are organised in
ways that enable people to draw on them for years
without prolonging their association with roles and
settings connected with a mental illness which is
now behind them. Such an enterprise could be open
to people who had left the day centre, people still
at the centre, and some people who had never
attended the centre but who otherwise qualified for
this particular opportunity. Such a scheme could
be started within a day centre, develop a degree of
autonomy then, maybe, move out to borrowed premises
elsewhere.

Finally it's worth noting some of the
variations which can be introduced to the basic
theme of a workscheme which finances a fund.

* You could have several funds per locality,
serving different groups or individuals or
different purposes. You could have a fund
earmarked for very specific purposes, like certain
traditional charitable funds. People could have
quite a choice as to which fund they worked for.
Plainly, too, it need not derive its income from
just one workscheme. It could be financed from
many sources, including the main service budget.

* One special type of fund is a loan or credit
fund which helped people without savings over
lump-sum expenses or emergencies when they suddenly
needed cash. Chapter Fifteen mentions an emergency
fund where membership is secured by a small weekly
per capita levy. Such schemes might also offer a
practical way of saving money to people too poor
for a bank account. A workscheme could supply such
a loan or credit fund with the capital it needs to

get started. A fund like this might offer an
important sense of security to people who can face
really very serious problems from sudden bills or
delays in Benefit payments.

*   Likewise a loan or grant fund might
significantly extend housing choices for people who
are using psychiatric services. It might help DHSS
claimants circumvent the problems they face in
raising advance payments to rent private bed-sits
or flats. Private landlords may require four weeks
rent to be paid in advance and sometimes another
four weeks rent as deposit against damage. While
the DHSS can, in fact, make such advance payments
to claimants, it can only be arranged after a let
has been agreed and may take quite some time.
Private landlords, however, tend to take the first
suitable applicant who can put down money there and
then. A 1986 survey by the Alone in London
counselling service identified this as a major
reason why young DHSS claimants could not rent
secure private housing.(3)
    If a fund can supply money for advance
payments, this can offer some individuals important
wider choices about where and how they live. Too
often people who lose their homes through
hospitalisation find their subsequent housing
restricted to Local Authority Lets, special mental
health housing projects and bed and breakfast
accommodation. Moving to another part of the
country, for instance, may prove extremely
difficult, however long one plans it. So access to
deposits for private renting can sometimes offer
important extra choices. Note that if advance
payments are either lent or given, one forgoes a
claim on DHSS.

*   Work activities can be devised in ways which
give people who have suffered mental illness social
contacts with members of the wider community.
Workschemes can be organised with an eye to the
social contacts they offer people. One option is
to seek enterprises which involve meeting members
of the public as customers - enterprises involving
market stalls, shop fronts, house-to-house
collections, or services like gardening. Another
is to recruit volunteers from the general public to
work alongside people who are recovering from
mental illness. Members of the public are
regularly recruited to do voluntary work to finance
charitable funds. A scheme of this sort could

recruit a mixed workforce in just the same way from people like those who volunteer for local mental health charities like MIND groups. There is a practical case for seeking volunteers with particular skills which your workscheme needs. But noteworthy too is the social aspect. Work seems to be such an extraordinarily good medium for people to form links with each other, providing appropriate tasks are chosen. In recent years 'Befriending' schemes have been quite widely discussed among voluntary sector workers as a valuable role for volunteers. A 'mixed' voluntary workforce on a small, part-time work enterprise can offer an unusually natural, unself-conscious opportunity for the gradual formation of friendships.

Schemes which can generate grant-giving funds may become increasingly necessary in coming years. The government's proposed Social Fund seems set to reduce availability of DHSS cash grants for essential items. Mental health workers may well find themselves looking elsewhere if their clients are to have bare essentials of furniture or clothes, let alone fuller social lives.

Other likely changes in Benefit regulations add reasons for community mental health workers becoming involved with work and making money. It seems particularly likely that the rules on what Supplementary Benefit claimants can formally earn before deductions will be eased for certain people who suffer illness or disability. Earnings up to £15 a week may be allowed for some groups of Supplementary Benefit claimants. Another way of alleviating poverty is to help people to work part-time or on a self-employed basis and earn directly, within the DHSS rules on earnings.

WORKING SELF-EMPLOYED WITHIN BENEFIT REGULATIONS

Chapter Eleven describes a sophisticated scheme for equipping users of psychiatric services to work self-employed. Developed by Kensington and Chelsea MIND Association, it offers thorough training in skills which have been identified as money-spinners for someone working self-employed in that locality. It aims to also provide an advertising and marketing service for its network of workers like an agency. Besides augmenting Benefit, it is hoped, in fact, that the earning potential of the trades taught should mean that some individuals eventually

become able to support themselves and will move off
Benefit altogether.   Such schemes offer special
opportunities to people on those Benefits which
permit earnings up to £25.50 weekly.

Chapter Fifteen includes description of a
smaller scale, less resourced venture, the Tontine
Users' Repair Collective. This gave members a
meeting point, premises, a loan for initial
materials and encouragement to follow their various
individual inclinations in chair repair, bicycle
repair, a printing service and other self-chosen
ventures. Otherwise it drew on the initiative and
existing work skills and business sense of
individuals who had an idea they wanted to try.

The DHSS regulations which sometimes permit
weekly earnings up to £25.50 for people on certain
Benefits have been described on page 161.   Clear
understanding of these regulations and possible
complications is important.

NOTES

1. Ann Davis, 'Confronting Poverty' in 'Life after
   Mental Illness? Major papers from MIND's 1984
   Annual Conference', MIND Publications, 1985

2. Ann Davis and Clare Hayton, 'Who Benefits?   The
   Rubery Hill Benefits Project', Birmingham
   Tribunal Unit, 1984

3. Guardian, 9 September 1986

Chapter Nine

MENTAL HEALTH WORKERS AND WELFARE RIGHTS: SOME
PRACTICAL STEPS

Teresa Leo

Editorial Introduction

Welfare benefits is a notoriously complex
area, which requires very specialised
knowledge. Many mental health workers start
off with minimal knowledge of the subject.
What should a mental health worker do, who
wants clients to get their full rightful
incomes?   Teresa Leo has been involved in
setting up and running an independent
Citizens Advice Bureau at Tooting Bec
Hospital since 1983. Through its advice work
the project has been particularly concerned
by the level of poverty experienced by
psychiatric patients and their families.
Entitlement to benefits and the difficulties
experienced in obtaining them is the most
common problem dealt with by the project,
representing a third of its total enquiries.
This chapter focusses on practical steps
which mental health workers can take to
respond to their client's welfare benefit
problems.   Please note that welfare benefit
entitlements quoted in the 1984/85 case
descriptions are regularly being altered.

A complex system, multiplicity of claims and
procedures, constantly changing legislation and the
belief that it is someone else's job all help to
create the barriers which keep most health and
social services workers well away from confronting
the daily poverty which faces many of their
clients.
      But those of us who use the mental health
services should be able to expect that our
financial circumstances are not treated as
irrelevant side-issues by those who are staffing
the services. Choice, control and a feeling of
well-being are all dependent on an adequate income.

171

This section aims to open up some of these
issues so that workers from different workplaces
with varying resources can place welfare rights
more centrally on their agendas. It outlines the
ways in which even mental health workers with
minimal knowledge of the benefits system can assist
clients in this area. The following suggestions
offer a choice of practical models for getting
effective welfare rights advice to your clients.
They range from simple liaison with a welfare
rights worker to a full scale take-up campaign for
a day centre or hostel.

ACCESS TO INFORMATION

Bernard is 61 years old and has spent the last
two years in hospital. Ready to leave this
summer, he talked to hospital staff and his
social worker about finding suitable
accommodation. Two addresses of boarding
houses were recommended and on the advice of
one of his colleagues in the Industrial
Therapy Unit, Bernard made his choice. The
landlord he chose is a staff nurse at the
hospital and for £65 a week he provides bed
and a breakfast (which boarders cook
themselves). In addition each boarder is
responsible for laundering his own bedding.

Bernard moved into his new accommodation
having made a claim for supplementary benefit.
When his first Giro arrived Bernard was "very
shocked" to find it was for £79.25 a week.
This meant that after paying his landlord he
was left with £14.25 a week to feed, clothe
and entertain himself. "It was impossible. I
couldn't get meals and provide for myself on
that amount." When he queried the Giro with
his DHSS office he was told that the 'new
benefits' meant that he was not entitled to
any more.

This news was devastating. Bernard didn't
know how he was going to manage to live
outside hospital on so little and his worry
showed. A nurse at the Industrial Therapy
Unit commented, "You don't look too good.
What's the matter?", and Bernard explained his
problem. The nurse directed Bernard to the
Citizens Advice Bureau at the hospital and the
CAB adviser worked out that he had been

considerably underpaid. The local DHSS had
not taken into account the fact that Bernard
was entitled to a further £16.15 for his
accommodation because of his disability and
that the personal allowance element of his
benefit should have been £10.30 because he did
not have to sign on for work.

A letter was sent which quoted the regulations
that should have applied and this led to a
revision. Bernard was also advised to make a
claim for a weekly laundry addition to cover
the cost of washing his bedding and he now
receives a total of £98.95 a week. He
described himself as "much happier - and more
relaxed now", and feels that he has a chance
of coping outside hospital with £33.95 a week
for food and clothes.

As the above case illustrates, access to basic
information about an entitlement to benefit can
have a dramatic impact on someone's sense of well-
being. In this instance, it made all the
difference between a successful and an unsuccessful
return to community living.
Information about welfare rights can be
obtained through local resources (if you have
them), national organisations and through written
material. The challenge, for both workers and
clients, is to discover where these resources are
and how to approach and use them.

USING LOCAL RESOURCES

Regular discussion on an individual or
group basis can be helpful in sharing worries and
learning from others how they have tackled them.
Some centres have found this to be a valuable way
of pooling information on the benefits system and
local services.

Contact local welfare rights specialists

Identify where your local welfare rights
specialists are. These could be:

* Citizens Advice Bureau
* Law Centre
* Consumer Advice Centre
* Tribunal Unit
* Local Authority Welfare Rights Unit

      * Social Worker with an interest in welfare rights

If your area is well served with these type of agencies it would be worth checking whether your clients are aware of their existence and if so whether they are using them. If not, why not?

A discussion at two day hospitals in South London about finding and using local advice agencies produced the following comments:-

"The problem is you need to know exactly what it is you want before you ask. You also need to know how to ask - just the right words."

"You can't understand them - they talk too quickly."

"I wish they would explain carefully - I don't catch what they're saying."

"It would be better if there was just one person you could talk to instead of going from one person to another with no-one really knowing what's going on."

None of the group members felt happy about using their local advice centres if they needed help.

To ensure a successful partnership with your local welfare rights advisers, be clear about why you are approaching them and what results you expect from the liaison. Contact them to discuss ideas for meeting clients' needs and how their services could be more accessible. This could include:

      *   Inviting the agency to your centre to discuss the service they provide;

      *   Setting up a formal link with the agency or a specific worker to ensure successful contact for referrals;

      *   Arranging for an adviser to hold benefit surgeries in your workplace;

      *   Establishing a training programme for workers and/or clients (see below -

'Training')

*   Collaborating on a benefits take-up
        campaign (see below - 'Projects')

Coulsdon and Purley Citizens Advice Bureau run
regular discussion groups at Cane Hill Hospital
Interim Secure Unit. The sessions were started
with a view to assisting the rehabilitation of
in-patients, mostly people who had spent a
substantial amount of time in psychiatric
hospitals. The discussions cover various welfare
rights issues. Patients are encouraged to visit
the CAB, initially by appointment with the worker
who leads the discussion groups.

Contact local statutory agencies - get to know
who's who and establish contacts for specific
problems at, for example:

*   DHSS - they may have a liaison officer,
        special cases officer or liaison
        committee for community groups which you
        could attend

*   Fuel Boards

*   Housing Department - invite key officers
        to your centre to talk about their
        agency and to discuss common problems
        experienced by your clients

A discussion at a day centre included this exchange:

"Last week I was moving from a flat to a house
and my social worker said, 'Just apply and you
can get the move paid for'. So I went to the
DHSS as she said. Well, this form, I just
couldn't understand it. In the end the lady
at the counter had to fill it in for me and I
just signed it. I still don't know what it
said. Then they sent me to the Town Hall. The
Town Hall said that they couldn't help me
because I was only on Invalidity Benefit - so
I was on the wrong benefit for them to help
me. They said that I would have to go back to
Housing. I spent a whole day in Housing
sitting and waiting and going backwards and
forwards from one person to another. In the
end they said they couldn't help me - after a
whole day. I was so tired and upset".

Mental health workers and welfare rights

"There needs to be better co-operation between all the people who are supposed to help you - better liaison."

National Organisations

If there are no local welfare rights agencies in your area, the following organisations provide welfare rights advisory services:

* Disability Alliance
  25 Denmark Street
  London WC2 8NJ
  Tel: 01 240 0806

Mon-Fri 2pm-4.30pm for urgent enquiries; otherwise write with full details of the problem enclosing a SAE.

* Child Poverty Action Group
  Citizens Rights Office
  1 Macklin Street
  London WC2B 5NH
  Tel: 01 405 5942/4517

Mon-Fri 2pm-5.30pm for urgent enquiries; otherwise write with full details of problem enclosing an SAE.

NB: This service is not for the general public - advisers only.

Local Information

Having established where your local resources are, compile information on useful addresses and telephone numbers such as the DHSS, housing departments, fuel boards, social services departments, etc. A local information system which can be regularly updated is essential. It is safer to have one set of information which is updated by one person, to ensure accuracy.

Reference books - A set of useful reference books held in the workplace would include:

* Disability Rights Handbook - a guide to benefits and services for people with disabilities. New edition every November. From: Disability Alliance, 25 Denmark Street, London WC2 8NJ

*   National Welfare Benefits Handbook and the Rights Guide to Non-Means Tested Social Security Benefits. New edition every November. From: CPAG, 1 Macklin Street, London   WC2B 5NH

*   Leaflets - These can be useful supplements to reference books but shouldn't be relied on as the sole source of information. DHSS leaflets describe procedures for claiming a particular benefit but tend to do so in isolation from other linked benefits which the claimant could be eligible for. However, it may be helpful to keep a stock of the leaflets which have claim forms. Leaflet NI146 lists all the available leaflets which the DHSS produces and includes an order form. Bulk orders may be obtained by writing to PO Box 21, Honeypot Lane, Stanmore, Middx.

Leaflets which are 'tailor made' to your clients' needs could be produced with the help of a welfare rights adviser. This could be part of a take-up campaign on a specific benefit, (see below - 'Projects').

TRAINING IN WELFARE BENEFITS

Alice was admitted to hospital suffering from severe depression. For eight months it went unnoticed by health and social services staff that she had not received any benefit payment. Alice had a privately rented flat and approached the Citizens Advice Bureau in despair when she had exhausted the savings she had been using to pay her landlord. After the CAB adviser had convinced the DHSS that Alice had 'good cause' for a late claim, she received a back payment of supplementary benefit and housing benefit totalling almost £1500.

Alice is typical of many of the people who use the CAB at the hospital where I work who have been known to the mental health services for years and yet have failed to secure their basic benefit entitlements.
Mental health workers at Rubery Hill Hospital found that an increased knowledge of the benefits system made a big difference to the way in which they worked with users of their services.(1) Ann Davis writes:

"Nursing and social work staff who took part in the project found that in raising issues of finance and benefits with individuals and their families, they touched on a topic of central importance. It became clearer to staff that successful rehabilitation and community care was in part dependent on tackling the problems generated by the social security system. At the end of the period of the take-up project a number of the nursing staff considered that benefits work was part of the nursing process and social workers found that successful resolutions of benefit problems often resulted in a more productive working relationship with clients and their families."

WHERE TO GET TRAINING

* Local Authority: Welfare Rights Officer or Training Department

* Voluntary Organisations: Citizens Advice Bureaux, Law Centres, Neighbourhood Advice Centres, Tribunal Units

* Local Education Authority: Colleges of Further Education, Evening Institutes

* National Organisations: Child Poverty Action Group, Disability Alliance, Federation of Independent Advice Centres (Tel 01-274-1839 for details)

SUGGESTIONS FOR USING THE TRAINING

* Invite a welfare rights adviser to give information talks on aspects of welfare rights on a regular basis.

* Arrange for staff to be trained in enough knowledge to give basic advice and to recognise clients who are missing out on their entitlement.

* One member of staff could take on responsibility for building up a specialist knowledge in this area, regularly updated through training.

Solihull Mental Health Welfare Rights Group was formed in November 1984, and meets

approximately every couple of months. It comprises
a number of social workers all working in the
mental health field - from hospital based teams,
day hospital, day centre, hostel and the community.
Recently two clients have joined the group.
The group has a number of aims. Mike Murkin,
Community Mental Health Social Worker and member of
the group explains:

> "It was acknowledged that we needed to
> increase our knowledge in this area and
> training, both formal and informal, has been
> arranged. We have collected information
> about local resources, useful books,
> contacts, etc. We hope to produce simple to
> understand material for other social workers,
> community psychiatric nurses, residential,
> day centre and hospital staff to use with
> clients. We have also planned a small
> take-up campaign and hope to extend this if
> successful".

PROJECT WORK

The last couple of years have witnessed a
growing number of projects aiming to promote the
importance of welfare rights in mental health work.
They range from projects like the Citizens Advice
Bureau at Tooting Bec Hospital, set up at the
instigation of an outside agency with the
co-operation of mental health staff, to initiatives
taken by health and social services workers
themselves, like the Solihull Mental Health Welfare
Rights Group.
The projects mainly fall into two broad areas
of approach. There are those which have gained
medium/long-term funding for a project worker to
provide advice sessions and regular training for
staff and clients. There are others which have
obtained funding for a more limited period to
develop a specific welfare benefits take-up
campaign. Most projects are examples of
partnership between mental health and welfare
rights agencies and many of them have produced
reports on their work. These provide useful
reading for anyone who may be thinking of
undertaking a similar project.
A full list of the various projects is
available from:

Mental health workers and welfare rights

Citizens Advice Bureau
Tooting Bec Hospital
Tooting Bec Road
London SW17 8BL

SUMMARY

A major priority for mental health workers
and planners should be to recognise the crucial
importance of an adequate income for every
individual's well-being. The urgent priority which
users of mental health services accord to this
issue should be reflected in the service and care
offered by those who are staffing the services. We
suggest the following areas for initial action:

* Mental health workers should ensure that people
using their services have more access to
information about their benefit entitlement.

* Mental health workers should arrange to have
regular training in welfare rights.

* Systematic benefit assessment and follow-up
should be available to all clients.

* Funding should be sought for the development of
a special project to provide regular assessment and
advice sessions; to provide training for staff and
clients in welfare rights; to undertake a welfare
benefits take-up campaign.

NOTES

1. Ann Davis and Clare Hayton, 'Who Benefits? The
Rubery Hill Benefits Project', Birmingham
Tribunal Unit, 1984

Chapter Ten

WORKSCHEMES AT THE PETER BEDFORD TRUST

Richard Grover

Editorial Introduction

The Peter Bedford Trust is a voluntary
organisation in Islington, North London whose
philosophy places special value on opportunity
to take the role of worker. One reason for
interest is the steps the Trust has taken to
make worker roles accessible to anyone who
wants them, without being limited by subsidies
or restricting work to commercially productive
people. Another reason is that some of its
work enterprises finance a grant-giving
amenity fund on lines like those discussed in
Chapter Eight.

We are a modest-sized organisation which provides
opportunities for about 85 people who have suffered
various serious difficulties and disadvantages.
Many have spent long years in psychiatric
institutions for instance. We provide housing. We
have also always aimed to provide work
opportunities. Our original means for this was an
office cleaning company, John Bellers Ltd, which we
started, whence people used to move on to open
employment. But the massive decline in employment
opportunities in the last decade has required us to
seek additional schemes which can offer many more
people a long-term opportunity to include an
element of work in their lives. We needed an
arrangement which was not constricted by the
expense of subsidising wages. This has meant
starting our scheme on the basis of people working
with the Trust while remaining on state benefits
rather than taking up paid employment. What we
have come up with is a flourishing furniture repair
business, two canteens, home cleaning and repairs
and a little gardening which currently offer 35
people regular part-time work outside of formal
employment. Worker-satisfaction is made a
priority in the way that tasks are organised. The
money the business makes all goes towards the

expansion of the work opportunities and payments,
grants and gifts to individuals who have
contributed to the scheme. These grants and gifts,
which comply with DHSS rules for Supplementary
Benefit, give our tenants opportunities for various
activities and amenities like proper holidays or
their own colour TV sets to which they would never
otherwise get access. This scheme now offers
generally well-liked and interesting work
activities to quite a lot of people who otherwise
have minimal chance of working again. Through the
grants and gifts which the scheme finances some
people have broadened their lives considerably.
When they had money to make it possible, people
went ahead and did things which no-one ever
expected of them. The scheme tries to be very
flexible. There are tasks for many differing
abilities and aptitudes. It can cater for varying
levels of commitment, too. Furthermore it does not
involve great financial costs, capital outlay or
risks. We are quite a small organisation,
deliberately quite small. We started this scheme
from very small beginnings, just an idea and a few
pounds outlay and it grew. It seems to me that
it's quite within the grasp of any group of workers
who might feel that this would suit the people they
work with.

It is important to clarify how the scheme
evolved. We didn't start off from the idea of
redressing our tenants' poverty. We started 14
years ago as a project based round the special ways
the activity of work can help people reclaim
identity and self-respect. We sought to reach
people living in institutions, mainly in large
psychiatric hospitals or single homeless people in
DHSS resettlement units, who include many people
with a psychiatric background. We sought a fresh
way of making contact with them in order to help
them leave those institutions. We sought ways
which did not involve the conventional 'care' ethos
of so many social work agencies or half-way houses
- which often leads to a passive role for the
person being helped, for instance. We felt that we
should not present an image of offering something
for which they, the participant, didn't have to
make any effort or we would risk being seen as an
extension of the all-controlling institution.
People would yet again be in 'care', in a passive
role. We wanted, as a starting point, to give
people coming to us a sense that if there was going
to be movement in their lives, it would be through

their efforts not ours.

This was achieved by offering work on a daytime basis to people still living in psychiatric hospitals or resettlement centres. We went round telling them: "We have work which needs to be done. Will you come and work for us? If you don't want to, it doesn't matter because we're a voluntary organisation and need take only people who want what we offer. But for anyone who wants to work, no matter what your difficulties or how poor your work record, we will try to find a work situation which suits you." So from the start we were presenting ourselves not as a caring agency but one which was interested in seeing what a person could contribute positively.

It was established early that quite a number of people wanted to take up this invitation. Work seemed to be a very significant element in their lives. Even if they had very little experience of working, quite a lot of people who were previously regarded as incapable seemed to respond well to the idea that they would work and be responsible for their work. We found that it was important that the work be interesting to people. It was important, too, that they could see the product of their labours as valuable to others and being appreciated as having value. So many people who have been written off as incapable actually desire quite strongly to do something worthwhile. In our society work is perhaps the most common currency for showing your worth and for being judged worthy by others. The opportunity of work offered them, in fact, a tangible, accessible vehicle for assuming a different social role and making some changes in their lives. This work has to many people with a psychiatric history, or who have a mental handicap for that matter, the same value as it has to many who are generally well placed in life. It is a source of identity, provides structure, gives greater meaning to leisure, provides a source of friendships, increases self-esteem and can be a source of income.

After some months people who were coming to work for us on a daily basis started to say they wanted to move out of the institutions where they were living. But as time went on it became clear that only a few were getting out to ordinary housing through their own efforts or those of social workers. It seemed that many of them saw us as their only practicable opportunity for housing. So the Trust developed a housing arm, then a housing association, and began providing housing in the community as well as work.

We began to note key elements about the sort of work which seemed to suit best the people who came to us. It tended to be tasks which could be learned quite quickly - at most semi-skilled. This was not because that was all our workers could manage, but because such work gives a sense of competence and mastery early on and that is what our workers needed. What did not appear to suit them was a task which involved a drawn-out, dependent relationship with a supervisor or skilled craftsman before you were properly on top of the job. Highly unsuitable were tasks where mistakes had serious consequences. We found this, for instance, when we tried decorating work in private homes where mistakes obviously have to be rectified and where a bad reputation spreads quickly. With our workers mistakes didn't just hold up the job. They made the workers panicky, lose confidence and sometimes they'd leave us soon after. It was important to seek tasks where people could take off on their own initiative fairly soon without lengthy teaching of technique or watching for mistakes.

Just as the work should have minimal consequences of failure, so a high chance of visible success seemed important. It mattered, too, that the work should be clearly useful, valued, wanted. Also, we sought work with a communal, sociable aspect. So we would seek easily learned, labour intensive tasks which gave an individual an evident impact on their surroundings.

We set up an office-cleaning business which employed people part-time. They came off their state benefits and worked for the company for a wage. This company, John Bellers Ltd, still exists and over 20 disabled people are employed there today. But in those days everything functioned very differently. It the early 'seventies unemployment oscillated between 2% and 3%. Many people started working for our cleaning company and then moved on to other open employment. In those days they were quite readily seen as valued workers because of the gross shortage of labour. But from 1975 came the first big rise in unemployment which meant that people who had been vaguely marginal as potential employees in the early 'seventies became first extremely marginal and then, after the huge rise in unemployment from 1980, unlikely to be employed by anyone unless a high degree of subsidy was made available. Once many people left us for open employment. But, very strikingly, in the last three years only two people have done so.

So we were becoming less able to offer formal employment because people weren't leaving their jobs with our cleaning company for other jobs outside. Yet at the same time more people than ever were coming to us hoping for work because opportunities for employment elsewhere were drying up. We came to the conclusion that for many people there would have to be some different basis for their working life other than the opportunities for open employment which were moving fast beyond their grasp. It certainly would not be conventional, highly subsidised sheltered employment because there was little or no growth in that field. Even at the best of times, in fact, people who have suffered psychiatric illness had great difficulty in getting access to such opportunities, let alone at a time when there is such competition for these subsidised jobs. So for increasing numbers of people, if they were going to work at all, it would have to be on some arrangement other than employment, be it open or sheltered. Having seen how much our tenants could value working, we rejected the idea that they needn't have the opportunity to work, that they should be offered 'day care' instead as though they had no further productive or giving capacity for the rest of their lives. It was to keep open the opportunity to engage in work that we developed our furniture repair business and other work schemes. We sought a scheme which matched the sizeable numbers of people needing such opportunity with the limits to finance available from earnings or subsidy.

We aimed to see if we could devise a workscheme which included all the best features of employment and which left out all the bad ones that might lead people to further illness. It should be 'good work'. For instance, it should be purposeful and produce something which was a visible achievement and clearly useful and valuable to people outside the workforce, to people in the wider community. If possible, that usefulness should get concrete expression through a chance for workers to see customers buying their products or their service. Furthermore it should be a social occasion. It should be organised in ways that give the workers the sort of social relationships which many people in mainstream employment value highly about their jobs. Note, though, how one attractive social aspect of mainstream employment is that you

meet new people through your work and you can make
new friends and enter new social circles. Too
often workschemes (and day centres) for people who
have suffered mental illness are organised in ways
which give workers contact only with people they
know already, for instance with people with whom
they are living, as in some hospital industrial
units. So another of our concerns was to try to
organise the work so it had an outgoing quality and
took people to meet others besides co-residents and
neighbours. Yet another intended positive
ingredient was the opportunity to develop some sort
of skill in which a man or woman could take pride.
We have always found that, given enough time and
space, the majority of our workers will show some
particular aptitude, one thing which they do very
much better than they do others. So we sought a
workscheme which would involve a wide range of
different tasks so people could try out different
areas and find one which really did suit them,
where they could develop a personal skill or
aptitude. Too often on workschemes for
disadvantaged people there is only one type of work
on offer and if this does not suit an individual
they can be declared unsuited to work. Really,
though, it is important to provide variety to suit
different skills and temperaments, just like at the
best end of the mainstream job market.

So we sought to devise a workscheme which
included all these positive elements of open
employment plus, of course, another - some element
of reward for your work, if not direct wages. We
also aimed to cut out the negative features which
one also can find in employment. Many people's
psychiatric problems are aggravated, even caused,
by aspects of employment like excessive demands or
pressure, abuse from workmates, boring, stultifying
tasks, or excessively long hours.

We ended up with a series of workschemes, the
main one of which is a furniture repair and
restoration workshop which has generally met all
these criteria. We started it with just a few
pounds investment. Over the last 18 months it has
grown considerably and diversified. It arose from
the direct, practical need of our tenants for
furniture for their flats. We collected
second-hand furniture and started doing it up.
That meant developing a system for contacting and
collecting furniture which people were giving away,
then repairing it, and delivering it to people who
needed it. After the workers had met their own

needs for furniture, we continued to use the system
we had built up and the skills people had developed
to repair and sell such furniture to the general
public. The public buy our furniture by visiting
the workshop where it is restored and also through
a shop we have acquired. Business has surged since
that 'Let's try it and see' beginning. Last year
the workshop had sales of £12,000 from the efforts
of its part-time workers.

The furniture business produces a wide range
of jobs. There is accompanying the van for
collection and delivery of furniture and doing the
house clearances, which is the main way we get
furniture. There is basic sorting, cleaning and
polishing of furniture. There is simple carpentry
like repairing broken drawers. There are more
skilled tasks like special staining and polishing
processes. A whole range of skills can be
developed.

We found quite a lot of people delighted in
various parts of this process. It is clear too
that pleasure comes from actually seeing the public
seeking out our workshop, now it is known locally
as a source of good furniture. Customers can be
seen handing over money for furniture which our
workers acquired as throw-outs but have transformed
into objects of value to others. You can see
smiles on people's faces at this.

But there is also the question of more
material rewards for work done here and on the
cluster of other small enterprises which we have
developed around this scheme. Money, after all, is
not exactly far from the top of your list of
positive features of employment if you have an
ordinary job. The people working on our workscheme
are really very poor. I have not calculated how
well benefits have matched inflation but I believe
from seeing the way our tenants live today that
people on Supplementary Benefit are much poorer in
real terms than ten or fifteen years ago. And,
moreover, people on the workscheme have so much
less chance of ever getting out of their poverty,
owing to the fall in employment prospects. So we
really had to think very seriously about what
element of reward we could bring into the
workscheme in addition to the intrinsic rewards
round which we were designing the work. Many of
the workers have also pressed us to find ways of
increasing their earnings. So the matter of pay
and of conditions of engagement took on
significance in the development of the workschemes.

How we have resolved the issue to date is outlined in 'Free of Old Tags' a report on the Trust's Development since it was founded in 1968.

"Everyone engaged on the workschemes remains on state benefit whilst doing so. This means that their earning capacity is limited more by benefit regulations than it is by their own efforts. The Trust pays 50p an hour to most workers and 65p an hour to a few who have some supervisory responsibility for other people. People can work anything from a couple of hours to 30 hours a week, but at 50p an hour they reach their maximum earnings after eight hours work since Supplementary Benefit regulations require that any earnings over £4 per week are deducted from benefit. In addition to the £4 'earnings disregard' (unchanged for over a decade), people are entitled to a meal whilst at work, their fares to and from work and protective clothing if the job warrants it.

These restrictions seemed at one time to severely limit the incentive that could be put the way of those who wished to work but quite reasonably wanted some reward for their effort. To try and alleviate the consequences of the severe restrictions of the earnings rule the Trust has adopted the system that makes use of the regulations regarding gifts and Supplementary Benefit. These regulations are not entirely clear-cut, falling into the ever expanding world of administrative law. But the essential elements are that benefit claimants can receive a series of gifts that do not affect their benefit but which are highly beneficial (relative to their earnings capacity) to the individuals concerned. In broad terms the gift should be an item that is not considered to be covered by the benefit entitlement. Food, for example, is intended to be met from benefit so a gift of food would result in a corresponding reduction in cash benefit paid. Amenity and leisure items, travel costs outside of ordinary daily travel, holidays and the like are, however, within the bounds of a legitimate gift. The leisure and amenity category can include televisions, radios, videos, garden tools and many others - an exhaustive list does not appear to exist.

Gifts can also include 'occasional' cash
donations, a guideline being £100 on a
birthday, and a gift at some other time in the
year.

All of these items have to do with gifts, not
with payments for work done. If there is a
direct correlation between work done and the
gift, then the cash value of the gift may be
set against benefit: the gift will be seen as
payment in lieu of cash.

Such a scheme has been accepted by the local
DHSS office as being entirely legitimate. The
use of such a device is necessary in order to
reduce the adverse effects of the highly
inflexible and outdated Supplementary Benefits
regulations which act as a chronic
disincentive to those wanting to work to the
best of their abilities. That the rules
remain so restrictive and unimaginative is
perhaps surprising given the accepted wisdom
of offering incentives to effort, and matching
this with the negligible employment prospects
facing many thousands of people whose chances
of a job were highly marginal even in times of
full employment.

A device such as this can also go some way to
removing the poverty that oppresses many
people living on Supplementary Benefit alone.
A personal allowance of £28.05 a week to pay
for everything outside of housing presents a
tight budget for anyone and the prospects are
all the more bleak if you are reasonably
certain that this will be your income from one
year to the next, without relief.

So workschemes become important because they
relieve poverty as well as giving cause for
people to feel that they have a capacity that
is appreciated by others. Relieving financial
poverty is important but alone this will not
change the personal bleakness that surrounds
the lives of so many people who have led an
institutional life. The social poverty can
only be relieved through a developing sense of
personal worth. This is not in the gift of
any social worker or politician: it can only
arise through people having the chance to
demonstrate their worth in some practical way

and to meet others on equal terms. Our
responsibility is to create that
opportunity." (1)

So the way it works is this. The Trust pays
people on workschemes a sum of up to £4 per week,
the limit of the DHSS earnings disregard for
Supplementary Benefit. But we aim to ensure that
those who attend our schemes for longer than they
would ordinarily need to in order to receive £4,
can do so with some form of encouragement. The
Social Security regulations prohibit any additional
payment or offering that might be construed as a
payment, without there being a consequent financial
penalty. The Trust therefore makes clear that it
cannot make any payments beyond the £4 per week.
People are, however, entitled to receive occasional
gifts without this affecting their state benefit.
Thus the Trust pays people £4 for attending a fixed
number of hours. If people then choose to attend
at other times, we note this fact and use it as an
indicator as to whether or not someone might
receive a gift. The gift is at the discretion of
the Trust and it is our intention to make such
gifts only to those participants who display some
wish to take greater control over their own lives
through attending our scheme.

This 'gifts' system is visibly improving
quality of life for workers on this scheme. They
are using it very actively. It means there's a lot
more going for many people. It makes it possible,
for instance, to have ambitions and goals to look
forward to, maybe activities like a holiday or
maybe a particular acquisition. As a tangible
reward it adds meaning and value to people's effort
in the workshop. But while this workscheme means a
great deal to the people who work on it, in
financial terms it is an offshoot from the Trust
where a large proportion of costs are met by sales.
It developed naturally, with some hiccups but with
very little capital outlay. So many other projects
could start something on the same lines. You can
start from the smallest of beginnings and just see
what develops naturally. All our business ventures
have started from very small, experimental
beginnings which we pursued if they seemed to be
working or abandoned if unsuitable. All you need
to start with is some sort of sellable product or
service, assuming you are not going to be able to
run on any great subsidy. It doesn't mean you have
to be a grand entrepreneur - just take a little

initiative in looking at your local environment and identifying any particular needs. Small scale gardening, for instance, is a venture which often has wide possibilities. Just about anywhere recycling furniture has a market. It does take some effort and initiative. But really it can be very interesting and sometimes great fun.

It can be a surprise, too, how easy some things are. Concerning our furniture recycling business, for instance, supply of furniture was no problem. The quantities were amazing. We just started by contacting an Oxfam shop. We found out that quite often these shops get more offers of furniture than they can handle. So often people who want their houses emptied of furniture or goods get angry when they learn the low prices paid by commercial clearance firms. They offer it to the Oxfam shop instead. So our local Oxfam shop started ringing us when they got such approaches. So that is how we got our first furniture.

From such furniture clearances other business opportunities can emerge. People who either want furniture or want rid of it are quite often soon to move house. So requests to do small removals could follow naturally once you are there with your van. Furthermore you get a lot more from house clearances than furniture. There'll be bedding, household goods, hundreds of books, all sorts of knick-knacks. Some of our workers love going out doing such collections because it's just like a treasure hunt. You never know what someone will be giving away. Of course, the possibility is there for selling some of these things as a side-line.

The premises need not be a great problem either. You only need quite a small work space because a lot of furniture needs no more than a thorough wash or paint scraping off. That needs neither expertise, tools nor great skill. Then spray it with Pledge so it smells nice and you have a perfectly saleable item! We've learned ways of selling by trial and error - leaflets and adverts in shop windows, DHSS and Social Services Offices, local papers. From our general publicity it is now known locally that we have a supply of furniture and people come to the workshop to seek it out. Demand is sporadic. There are sudden rushes and our stock is suddenly cleared out. In fact we could expand the furniture side of our business if we could supply it on a more regular basis. Pricing, again, is something you can learn by trial and error. We assess a price per item below which

191

we should not sell but need to acquire greater expertise on such assessments.

For us this furniture business has grown from those small beginnings when we lacked the money for furniture for our tenants and so had to learn to recycle unwanted furniture. We have chosen to steadily expand it when opportunity arose. Recently we have acquired a skilled supervisor. But there are probably plenty of other such opportunities if you seek them out. Besides the offshoots already mentioned like removals and gardening, we do work around the houses we manage that would otherwise not get done. These are areas of needed work that lie outside the realm of paid employment and can legitimately be claimed for a workschemes arrangement.

So really there are many ways you can give people opportunities for genuinely useful productive work. And even if this work may not bring in anything like enough money to support the worker, it can finance an amenity fund which makes a real impact on people's quality of life and the roles they can play in society. This is something we really ought to organise with those many people who are keen for such opportunities. I once thought open employment was the proper goal for every person who came our way. I have changed my mind both because that's obviously no longer possible in today's high unemployment society and because I also recognise that there is nothing actually holy about employment as such or even about work. But we must recognise that work does have a particular meaning in the social vocabulary used by very many people in our society - and that includes people who have suffered long-term mental illness or institutionalisation. Work is the commonly accepted means for showing your worth and being judged worthy by others. Individuals who come to us often have had protracted experience of roles as incapable or non-productive people. They feel strongly about this. They want to do something worthwhile. They speak the 'work' vocabulary. Yet, without schemes like ours, unless you are able to hold down a proper job or are lucky enough for a place in a highly subsidised sheltered workshop, there are no opportunities for you, not from the helping services nor from anyone else. You can be treated as redundant for the rest of your life as far as your productive, giving capacity is concerned. You may be relegated to 'day care'. There, 'care' is the operative word.

Workschemes at the Peter Bedford Trust

It is there with the best intentions, but it marks
out everyone who receives it as unable to
contribute. This is an utterly unbalanced notion
of a person's future. Nor is it in any way
necessary to characterise people in this way when
there are perfectly good alternatives. With our
workschemes, for instance, we offer people a chance
to become contributors and participate in the
valued and familiar role of the person who carries
out work which is of value to others and which
brings rewards as a recognition of this fact.

NOTES

1. 'Free of Old Tags: the Peter Bedford Trust
1968-85' available from the Peter Bedford Trust,
Legard Works, Legard Road, London N5 1DE

Chapter Eleven

A WAY TO TRY SELF-EMPLOYMENT

Judy Scott

Editorial Introduction

An innovative scheme with flexible
opportunities for both part-time earnings on
benefit and full-time earnings in the
long-term is being developed at Kensington and
Chelsea Mental Health Association in West
London. It involves training people in
particular skills which local market research
has shown can earn high hourly rates for a
self-employed person. The dual aims of this
scheme enable trainees to supplement their
Benefit through part-time work, building up
confidence and ability to sustain earnings.
Through this opportunity to establish
professional standards individuals may
increase their earning power sufficiently to
come off welfare benefits. Full-time work on
a self-employed basis can be supported in a
number of ways through an Agency. Thus the
scheme is designed to give each person the
means to achieve their own potential in work
and for some a way to escape altogether from
the long-term unemployment and dependence on
benefits which trap so many after mental
illness.

The Agency provides six month courses giving
the basic grounding in skills, followed by
continued part-time training in conjunction
with part-time work. The staff act as
enablers and advisers to the teams, promoting
self-support. The staff also obtain the work
and handle the many financial aspects of
self-employment that cause common
difficulties, such as customer invoicing, tax,
NI, etc.

If ways can be found round such familiar
problems, then this sort of self-employment
may offer a special opportunity for people
recovering from mental illness, since it
avoids a number of problems which makes

conventional employment difficult for them.
There will be no employer to refuse a job
because of medical record or lack of recent
references. Relapse will not cost a worker
their job - you can return to the scheme when
you are able. There is flexibility concerning
the number of hours a person works. The
decisions about work rest in the hands of
yourself and team members. You can choose the
people you work with from amongst your team.
Currently this scheme is in its second year.

This scheme grew out of some lessons we learned
from running a couple of conventional MSC funded
projects offering waged employment for one year
each. The aim was rehabilitation through work and
a stepping-stone to subsequent employment
elsewhere. One of these schemes, for instance, was
an open-air building project which laid out a
formal, scented courtyard in our local community
park. The other project involved repair and
restoration of furniture belonging to pensioners
and community organisations. These workschemes
lasted two years. They employed a total of 32
people. Many had suffered serious recurrent mental
illnesses. Fourteen of the workers had been
diagnosed as suffering from schizophrenia, for
instance, and 22 were receiving long-term
medication. All of the latter had a history of
relapse and readmission to hospital.
      Our first lesson from these projects was how
extraordinarily well such work appeared to suit our
workers. Despite many workers' histories of
relapse, during those two years just none of them
were re-admitted to hospital. Yet we were, in
fact, offering quite a challenging environment
which required the continuous learning and practice
of new skills. The speed of work was extremely
slow, possibly as a result of lack of training or
work experience, possibly lack of self-confidence
and the effects of medication. It is difficult to
tell. But the standard of work on both projects was
more than acceptable. Good social networks formed
among workers and attendance and time-keeping were
good. The building project achieved an attendance
record of nearly 100% in the second year - this
must surely be unusual in any sort of employment!
      But our second lesson came when the projects
ended. The people who had worked on them generally
expected that they would get jobs on the open

market. We expected this as well, particularly in
view of some individuals' good previous work
records. For a short while we were almost
convinced that this rehabilitation process had
worked. Eight of the workers obtained full-time
jobs. Six more got part-time jobs. But by now we
have been following people's progress for between a
year and two years. We have seen that in fact
those who got jobs did not succeed in keeping them.
For the others, too, employment just finished with
the workscheme. Of those 32 people only one person
now is in employment. Moreover there have been a
number of relapses, including six re-admissions to
hospital. It is, in fact, chiefly the most able
workers among the large group on long-term
medication who have relapsed since our workschemes
finished. Maybe there is some connection with the
contrast between their sense of their own ability
in the environment which our workscheme offered and
their feeling of disability when they become
unemployed again.

So those MSC work projects taught us that a
certain type of work situation can really benefit
people recovering from mental illness, including
people with serious, recurrent illnesses. But they
taught us, too, that there is no way that people
like our workers can get long-term access to those
benefits if you rely on today's open employment
market. We still see MSC funded projects as very
useful for short-term rehabilitation as a
stepping-stone to somewhere else. We have
developed this new scheme in response, linking
longer term opportunities to temporary employment.

Something else we learned on those work
projects gave us a pointer to the new scheme we
have developed. We found that relatively brief
training in certain skills can sometimes
dramatically boost the earning power of someone who
may have pretty low productivity or employability
in unskilled tasks. At one stage on the building
project we needed some welding doing on a stretch
of railings we were putting up from scrap metal.
Two of the workers volunteered to take a three week
welding course at Perivale Skill Centre. Both in
fact were on long-term medication. One suffered
from manic-depressive illness, the other from
schizophrenia. Both had been working on
semi-skilled jobs on the project. They were
learning fast but their work was slow. They needed
constant advice and supervision. Their earning
power in open market terms would have been very low

196

indeed.

The welding course was very high pressure, we were told. Indeed the two workers arrived back at the end of each week exhausted, apparently to their limits. However they survived the three weeks and, on return to the project, between them they welded up the fifty foot stretch of railings. After they had done this, they found themselves getting offered a number of small, private welding jobs - mending someone's fence and so on. For a short while, when the welding equipment was still available, they found several small jobs which brought in £40 a day.

Now all of a sudden we had two people who at one point could hardly earn even £5 a day in the open market. Then they had this three week course in welding. Of course they remained slow workers with their limited experience but the skill the course had given them enabled them to increase their earning power dramatically. They had a skill which could readily bring in £50 a day if you could get hold of the work. You could live adequately on two days work a week at this rate. So this was a very striking, radical change.

Now this incident and others made us think about training. If particular skills meant you could have interesting work, do it at a slower pace and for shorter hours, and yet still make enough money, then providing such training was what we had to do. We have come to see such skill training as a central issue. Of course some people who come on our schemes already have skills they have developed in previous jobs. But often these are not relevant to the sort of work they are seeking now. It seems that these are frequently skills related to roles, expectations or a way of life to which they do not seek to return.

So skill training is one major element in our new scheme. Another is self-employment. If one of our workers trains in a particular skill he or she will certainly increase their earning potential. But if they use their new skill with limited experience in conventional employment, the same old pressures will be present again. That person will steadily suffer as it becomes apparent that in one way or another, whether through lack of speed or inability to withstand stresses, they cannot compete in the job market today. So this led us to consider self-employment as a framework through which people using our schemes could employ the skills if we provided training. We sought a way

round the pressures which come from the standard
expectations of output, hours worked and so on in
most conventional employment. Hence we arrived at
our present scheme. To make such self-employment
possible we needed:

*   Market research to identify skills which are in
    demand and could command high prices.

*   Training courses in skills identified as both
    in demand and preferred by people leaving
    temporary work projects and day centres each
    year.

*   Training in business roles required for
    self-employment like negotiating with
    customers, estimating for jobs, basic
    book-keeping.

*   Some means for getting customers for the
    workers: advertising, booking orders and
    channelling customers to workers.

*   Some overall means for co-ordination, financial
    advice to workers, general administration and
    paperwork.

*   Some means whereby workers could build up
    confidence, business and earning power
    gradually: ie. explore the possibilities of
    self-employment while initially still on the
    safety net of welfare benefits.

    Our answer to the last point is to either use
the DHSS rule for people on Invalidity Benefit or
Severe Disablement Allowance (without top up of
Supplementary Benefit) and for others to use the
rewards and concessions agreement as described by
Richard Grover of the Peter Bedford Trust in
Chapter Ten. This opportunity for testing out
earning power and gradually building experience and
skills on the open market is absolutely integral to
the scheme.
    Our market research pointed to three
particular lines ·of skilled work which were in
local demand, commanded high prices and which were
teachable to people coming on our scheme. One was
painting and decorating, possibly including special
finishes like rag-rolling, marbling and stencilling
which are fashionable and popular at present.
Another was carpentry, maintenance, repairing and

refitting doors and windows, installing locks and security fixtures in addition to general work. A third distinct area of local demand was gardening and plant care and supply to offices and hotels.

We developed the idea of setting up a time-limited training course in each particular skill, like painting and decorating, for teams of between six to eight people. The team would train together. As they became capable of taking on their first paying customers, they would be encouraged to help each other out and form a sort of a co-operative association of self-employed workers. Different members would take on particular roles, like buying materials, or take the roles in turn. They could carry on supporting each other in this way when their training was completed. We would ourselves run a permanent central office which would advertise the workers' services, take and pass on customers' orders, monitor customer satisfaction, do all paperwork and generally co-ordinate things. After the painting and decorating course in basic skills was completed, a second time-limited course in a different skill would be run for another team of six to eight people. Then those workers, when they 'graduated', would also move on as a second co-operative, mutual aid team to take on customers under the auspices of our central 'Agency'. Then, likewise, a subsequent group.

What we are proposing is in very broad and general terms similar to an employment agency but with membership limited to 30. The agency staff will be assisting a series of small self-help teams structured on a co-operative basis to generate and sustain themselves with part-time or full-time self-employment. Membership is reserved for people whose emotional vulnerability and recurrent illness have previously led to their unemployment. Priority is given to applicants who have completed a rehabilitative programme at a Borough Day Centre or a temporary work experience project. Some experience of the skill is essential for a realistic choice to be made.

Our aim is to create real and lasting work opportunities, to offer open-ended opportunities which enable each individual to find and sustain their maximum potential in either part-time or full-time supported self-employment.

In a nutshell the basic structure of the system is as follows:

A way to try self-employment

TRAINING

We are setting up five training courses in specialised technical skills, which are in demand, as services to businesses and householders in the Borough. The training courses are chosen by applicants and adapted to their aptitudes. The first course was agreed with prospective applicants to be painting and decorating. It started mid 1985. The second course in carpentry maintenance started March 1986. The third course, starting November 1986, represents a change of plans in order to ensure that women were able to use this opportunity. We had found ourselves with twelve men and only one woman in the first two teams so we researched three practicable alternatives and offered these to women in a poster campaign. Interior decorating or gardening/plant care or office skills? Overwhelmingly the choice was for office skills. The fourth and fifth courses will be agreed in conjunction with applicants.

Different tutors are employed for each six months course on temporary contracts. The courses begin at approximately six monthly intervals. We start with eight trainees on each course. Additional training provided by outside facilities includes work-related assertion courses, driving lessons, and other skills as required. Concerning the driving lessons, Provisional Driving Licences for a person with a history of mental illness are granted subject to the agreement of the GP and the Licensing Authorities.

THE 'EMPLOYMENT AGENCY'

The Agency has initially three permanent staff members employed by Kensington and Chelsea Mental Health Association: the Work Development Officer responsible for overall management and co-ordination with two new staff members, the Administrator and the Technical Adviser. It is hoped that after the development stage and training courses are completed the Agency will require only two staff.

The Administrator and the Technical Adviser will be responsible for marketing the services of the teams, the financial administration and technical aspects of the work. Their roles are to advise and enable the teams to prepare accurate costings, keep records, and maintain a high standard of work. They also supply supplementary training in management, accounting, budgetting, costing etc.

Each team commences real part-time work as soon as possible. The painting and decorating team started their first real contact three months into the training course. Work for customers is initially with the staff member present. This input decreases as the team gains in experience. The training period flows into the part-time working, the main difference being that the training continues on real jobs for customers with increasing emphasis on self-management. As new teams complete training with the tutor, the Technical Advisor takes on this role thereby having less time for the previous team.

Full-time work and coming off Benefits will commence as and when the individuals or teams concerned have:

(a)   sufficient confidence in their ability to sustain the work

(b)   sufficient experience to achieve a professional standard of work

(c)   obtained contracts ensuring a regular supply of work

The eventual structure of the 'Agency', with five teams and 30 members working either part-time or full-time, is likely to fluctuate according to individuals' needs and potential. Some members may not be able to take the step into full-time work and therefore continue in part-time work continuing to claim Benefits, using the base as a network support. Other members may become self-managing, using the 'Agency' as a marketing and accountancy service in return for a small fee.

And if there are relapses, after one or two months absence that person can return, take up part-time work for a while and steadily increase their workload as and when they feel able. It is important to clarify that the MIND staff play the roles of advisors and enablers. This is another very important aspect of the scheme. The staff members are not supervisors, employers or bosses.

So, for example, the painting and decorating team has developed like this: their initial six month training programme taught the basic skills. The tutor with many years experience in the trade used our workshop facilities, mini-rooms with doors and windows, combined with work outside at customer premises. The instruction covered care of tools, ordering materials and organising the various processes in each job. Workers took on responsibility for differing aspects of the work on a day-to-day basis. The training programme has been followed by a series of contracts for customers, the team working 9.30 to 4.00, initially as one group. In May they decided to take on increased personal responsibility and commenced working in twos and threes on each contract. This resulted in greatly improved attendance (which had been a problem prior to earnings), and also increased earning power per hour.

The lynch-pin of work management is the weekly team meeting. This is chaired and minuted in rotation by team members. Work progress is reviewed, offers of new contracts are discussed and it is agreed who will be available for the work and therefore who will visit the job to prepare the estimate. Contracts completed are reviewed and site book records of hours worked are tallied and agreed between co-workers for payment into the Agency Amenity Fund. This emphasis on team members taking responsibility has resulted in the staff member only visiting work in progress when requested. Recently this has been as little as an hour every couple of days. Although this may be apparently minimal there is no doubt that it is crucial. Minor technical problems have been presented as insurmountable crises. From time to time morale drops and work pace likewise - staff availability and input is needed quickly if we are to maintain our reputation for reliability. It is worth mentioning that we have had a plentiful supply of work from both private customers and the council and it would seem that the carpentry team will have the same.

At the time of writing some of the first team are considering the Enterprise Allowance as their next step but are somewhat apprehensive despite their success. Others, as expected, are content to earn within the Amenity Fund agreement, finding that their present energy levels restrict the hours they can work. The staff anticipate that this stage, of establishing a professional standard of work, will continue to next January, eighteen months from the start. Hopefully sub-groups working either full-time or part-time can continue working in collaboration providing each can respect the other's need. It seems quite probable that all members will fluctuate in their working pattern. It is our aim to provide the options.

Following the launch of the painting team the same process will be repeated with the carpentry team. Our selling point is both a good standard of work and reliability. It is a line of work where cowboy operators thrive. Potential customers have learned to be wary of tradesmen who do not deliver or who disappear before finishing the job. Already by word-of-mouth we are receiving a stream of calls from local businesses and agencies to fit locks and replace doors. Due to the nature of the work, each job is usually suitable for no more than two. This team will be working in pairs from the outset. The technical member of staff will have his work cut-out to start with; up to six jobs in progress at any one time.

The third training course in office skills has attracted mainly women as intended - to right the balance of our mainly male scheme. We are offering tuition in typing, word processing and related skills such as phoning, filing and brush-up spelling and grammar. Individuals will be found part-time voluntary placements (one or two mornings a week) in local offices as soon as possible. The training programme will be followed by part-time paid work via us as an 'Agency' providing a mini-alternative to commercial employment agencies, probably to voluntary agencies. We will also look to attract some work back at base if necessary. Special training sessions will continue as will weekly work support and planning meetings.

Office skills represents a change of direction in that eventually most individuals will not be working with team members but in local offices. However the same flexibility to work part-time or full-time, to stop or to start, and importantly, to count on support at base remains. Eighteen months from now we will be able to report on how trainees' hopes have been realised.

In the meantime members of the first team are enjoying the rewards of their work through the Amenity Fund. One member has been taking guitar lessons. He has bought an electric guitar and sound equipment and played at our anniversary party. He is saving for a moped now. Another, who took a refresher course in driving lessons was able to take a two week touring holiday with a friend. An artist buys his oils and canvasses. An inveterate collector has filled his flat (recently established) with interesting objects from our

local market and installed a 'phone. Each has
developed and broadened their options.
The general pattern of the scheme should be
clear now. There are a couple of extra points
worth noting about the overall role of the
'Agency'. One obvious aspect is that it enables
goodwill and customers gained through one line of
business to be passed on to Agency members offering
other services, if the customer later seeks these
too. While the major role of 'Agency' staff is
business advice, advertising, booking of customers
and administration they are also intended to liaise
with the DHSS on behalf of 'Agency' members, when
necessary. There are many possible complications
in relation to the earnings rule on Benefits. It
can be very important to have some channel of
communication for sorting these out fast, rather
than leaving it to each individual worker.
Another aspect of the 'Agency' is that when a
worker has achieved a satisfactory level of
full-time earning, we'll be making a service charge
of between £5 and £10 a week per person, just as
one would pay an accountant. We see this as an
important principle and an expression of our
expectations of the workers. When the scheme is
fully operational, this charge could, in fact,
bring in around £10,000 a year to the 'Agency',
which would reduce the scheme's costs considerably.
Talking of costs, once you exclude capital outlay
and initial training costs, were the government to
finance the running of this scheme, it would start
to represent a net saving to the national exchequer
if just half the workers, 15 people, could move off
Benefit.
Certainly this scheme is complicated, mainly
as a direct result of DHSS Benefit regulations
which are not geared to present conditions. But it
can hopefully offer people some opportunities which
are not otherwise available. It offers them a way
past the obstacles which mental illness places in
the way of their ever working again. It is
designed to bypass that stark choice between
full-time employment or full-time unemployment. It
offers opportunities for people across a wide range
of abilities. At one end of the range are those
people who are able to work their way to
self-support through self-employment. Towards the
other are those many people who actually have
little prospect of ever being able to work well
enough to support themselves - but who nevertheless
could manage a number of hours a week using one of

these high-earning skills, to alleviate the extreme
limitations that living on Benefits brings. This
brings people who suffer long-term mental illness
many more choices and opportunities in their lives.
They are no longer confined forever to a very
restrained existence by shortage of money. They
are no longer squeezed down to always buying the
same bargain food, to never travelling anywhere,
never going to the cinema for instance. The scheme
opens to them a level of income which gives some
choice to explore living. Another notable feature
is that another breakdown or another psychotic
episode need not destroy the friendships and social
systems a person has built up.

This is, of course, a sizeable scheme which
has taken a lot of planning. It has also depended
on other schemes to provide prospective applicants
with a stepping-stone to reach this stage and to
find a skill they enjoy. But there are certain
ideas or basic components which anyone could draw
from this scheme and use on a much smaller scale.
Here are some things I would do if I were working
for a MIND Association with limited staff and
resources.

EDUCATION IN BENEFIT RULES

You could promote use of the earnings
allowance for Invalidity Benefit and inform people
about the possibilities for legitimately financing
an Amenity Fund for people on Supplementary
Benefit. Many people don't know. You could also
help their negotiations with the local DHSS Office.
You could become the Agency or organise the fund to
which earnings were paid, although this may be more
time consuming.

RESEARCH LOCAL DEMAND

We got help from the local Chamber of
Commerce. In many places there are local business
associations. I would urge you to examine services
you can provide, rather than manufacturing goods or
products. Unless you are manufacturing goods which
are really distinctive as well as high quality, you
face impossible competition from mass-produced or
imported goods. Dreams about making spice racks
and wooden tongs may be attractive because of the
process but earnings are hopelessly low. It is in
providing services which are accessible on a local
basis that you do not face competition from

automation or imports and realistic earnings can be achieved.

OPPORTUNITIES FOR TRAINING

The local Adult Education Institute, for instance, might be willing to arrange short courses in various useful skills which might earn money in your area, teaming up with members of a local unemployment centre.

You could perhaps form work groups with volunteer leaders such as retired tradesmen. Most of all you could provide a base for people to make plans. So you don't have to try an extensive scheme. You could actually do this sort of thing with just three or four people who drop in and say they don't know what to do and they can't get a job. The possibilities are there, in fact, for many mental health workers to do something of this sort.

Chapter Twelve

GETTING A REAL JOB AND THE RIGHT JOB

Corinne Brewer

Editorial Introduction

This chapter reviews issues involved when a
person who has suffered mental illness is
seeking employment on the open job market.

We have four million people out of work and no sign
of improvement. Undoubtedly talk of helping
people obtain paid work gets dismissed as
unrealistic. Certainly it is not easy to find work
in these times of high unemployment. For people
who declare a history of mental health problems it
never has been easy, let alone nowadays. But
admitting that it is not easy is not the same as
saying it is not possible. For some people there
is no acceptable substitute to paid work. For some
it represents a return to normality, a return to
society after a period of segregation. Certainly
it is more likely to offer chances of a reasonable
standard of living, of meeting a wide range of
people, and escape from the role of 'patient' or
recipient of services than many alternatives.
    What follows are some ideas of ways in which
people can be helped to think about themselves and
work, to match their needs and skills to those of
different jobs and some practical information about
finding and applying for jobs. It is not specific
to people who have had mental health problems.
Most, if not all the points made, are relevant to
anyone looking for employment. And it is not in
any way meant as an exhaustive list of points or
issues. It focusses on individuals thinking of
themselves - what they can do, things which they
should avoid or would find unenjoyable, and
likewise analysing jobs and work situations.
    But while most advice given here applies to
any job-seeker, there is one particular issue which
faces people who have suffered mental illness. If
you have had a period of mental illness, on
applying for a job you will be immediately
confronted with the dilemma of what, if anything,
to tell a prospective employer about your health.

There is evidence to show that employers are
prejudiced against employing people who have
histories of mental illness. But it is important
to remember that this is not the same as saying
employers do not employ such people.

In any discussion of this issue it is
important that the following points are raised and
dealt with. Fundamental to the 'to tell or not'
dilemma is understanding of people's anxieties
about mental illness and in particular what
concerns employers with respect to past illness.
Perhaps these four questions sum up the major
fears:

> Is s/he able to do this job?
> Will s/he be ill again?
> Is s/he well now?
> Is s/he going to be reliable?

Understanding these fears may help people
prepare answers which will allay them. Other
points to bear in mind would be whether the past
mental health problem, or any current medication,
affects a person's ability to do certain things or
to work in certain situations. An awareness of
public ignorance about mental health and
misunderstanding of jargon is important - certain
psychiatric labels conjure up frightening images in
the public's mind. It may be worth bearing this
in mind when talking about illness or treatment.
Certainly there is no right or wrong way to tackle
this issue. It can be argued that, if past mental
illness will have no effect on how one does a
particular job, then there is no justification for
an employer to be informed, any more than
concerning a previous marriage or home ownership.
The counter argument is that failing to disclose
information at an interview or on a job application
form is grounds for dismissal - no matter how well
you are doing your work. In the end it must rest
on what the person going for the job feels
comfortable about saying or doing. Discussion and
preparation will certainly do no harm and may help
to make someone more confident about the way they
handle this issue. Confidence about the decision
is probably more important than whether or not an
individual decides to tell or not.

Getting a real job

WHICH JOB?

      With a declared aim of helping people to find
work wherever possible, it is important to think
about how one chooses the jobs to go after. With
four million unemployed and many people chasing
after each available job, choice may seem an
unaffordable luxury. But people do make choices,
often based on whether or not they possess the
practical skills required by the job. If the
decision of job suitability is based on this aspect
alone, it may well be the wrong one. 'Unskilled'
jobs call for a variety of skills, often not ones
that can be learned. For example, an office
cleaning job may be classified as 'unskilled' -
anyone can wield a duster or push a hoover over a
floor. But in terms of initiative, judgement,
ability to work alone, or to take responsibility,
it may require quite a high level of skills. It is
one thing to hoover a floor. It is another to know
when one office is clean enough to move on to the
next one. If the wrong decision is taken then
either the office is left dirty or the work isn't
finished in the time available. For some people
the responsibility and decision making involved
would make the job very stressful. On the other
hand some seemingly 'skilled' jobs, for example
copy typing, may involve the practice of a learnt
skill but require very little in the way of
initiative, judgement or individual decision
making. The point may seem simplistic but it is
possible that many people either do not convince
employers at the interview stage or do not cope
when actually at work because they are unaware of
such subtle demands of the job. Practical skills
can possibly be learned on the job. But 'coping'
skills, like the ability to work without
supervision, to be relaxed with a group of other
people or even having a good memory or long
concentration span, cannot be as readily 'picked up
on the job' - and they are skills which an employer
will not be expecting to have to teach. It is my
experience that people rarely lose jobs because
their practical skills weren't quite up to scratch.
More often it is because they were unable to
socialise or failed to ask for more work when
they'd completed one task. It is vital that people
applying for jobs are aware of the whole job and
feel that they have the necessary skills and are
comfortable about using them.

POSITIVE PRESENTATION

One of the problems of looking for work is
that it can be utterly dispiriting. The lists of
jobs which are out of reach, that you feel you
cannot do, can seem overwhelming. It is important
to redress this imbalance. 'Positive presentation'
is vital. Everyone has a variety of skills - no-one
is 'unskilled'. As with job demands, people's
skills can be divided into practical, learnt skills
and those that are personal aptitudes or 'coping
skills'. Learnt skills may be more readily
identifiable. They can be things you learned at
school, in past jobs, through hobbies, on training
courses or through voluntary work. The 'aptitudes'
list may be less immediately obvious but with a bit
of thought, no less encouraging. Abilities to
concentrate, remember things, take responsibility,
work alone, solve problems, get on well with other
people or even to keep busy or cheerful - all these
could all be vital in getting or keeping a
particular job. They are skills which can be
developed with practice - but rarely do employers
consider them in training. As mentioned, I find
that the lack of one of these 'coping' skills means
greatest risk of someone being dismissed as
'unsuitable'.

To be successful then, the job seeker must
look at him/herself in terms of all his/her skills
and do a similar breakdown concerning different
types of work. The next stage is called
'matching'. As the name implies, it involves
trying to find a job which is attractive and calls
for those practical skills and coping skills that
the job seeker possesses.

JOB HUNTING

I have raised some of the points which I feel
are vital to consider before embarking on job
hunting. I now want to touch on how the hunt can
actually be carried out - and who or where might be
useful sources of help. A few years ago an
analysis of the ways in which people obtain work
showed that the majority of jobs were obtained
through newspaper adverts, but many were also found
through friends or family members. Job centres or
agencies played a smaller part. Maybe this has
changed of late, but both adverts and personal
recommendations are very important to consider.
Personal recommendations are obviously popular with

employers, though they may raise doubts in some
people's minds on the morality of preferential
treatment. If a trusted, reliable employee has a
friend who s/he believes would be able to do a
particular job, the employer has good reason to
feel that employing this recommended person
involves less risk. They are likely to be more
successful employees in terms of knowing more about
the firm and the job, perhaps, than someone who the
employer has only talked to for half an hour at an
interview. It is worth exploiting this. It is
always worthwhile to ask friends working in places
which might have suitable work to ask on one's
behalf or talk to friends and family and other
contacts on the off-chance of a lead to a job.
    Newspaper adverts are the other major source
of information on available jobs. People who have
no experience of reading and interpreting these may
need some initial help - the abbreviations can be
confusing and time can be wasted going after jobs
which turn out to be unsuitable. It takes courage
to pick up a phone and talk to a potential
employer. Even to ask for an application form can
be a trial if one is not used to the phone or
talking to strangers. For some jobs the
phone-manner of the applicant may decide whether or
not they are considered worth interviewing. It is
vital that people prepare for this. A simple
written checklist of questions that need answering
can help. For example - hours or location of job,
training given, qualifications needed. For some
reason employers don't appreciate the first
question being about pay - even if it's not
specified in the advert. Asking if references are
needed often arouses suspicions that the applicant
doesn't have any. Think of the initial phone
conversation as the applicant's first chance to
'sell' themselves to the employer - and to sort out
for themselves whether it is a job they really
want. First impressions are important and the
telephone call may well form the first impression.
It is worth practice and preparation and both are
relatively easy to do.
    If the phone call is often stage one, the
application form or the letter of application is
often the next. And this is the chief filtering
stage for employers. Some of the advice that
follows is very obvious. But it's important to
remember how it can feel when confronted with one's
first application form in years, - maybe the first
one ever. Bear in mind how devastating it can feel

if you make a mistake and know your messed up form
may cost you an interview for a desperately needed
job. So - basics - it's well worth keeping a list
of information to use for each form and letter.
It's important, if you are not going to declare
periods of hospitalisation, that you have a clear
way of accounting for those periods of time.
Reading and re-reading the application form all the
way through pays dividends. There is no point in
cramming important but unrequested information in
at one part of the form if it's asked for
elsewhere. Filling in the form in pencil first is
useful. If one is not confident about spelling or
grammar, getting someone to check the form before
inking it in might be worthwhile. Some jobs
require application by letter. While this seems
harder than filling in an application form, it does
give the applicant more scope for putting
themselves across. Again, preparation and practice
pay dividends. The letter should not just describe
the applicant - previous experience, a few personal
details like age perhaps. It should also show that
thought has been given to why this particular job
is wanted and why the applicant feels they will be
the best person for it. Bringing in any relevant
past experience that relates to the tasks involved
in the job will help. The experience doesn't have
to have been in a previous job. Hobbies, school
work, house work, voluntary work, help given to
friends, may all be possible evidence of relevant
aptitudes and a clear understanding of what a
particular job involves.
     Before coming on to the next stage in job
application - the interview - a brief look at other
sources of jobs. The Manpower Services Commission
(MSC) have job centres, which offer applicants the
opportunity to self-select jobs and obtain
interviews with the minimum of fuss. Usually only
very basic information is required before an
interview is arranged by the job centre staff with
the prospective employer. This has the advantage
of speed and ease but the disadvantage of minimal
advice or help in making sure the job is what is
wanted by the applicant - or a realistic choice.
Specialist staff are employed to help people who
have identified themselves or been identified by
staff as needing extra help. The Disablement
Resettlement Officer (DRO) is specially trained to
help people with disabilities or a history of
illness to find suitable work. They also spend
time canvassing employers and may well have

personal contacts with a range of local firms which
can smooth entry for a job applicant they
recommend. They can be valuable allies and useful
sources of information on the local job market and
training opportunities. However they can also have
the same fears and prejudices about 'employing
someone after mental illness' as many employers.
Sometimes a worker in Social Services or hospital
may be considering encouraging an individual to
seek the DRO's help. In this situation it's worth
checking out whether they would like you to act as
advocate, should the DRO seem to feel unconvinced
about their employability or 'wellness'. It is not
unknown for DROs to simply fob off people they
don't feel would be able to get work. Sometimes
their assessment is accurate and an individual is
not able to work. But sometimes this assessment
can be made on the basis of a psychiatric report
full of labels and negative aspects of the person's
experiences whilst ill. DROs often have only
limited training in working with people with mental
health problems. It is hard for them always to
feel confident enough to carry on working with
someone who may superficially appear damaged by
such difficulties. And the fear of someone
'relapsing' whilst in a job that the DRO has helped
them obtain, does influence how far a DRO may be
prepared to persuade an employer to take a chance.
The offer of support or a positive second opinion
from someone else who knows the client may help.
     Some workers, working from a day care base or
perhaps a MIND Local Association, have themselves
taken on the DRO function with great success. This
does involve considerable amounts of time and the
development of expertise in job counselling.
Helping people to assess their job needs and
personal skills and match them to an available job
is not an easy task. It is never one to be taken
lightly without thorough knowledge of locally
available jobs, and the qualifications and
practical and 'coping' skills needed. Without this
knowledge people's hopes can be unrealistically
raised and then dashed. Reading the newspaper
adverts, visiting Job Centres and talking to people
doing a whole range of jobs about what each job
involves can provide a lot of information. And if
one has never spent time talking with different
employers or personnel staff it would be worth
setting up some meetings to hear exactly what they
look for in potential employees. Perhaps, too, you
can use the opportunity to allay some of their

misconceptions about the effects of mental health
problems and the reliability of people who have had
these in the past.

Additionally, you may be able to offer
potential employers support and advice on an
ongoing basis. This may well make the employer
more confident about what he or she perceives as
'risk-taking'. It is worth keeping this 'risk-
taking' in mind throughout any help you give over
job-seeking. Employers by and large want to employ
the best person for the job. Because of commonly
held misconceptions about the effects of mental
health problems, people who admit to these are seen
as coming bearing risks. This distorted picture
must be corrected if the person is to stand a
chance of being employed. Again, knowing one's
skills, knowing those that the employer is seeking,
and having confidence that they match can go a long
way towards convincing the employer to take a
prospective employee seriously.

RISKS AND REWARDS

It is important to encourage and support
people while seeking work. The rewards are huge
for an individual who succeeds in getting and
keeping a job in which they feel happy and
competent. But the disappointment involved in
continual rejection can be devastating. Likewise
for failure to keep a job if you do get one. It is
vital to remember this. Too often advice is given
and an individual is sent off alone down a road
which can be depressing and dispiriting. At the
beginning of this piece, I said that the difficulty
in obtaining work shouldn't be an excuse to exclude
people with a history of mental health problems
from the world of employment. It should make
everyone work harder to overcome prejudice and
ensure that advice and information about work or
training is readily available. I feel equally sure
that this work shouldn't be undertaken without a
commitment to support the individual, if they want
this, throughout their job seeking. If necessary
you should also offer some continuing support in
the early stages of their new job.

Chapter Thirteen

A ROAD TO SOMEWHERE: FOUNTAIN HOUSE AND
TRANSITIONAL EMPLOYMENT

Jane Richardson

Editorial Introduction

A well developed system for opening
opportunity after mental illness is the
Transitional Employment Programme originated
at Fountain House, New York. Through special
business contracts with local employers, a
person getting ready to leave this famous
mental health service can be guaranteed
appropriate temporary jobs in ordinary
workplaces and thus can build up confidence,
work experience, and references from
mainstream employers. Jane Richardson
describes how Transitional Employment works -
and how it interlinks with Fountain House's
'clubhouse' model for rehabilitation.

A major current concern for everyone involved with
the mentally ill is responding to the planned
closure of the old psychiatric institutions in ways
which ease the transition from hospital and promote
re-integration in the community.

I am grateful therefore for the opportunity to
share my experience of having worked for three
months at Fountain House in New York City. It is
parent of the clubhouse model of rehabilitation for
people chronically disabled by mental illness, very
many of whom have a diagnosis of schizophrenia.
Fountain House is a large but homely,
non-residential 'clubhouse' for its mentally ill
'members' which attracts a daily attendance of over
350. It has excited much world-wide interest, most
notably for its unique Transitional Employment
programme with which this paper will be largely
concerned.

I propose firstly, however, to enlarge upon
the daily life and philosophy of the clubhouse, of
which the Transitional Employment Programme forms
an integral part. Then I will describe the work
placements scheme in more detail.

THE PRE-VOCATIONAL DAY PROGRAMME

"People don't dwell on limitations here!"

Member

Fountain House is essentially based upon a profound belief in the potential productivity of those suffering from chronic mental ill-health. To illustrate this, the members take responsibility for the day-to-day running of every area in the life of the clubhouse, the staff to member ratio being kept deliberately low so that the club could not possibly function without its members.

There are six work units whose activities comprise what is known as the pre-vocational day programme. These are, the kitchen, first floor reception, clerical, education/research and snack bar. Each new member selects the unit and key staff worker of their choice and begins by participating in the various activities and twice daily unit meetings. They learn to relate to other members and staff in a working environment which does not involve any 'make work' tasks.

Thus, in the first floor unit members help to operate their own bank and to man the busy reception area, checking members in and out and attending to the persistent demands of the telephone.

Likewise, other members are to be seen handling enormous trollies laden with foodstuffs. They will soon re-emerge as the midday meal, prepared, cooked and served by the members in the large basement dining room or as snacks to be consumed in the fifth floor coffee bar.

Again, in the extremely busy clerical unit, a large room filled to capacity with desks, typewriters and filing cabinets, numerous members are involved in every aspect of the publication of the daily house newspaper. Others are engaged in operating the complex switchboard or in performing many varied clerical tasks. Still others act as tour guides for the two thousand annual visitors to the house. Each unit is also in turn responsible for its own cleaning and general maintenance.

PEOPLE NOT PATHOLOGIES ...

"Rehabilitation is about enabling people and
allowing them to become enablers."

David Goldberg

Implicit in all this is the fact that the
members and staff work alongside one another in a
reciprocal relationship based upon mutual
dependence. Both work together, the emphasis being
upon doing with not to.
Thus, through the concept of membership, the
mentally ill regain the confidence and sense of
self-worth which come from the knowledge that each
has a valued contribution to make, whether it is
simply the cleaning of an ash tray or the teaching
of a task to a fellow member, and from knowing that
these contributions are recognised and applauded.
As John Beard, late Director of Fountain House for
nearly thirty years, noted:

"There is need for an environment where
someone has significance as a person, despite
their pathology."

This sense of personal investment, of having
worthwhile expectations upon one's time, and the
fulfilment of the need to be needed, goes far to
explain the very high energy and morale which so
immediately impress the first time visitor to the
house. At every opportunity the staff workers
encourage and promote the members' strengths. They
focus on the healthy, functioning part of the
individual. This obviously doesn't make the
pathology go away. But it does gradually assume a
lesser importance and, indeed, clinical improvement
is noted.

TOWARDS A TRANSITIONAL EMPLOYMENT PLACEMENT

"I had 20 years experience as an executive
with Rolls Royce cars. I had been
hospitalised several times in Bellevue and New
York University Hospital. I work in the
Programme Office where I answer the 'phone and
keep up to date the permanent files of members
who are on TEPs. I had been very sick before
coming to Fountain House every day. Now my
medical doctors are very pleased with me."

Fountain House and transitional employment

Lyn Perkins, Member

Importantly, during the pre-vocational day programme members are encouraged to develop better work habits, notably punctuality, improved concentration and acceptance of a degree of supervision - all essential prerequisites for sustaining employment in the community.

Likewise, there is a marked similarity between many of the tasks required daily at the house and the work required during a TE placement. Members have the opportunity to learn a number of practical skills, such as filing, typing and so on and are encouraged to 'brush up' on old talents.

"Prior to my hospitalisation, I had not worked for six years. Before my first TE placement I worked in the membership office at Fountain House. This experience gave me confidence to accept my first assignment at a bank. I have had several placements and my confidence and skills have improved with each one. I am presently working as a numerical file clerk at a Manhattan Insurance Company. The job is ideal. I look forward to going to work each morning."

Helen Farrell, Member

Whilst working at Fountain House, I was given the role of staff worker in the house 'Thrift Shop', a large, smart 'nearly new' store on nearby 9th Avenue. The Thrift Shop neatly illustrates how a work unit closely simulates a real working environment.

A team of members participate in every aspect of the running of the store. This involves sorting through and pricing the enormous volume of donated goods, operating the cash register or acting as security guards and shop assistants. Even those members with active symptoms were able, with guidance, to redirect their thoughts towards such tasks and perform them successfully.

Thus, given a rehabilitation programme which focusses on the doing of normal, everyday activities, the members begin to perceive themselves, and are in turn perceived, as being capable of normal activity. This contributes not only practical skills but a greater confidence to attempt a work placement in the community.

218

SO WHAT EXACTLY IS A TRANSITIONAL EMPLOYMENT PLACEMENT?

When a member feels sufficiently confident and has been participating well in the day programme, he or she may take advantage of the opportunity to go on a TEP. These are jobs secured by Fountain House. They are real, entry-level positions in industry and commerce where members receive the regular wages and are given no special favours. Each day some 110 members go out to work on a part-time basis, the remaining half of the day being spent in the clubhouse. This means that two members can take advantage of any one job placement and ensures continuous monitoring of the progress of the placement and support for the member concerned.

Currently, some 44 different employers in New York City are involved in this arrangement. They range from large, national corporations to small local firms. Typical placements include banks, department stores, messenger jobs, insurance and advertising companies and placements in fast food restaurants.

One member of staff at Fountain House has the major responsibility for negotiating with employers for new placements. Each unit at the house is then in turn responsible for the management of certain TE placements, individual staff workers being responsible for initiating and supervising specific placements. This means that a staff worker is required to spend a few hours or days on the job to familiarise themselves with the demands of the work before introducing the member to their role. The member then works for a period of approximately six months before helping to train another member who is about to replace them. Staff commonly develop good relations with the immediate supervisors within the respective firm and respond promptly to any difficulties which may arise.

Most placements are for individual members but there are a few group placements involving some six to ten people working on a TEP together.

It must be stressed that TEPs are not an act of charity on the part of the employer. Rather, they represent a unique collaboration between Fountain House and the business community to their mutual benefit. The employer is assured that if a member is unable to attend at any time there will always be another member or staff worker to take

over the job, offering a guarantee that the job
will always be done. Employers also state that
making one of these entry-level jobs into a TE
placement means certainly no greater employee
turnover than would occur anyway. Also, since
members place a high investment in their placement
their work tends to be of a good standard.

In turn, Fountain House is able to secure jobs
for members whose record of hospitalisations,
sometimes limited education or poor work record -
or indeed the absence of one - would normally make
obtaining work exceptionally difficult. Many
members lack job references and experience
difficulty in dealing successfully with a stressful
job interview. (In practice little correlation has
been found between the ability to pass an interview
and the ability to perform a job successfully).
However, since Fountain House itself screens
members who feel ready to seek part-time work,
these difficulties are immediately eliminated.

WHEN AND HOW?

> "You start out when you're ready as a simple
> job-messenger, very simple jobs for 20 hours a
> week. You progress slowly, gradually to more
> and more."

Ronnie Peterson, Worker

The process of selecting members for TEPs and
its timing is informal. Staff stress, however,
that it is crucially important to know the
prospective member well and preferably to have seen
them at their worst as well as their best.

It is important also to be familiar with the
placement itself to know the working environment,
job requirements, likely pressures and to be able
to evaluate its compatibility with the needs of the
individual member.

In practice, members may make use of the
opportunities of the TEP programme very gradually.
In this sense the clubhouse may be likened to a
family. As with the family unit, there are no time
limits. Rather, it is a place where members can
learn and from which they can develop and grow in
their own time.

Some members use TEPs as a stepping-stone to
seeking full-time independent employment.
Sometimes this will be in skilled jobs. As one
remarked, "Some of us use a TEP to learn to follow

a routine and take responsibility, not because we want a vocation as a Staff messenger or clothes tagger". Some TEPs are more demanding than others and members may make use of any number of placement opportunities. For those wishing to eventually go on to full-time work, TEPs make it possible to evaluate their potential in a normal working environment rather than that of a sheltered workshop. There are other TEP workers who have no intention of seeking full-time employment. These members likewise are able to make use of TE placements for as long as they wish.

THE RIGHT TO FAIL

"I was sent to try the placement at Benton and Bowles last year. I was to be trained by Barbara Baxter, who was finishing her 6 month TEP. I felt eager and sure of myself. Then I became nervous and over-anxious. I started to sweat and couldn't get the feel of the job day. I never went back .... I am now employed at Benton and Bowles doing the job at which I first tried to succeed. I am doing fine now. It shows that if you're going to succeed try, try, try, again!"

Lucille Anderson, Member

"The TE programme gave me the challenge to try to keep a job. I stumbled many times but became all the more sure-footed for it."

Nancy Schell, Member

The transition from working in the secure environment of the clubhouse to that of working on a TEP is difficult. Many members, especially those who have never held a job before, are anxious and afraid. It is crucial, however, to the philosophy of the house that whenever a placement breaks down, the member can simply return to full-time participation in the day programme and try again in their own time. Members often attempt two or three placements before finally completing one successfully.

Indeed as John Beard once wrote: "Failure is considered a step one must take in overcoming disability". Fountain House offers its members an environment where they can overcome the fear to try and where they know that failure, especially on

placement, is considered just another step in
learning to readjust to the demands of life in the
community. It is seen as part of the continual
process of learning in which all of us are involved
throughout our lives.

THE FOUNTAIN HOUSE COMMUNITY

"I don't think I would have made it through a
TEP at McGraw Hill on the indoor messenger
placement, if it wasn't for the list that
Scott Martin (member) made of all the stops we
both made whilst we were doing the placement.
It's the help of all the members which makes
TEP work."

Ronald Galan

Behind all this the Clubhouse is crucial in
providing an environment of mutual support where
members can discuss their placements or their
regular activities at the house. Achievements can
be celebrated and failures shared.

A poignant example of this is the weekly
evening dinner for all those on TE placements. On
these occasions members sit down to a meal prepared
and served by fellow members and staff. Member
after member then stands up to address this large
audience, speaking of their achievements or their
difficulties, stimulating dialogues with various
members and staff in the hall. The support thereby
generated is a very potent force. It reinforces
the belief that in sharing of ourselves we promote
our own health and rehabilitation.

The members' support for one another is
fundamental in the life of the clubhouse, both in
providing models for those considering a work
placement, and throughout the duration of the
placement itself. Integral to the clubhouse model
is the belief that mutual help between members is
extremely regenerative. Members pass on the
benefits of their experiences, and energy and hope
is channelled back into the house.

"I came to Fountain House when I was
discharged from St. Vincent's hospital. I was
placed in reception. I have met and made many
friends who are co-operative and supportive in
all my endeavours and future plans. I am
grateful to Fountain House for my new lease of
life and hope to stay here and help others as

222

I have been helped".

Sara Black, (retired) Member

IS FOUNTAIN HOUSE A VIABLE MODEL FOR BRITAIN?

"Chronic illness doesn't have to mean chronic patienthood. "

Staffworker

Fountain House sharply contrasts with many day programmes catering for a similar population in Britain - frequently characterised by passivity, low morale and poor motivation. Much of this inertia is often considered inherent to major illnesses such as schizophrenia. It is also often in part attributed to long-term use of major tranquillisers. Consequently, these people are commonly thought to have little real potential and are for the most part passive recipients - consumers - of services rather than taking a more active involvement in the running of the services themselves.

It has already been noted that the majority of members at Fountain House suffer from schizophrenia and many others from affective disorders. Many of the older members have been hospitalised for several years. The younger members have typically experienced recurrent hospitalisations.

The staff at Fountain House would not deny that withdrawal and energy loss are features of mental ill-health. However, it is felt unproductive to reinforce these limitations by developing programmes which assume little initiative or resourcefulness on the part of participants.

Furthermore, Fountain House is not based upon an exclusively American philosophy. Rather it is a response to the universal human needs to belong and to have some sense of purpose. It thereby breaks the cycle of dependency which is such a feature of the life of the mentally ill.

There may be lingering scepticism, however, that the TE programme is a particularly dubious import, which may work well only in New York, an affluent business centre with relatively high levels of employment. In response, it is worth noting that since the founding of the National Training Programme ten years ago, some 170 sister clubhouses have been established in 33 States throughout America. Many of these are in areas far removed from the busy commercial world of Manhattan. Likewise, clubhouses have also been established in cultures as different as Pakistan and Sweden. In the United States:

> "Fountain House has a list of 634 employers who are making it possible as of December '84 for 1,579 members to work each day as part of their vocational rehabilitation, earning total annual wages of $5,972,884".

HOW MIGHT TRANSITIONAL EMPLOYMENT BE APPLIED IN THIS COUNTRY?

> "Transitional employment is a dimension of rehabilitation - not an isolated system."

John Beard, Author of the TE programme

This year, with the aid of a research grant from the King's Fund, I was able to return to the States in order to visit some examples of smaller, sister clubhouses along the East coast of America. Several common factors emerged as useful guidelines towards establishing the clubhouse programme.

One key factor is perhaps self-evident, namely that the clubhouse must be well established before TEPs can be sought. Unlike the British MSC funded Sheltered Placement Scheme where a placement, once established, is monitored monthly, these placements need to be structured differently. Due to the way mental illness is episodic and exacerbated by stress, those on placement require more long-term, on-going support. Placements must therefore be seen in the context of the overall clubhouse programme which simultaneously monitors the placement and provides moral and practical support for the member concerned.

John Beard initiated the TE programme a year after his arrival at Fountain House but in practice there is no hard and fast time-scale for its development. However, some clubhouse directors suggested that TE programmes risked getting started later than necessary. Philip Emory, director of Gateway House in South Carolina, for instance, candidly stated·that one of his greatest obstacles to developing the TE programme had been his own hesitancy. It is undeniably a major change of direction for a social worker to approach industry and commerce in order to attempt to secure placements. It was emphasised that the approach must always be that of a business arrangement with no expectation of reduced production levels for members - "There is no such thing as equal but special".

A DIFFERENT PERSPECTIVE

A visit to an example of a programme which was struggling to develop the clubhouse model made clear that this model cannot simply be superimposed upon existing structures and attitudes. Note the heavy irony in the remark made to the Training Officer at Fountain House - "We call them 'members' now".

Most essential is the early and continuous education of both members and staff workers and the involvement of the membership throughout every stage of the development of the house. It is important that staff have a clear grasp of their role as enablers - motivating, encouraging, supporting, guiding - and always involving. Staff must demonstrate to the members a belief in the latter's potential within the clubhouse, if they are ever to believe in their potential to take responsibility in the form of a work placement in the community.

The actual clubhouse itself should start small and gradually evolve with its membership. Not all the units need to be set up at the very outset and unit meetings might initially take the form of a gathering of the whole house. Likewise, the clubhouse premises may be far from ideal. A building may be rented and might simply consist of a couple of rooms, one of which should have a kitchen facility. A newly established clubhouse programme in Brooklyn, for example, operates well in the basement of a community centre.

Indeed, although funding, locations and the actual mechanics of starting the clubhouse differed from area to area, the philosophy and structure of the clubhouse programme were the same.

TO CONCLUDE - AN OVERVIEW

"We collect, edit, type, proofread, collate and distribute the news we feel is relevant to each of us in our continuing effort towards our personal rehabilitation."

A statement which appears daily in the house

newspaper.

Community care, in which so much hope is currently invested, is not about 'containing' the mentally ill - although such institutionalised thinking does not just disappear when facilities are placed in the community. Rather it is about looking outwards towards the communities of which they are members - which means the working community as well as that of social and recreational life. Perhaps at a time of high unemployment this might appear naive. But we must not make excuses for any reluctance to make concerned efforts towards vocational rehabilitation. It could be argued, too, that the concept of the disabled doing the same work as the non-disabled is somewhat disconcerting or that even in areas of high employment, such as the South East, there are few schemes which take very seriously the idea of rehabilitation towards paid employment.

If community care is also about seeing people as resources for one another, then Fountain House has much to offer us. Implicit in this view is the involvement of those for whom our psychiatric day care services operate. We are surely bound to acquire a deeper appreciation and understanding of what sufferers from mental illness find helpful and constructive in the process of rehabilitation.

Again and again, members at Fountain House talk of the importance of a sense of involvement in their own rehabilitation by the doing of what they perceive as relevant activity both inside the clubhouse and out of it. Rehabilitation is thereby seen as a natural process. To conclude, this comment by a former member neatly expresses this philosophy:-

"For me, rehabilitation is not having something done to me. Most people I'm with at Fountain House don't feel they're being rehabilitated or having something done to them. Our lives are real, like the lives of others. We feel this way because we have the chance to be together, to be with staff who feel the same way, to do things which have meaning to us, to each other".

Ronnie Peterson
Staff Worker and Former Member

Chapter Fourteen

THE SHELTERED PLACEMENT SCHEME

Mike Twomey

Editorial Introduction

The MSC's Sheltered Placement Scheme opens
jobs in mainstream workplaces to people who
cannot work productively enough to compete in
ordinary full-time employment. Under the
scheme, which is intended for people who can
be registered as disabled, an employer pays
the proportion of the standard wage which
reflects the worker's actual output; an MSC
subsidy makes up the rest. This arrangement
can open a remarkable variety of jobs in
mainstream workplaces and in principle can
make it possible to select a long-term job
opportunity, which delivers an open market
wage, to match the aptitudes and travel
situation of a disabled individual. Mike
Twomey, who has been developing the Sheltered
Placement Scheme at MSC Headquarters,
describes how to make use of it.

A sheltered placement is an individual or a small
group of severely disabled people working in an
ordinary industrial or commercial setting alongside
the rest of the workforce. The people concerned
work normally and are no different from their fit
colleagues except for their lower output. There is
no limit to the size of the groups but schemes
providing opportunities for individuals are the
most popular.

The purpose of the Sheltered Placement Scheme
(SPS) is to provide integrated job opportunities
for people with severe disabilities who, when given
the opportunity to work within their own capacity,
have the ability to do a useful job of work. Their
capacities vary but for the most part the people
concerned can manage 50% of the fit person's output
and so could readily occupy a job that would
otherwise be part-time. Alternatively, two
disabled people could do as much as a fit person.
Notwithstanding their lower output, the disabled
people receive the full wage for the job.

The Sheltered Placement Scheme

The SPS is suitable for all kinds of disabled people, though they must be registered as disabled with the Manpower Services Commission (MSC) and the Disablement Resettlement Officer (DRO) at the local job centre must be satisfied that they are eligible for sheltered employment. About 6% of people supported under the scheme are mentally ill.

First the basic idea of the scheme, then we can consider the detailed responsibilities of the various parties.

The scheme involves a sponsor, which must be a local authority, a voluntary organisation or Remploy, which employs the disabled person, and a host firm which provides the work. There is a contract for service between the sponsor and the host firm whereby the services of the disabled person are made available to the host firm in return for an agreed payment based on the disabled person's output. The MSC approves schemes and gives a grant to the sponsor. Local authority sponsors receive 75% of their per capita costs back from the MSC up to a ceiling (£2,500 in 1984/85) which is reviewed annually. Voluntary body sponsors receive 100% of their per capita costs up to a ceiling (£3,000 in 1984/85) which is also reviewed annually. Before examining the fine detail of the relationship between worker, host firm, sponsor and MSC it is worth considering some of the special advantages and opportunities which this scheme opens.

An initial, very fundamental advantage is that the scheme permits the provision of sheltered employment in rural areas where this would not otherwise be possible because there are too few disabled people locally to justify a conventional 30 place sheltered workshop. Sheltered employment is one of the many opportunities which disabled people in rural areas either miss or which involve serious travelling problems. But with the SPS you can start off seeking a host employer for someone right on their doorstep. In the last few years, in fact, many schemes have been provided in rural areas, including in particular South West England.

Secondly, the scheme provides integrated job opportunities in the open labour market with, perhaps, the employment providing a route through which disabled people can mix with non-disabled people in mainstream society. This, I think, is what disabled people want for themselves, particularly younger disabled people, who often are not keen on institutionalised or segregated provision.

Of course, it also opens the possibility that a person may increase their productivity, gain their employer's confidence, and eventually get offered employment on a conventional basis. This feature perhaps will be attractive to those helping people recovering from mental illness, since they can often overcome their disability in the course of time.

Thirdly, by offering opportunities in open employment, the scheme is able to vastly expand the range of opportunities available to disabled people. The range of types of jobs in sheltered workshops is necessarily limited. But, in contrast, there is no limit in the SPS. We have placements in jobs which fit as broad a range of aptitudes and interests as the following:

Kennel Maid
Fishing: Porters, Picklers and Packers
Fish Fillet Inspectors
Editor/Compiler of Tapes
Playgroup Assistant
Archaeological Assistant
Project Engineer/Design Draughtsman
Social Worker
Field Worker (For a voluntary body interested in family support)
Coach Builder
Livestock Supervisor
Supermarket Trolleymen, Cashiers, Sales Assistants and Storemen
Traffic Manager
Physiotherapist's Assistant
Child Care Assistant
Saddlery Assistant
Gold Starter
Painter and Decorator
Trainee Modelmaker
Braille Transcriber
Pom-Pom Assemblers
Parks and Gardens (33 Schemes)
Agricultural and Horticultural Workers (14 Schemes)
Service Occupations: Domestic Staff (7 Schemes), Care Assistants (5 Schemes), Catering (6) and Home Helps
Clerical Occupations: Trainee Life Assurance Clerk; Production, Quality and Stock Control Clerk; Tracer; Airline Payments Clerk
Pottery Trades: Potter, Pottery Machine

Operative and China Flower Maker

So the increase in potential choice of employment opportunity for disabled people is really very significant.

A fourth advantage is one which appeals to me as an administrator looking to the future development of the programme. This is that the scheme keeps sheltered employment up-to-date and in line with changes in the open economy. This is very important, given the pace of technological and other changes, like the expansion of service industries and the contraction of manufacturing. Particularly when we are talking of people with sometimes transient disabilities like mental illness, such links to skills which are in current local demand increases the likelihood that a placement can become a bridge to open employment.

A fifth advantage is the ability of the scheme to provide opportunities for those disabled people whose productivity is notably low. They are finding it increasingly difficult to secure places in sheltered workshops, which because of the need to control rising costs are tending to select those people capable of higher output so as to increase workshop income. But with sheltered placements a low output worker need not disadvantage the host firm. The firm's payments simply reflect the lower output.

The sixth advantage I would mention is the cost. While the scheme has considerable merit without this last advantage, it is icing on the cake. The average cost in this scheme is about £2,500 per annum - that is about half the cost in a workshop. This means that we can provide twice as many employment opportunities for disabled people for any given level of spending.

Finally, sheltered placements offer special opportunities for people who have suffered from mental illness. They differ from many other disabled people in that their ability to work can greatly improve over time as they recover - or sharply get worse during bad spells. If worker performance changes in either direction, then the output figure which determines the host firm's contribution can be simply renegotiated. Thus the SPS offers a solution to the long standing dilemma of how people recovering from mental illness can get work which is neither dangerously over-demanding nor which restricts them to a more sheltered role than necessary.

The Sheltered Placement Scheme

That is the scheme and its merits in a nutshell. The finer details of the worker/host firm/sponsor/MSC relationship are as follows:-

The host firm provides the work, the work-place, tools and training etc, and pays the sponsor for the amount of work done by the disabled person. The payment made by the host firm is based on the disabled person's output. Thus, as mentioned, if the disabled person is capable of 50% of a fit person's output, the host firm's payment would be 50% of the costs (mainly wages) of employing a fit person to do the work.

The sponsor must be a local authority, a voluntary organisation or Remploy. The sponsor is the legal employer of the disabled person and is responsible for paying wages and National Insurance Contributions, making tax deductions and meeting the requirements of Employment Legislation. These sponsor's costs are offset by payment from the host firm for the work done and by a contribution from MSC towards the net costs.

The role of the MSC in all this is to approve the scheme and share the cost with the sponsor - ie. the amount which has to be added to the host firm's payment for work produced in order to make up conventional wage and employment costs. If the sponsor is a voluntary body, the MSC will cover the costs entirely. There is, though, an upper limit to the annual subsidy per worker which the MSC will refund to the sponsor.

Voluntary body sponsors are playing a significant role in providing employment under this scheme, in contrast with sheltered workshops which are mainly provided by local authorities. Two years ago about 80% of the proposals for sheltered placements were from local authorities. But today at MSC we are receiving as many proposals from voluntary bodies as from local authorities.

We are looking for caring voluntary bodies to undertake the role of sponsor. Organisations which are considering sponsorship should apply to MSC before they get into any detailed discussions. This is so that their eligibility to sponsor schemes can be checked. There are three points on which we need to be satisfied. They are:

1. That the voluntary organisation is allowed by its constitution to employ disabled people under sheltered conditions.

2. That it is non profit distributing.

3. That it has the financial and administrative resources and expertise to run the schemes.

People eligible for MSC funding under this scheme must be severely disabled people. This generally means people who are not able to compete for jobs in open employment for a period of at least 12 months. The people concerned must be registered with the MSC. Those familiar with registration arrangements for disabled people will know that the group we are referring to are 'Section II' of the disabled persons register. Disabled people who are thought able to compete in the open labour market are on section I of the register. The Disablement Resettlement Officer (DRO) at the local job centre is responsible for determining whether an individual disabled person is eligible for MSC funding on this scheme and calls for medical evidence where this is necessary.

It is open to the sponsor to nominate individual disabled people for this scheme. Alternatively the sponsor may ask the DRO to nominate someone from MSC's register. The disabled people nominated are then put to the host firm for consideration.

The sponsor is the employer of the disabled person, and has all the usual responsibilities of an employer. As well as issuing a contract of employment and paying wages, this includes, where appropriate, paying wages in lieu of notice and making any redundancy payments and other statutory payments along with contractual ones. Under the scheme the disabled person is paid the same wage as able bodied people employed directly by the host firm to do that particular job. Because of the nature of the scheme, some of the usual employer's responsibilities, such as supervision and control and health and safety, are shared between sponsor and host firm. This demands a close and effective liaison between the sponsor and the host firm. Beyond that, the sponsor has to bill the host firm for the work done, prepare a simple set of accounts, and claim grant from the MSC.

At the heart of the scheme is the contract between the sponsor and the host firm. This should be a written contract to avoid the possibility of any misunderstanding which could prejudice the employment of the disabled person. A major point to be covered in the contract is the payment by the host firm for the work done by the disabled person. There is a standard method of fixing this payment which is reasonably straightforward.

It depends on two things. First, determining the output of the disabled person and, second, establishing the wage the host firm would pay if a fit person was employed directly to do the work involved. The latter is easy. Nor is determining the output of the disabled person a problem in practice. It is often necessary to estimate this at first, taking into account the disability and the type of work. The accuracy of this estimate is then monitored and adjusted, and the host firm is expected to keep a record of the disabled person's output, so that this can be done. The payment by the host firm to the sponsor is the proportion (depending on the disabled person's output) of the cost (mainly wages) that would be incurred if a fit person was employed directly to do the same work. So if, for example, the wage was £80 per week and the disabled person's output 50%, the host would pay about £40 per week to the sponsor.

Then there are the arrangements whereby the MSC funds these jobs. The MSC grant is based on the cost which remains after the income from the host firm has been deducted from all wage costs and other employment costs. Local authorities and voluntary bodies get different degrees of MSC subsidy for being sponsors. Local authorities receive 75% of the cost up to a maximum annual payment per person. This maximum level, or 'ceiling' as it is known, is reviewed annually. Currently it is about £2,500 for local authority sponsors. Voluntary bodies receive 100% of the cost up to a 'ceiling' around £3,000.

In actual practice the average per capita costs of this sort of employment are about £2,500 per annum - this figure includes the sponsor's administrative costs. So as you can see, voluntary bodies can reasonably expect to recover their costs from the MSC, certainly most if not all. Just two qualifications need making about refund of sponsorship costs to voluntary body sponsors. First, we are talking about average costs, and some

schemes will cost more and some less than average.
The second point, is that because the offsetting
payments by MSC and the host firm are made in
arrears, the sponsor will need to have some
financial resources to meet the costs of the
disabled person's wages pending receipt of these
payments.

So that is how the MSC Sheltered Placement
scheme works. It is expanding at a fairly rapid
rate. In this financial year we expect to add
about 400 jobs to the 620 we were supporting in the
year ended in March 1984. The MSC's plans involve
a significant expansion in the number of
opportunities provided by this scheme. I commend
this scheme to you. Please consider if you can
help directly by acting as the sponsor in such an
arrangement. Maybe you have a particular disabled
person in mind. Maybe you have a host firm in mind,
too. But, if not, MSC will identify a prospective
host firm and a disabled person if you wish. For
further information, please get in touch with the
Disablement Advisory Service who can be contacted
through the DRO at the local job centre. If you
cannot sponsor or get involved directly, then you
can still help by describing and recommending the
scheme to others.

Chapter Fifteen

THE NORTH DERBYSHIRE MENTAL HEALTH SERVICES PROJECT:
A COMMUNITY-INTEGRATED SYSTEM FOR SOCIAL SUPPORT

Andrew Milroy and Rick Hennelly

Editorial Introduction

This chapter describes many different features
of The North Derbyshire Mental Health Services
Project, based at the Tontine Road Centre,
Chesterfield. One distinctive aspect of this
service is its series of self-managing social
groups which offer project users an informal
network for social and leisure opportunities
and mutual support. This has led to a
distinctive democratic philosophy which
emphasises how much service users can
contribute to each other and involves them in
shaping and running the service. Another
emphasis is on developing a diversity of
such groups and on a local basis where
possible, a special issue in this large,
partly rural catchment. Other areas covered
in this comprehensive description include the
service's involvement with work and leisure
opportunities, housing and income support.

The continuing collapse in the range and quantity of
employment requires us to seriously question the
traditional objectives of our mental health
services. In particular, we are forced to re-think
our concept of day care which conventionally has
been very dependent upon the availability of paid
work. Day care services give the sharpest focus to
the new problems which confront us, faced as they
are with the task of 'finishing off' the 'treatment'
and 'rehabilitation' process or offering continuing
support to people who continue to experience a
marked degree of disability. Nowhere in the range
of services will the question, 'Is there life after
mental illness?' have greater meaning to the people
who provide and the people who use the help
offered. Nowhere is there greater challenge to

confront traditional practices in the face of new problems. People are still leaving hospital but they are not leaving day centres. How can we cope? This crisis in our affairs requires us to radically re-think our whole philosophy. We must do more than fine tune our systems.

Traditionally day care has been concerned with either employment or a mixture of employment and social rehabilitation and support. This has been usually carried out in isolated single purpose units which inevitably accentuate the disconnection people experience in their lives. Such day care activities often seem fragmented and lack the usual incentives for participation like pay for work, or power and influence in social activities. In isolation from wider social experiences, they seem to fail to address the powerlessness and devaluation of skills and abilities which are a central feature of a person's experience of mental health problems. Right from the beginning we have seen such powerlessness as a central social experience for people who have had difficulties in how they think, feel and behave. Many people lose, forfeit or are deprived of power and control over their own lives. The consequences of this state of powerlessness is exclusion from the processes of ordinary life.

Over the past three years, the North Derbyshire Mental Health Project has been evolving a method of working which attempts to respond to the wide range of problems people experience during and after serious mental health problems. Our experience suggests that 'day care' services can be re-organised to afford the most appropriate focus for a community-integrated, dispersed system for social support. The boundaries of the buildings we work in must not limit our activity which must respond to the choices and needs of the people we seek to support. The development of our work also requires the transformation of the relationships between those who provide and those who use the service.

The North Derbyshire Mental Health Services Project was established by Derbyshire County Council in February, 1982. It is based at the Tontine Road Centre in the middle of Chesterfield, a town of 96,000 people which is the largest conurbation in North Derbyshire. The Project serves an area of North Derbyshire which has a population of approximately 280,000.

The North Derbyshire Mental Health Services Project was originally planned as a joint staffed,

joint funded community mental health centre. Joint
funding plans fell through but the Project went
ahead, though without Health Service personnel
employed directly in the organisation. At the time
it represented the only specialised local authority
provision in North Derbyshire. Since then the model
we have evolved has reflected these historical
circumstances. The philosophy and character of our
work is further influenced by the principles of
'normalisation', the personal experiences of those
who are paid to develop the service, and, most
importantly, the skills, abilities and aspirations
of the people who have used the service. In
particular we have sought to devise our theory
directly from our practice.

We are committed to respond to the needs of
individuals. Since these are forever changing,
consequently so are our responses.

But although details are continually changing,
several principles have emerged in our work which
remain constant. We commenced our work as something
of a hybrid between a local authority 'day centre'
and a 'community mental health centre'. Our
resolution of the possible conflicts between these
concepts led towards a community-integrated,
dispersed system of social support. However such a
system requires the contribution of many people and
organisations. It cannot exist in one place and
cannot be controlled by any one group of people. It
is a social process which must be worked with by all
those with a contribution to make. In common with
all social processes it cannot be run. Working with
this social process has required us to develop a
clear philosophy upon which we can draw to inform
our actions. Here are some core principles of this
philosophy.

OUR TASK AND ITS PRINCIPLES

The people we seek to assist have wants and
needs which are the same wants and needs, in broad
terms, that we all have. The thing which
distinguishes them is the extent to which they are
obstructed in achieving their wants or meeting their
needs because of the difficulties they have in how
they think, feel or behave. These people are likely
to experience a degree of difficulty in their
ability to make and sustain friendships, maintain
regular employment or involvement in purposeful
activity (this exists as both a personal and
political problem), manage ordinary life problems or

use the range of typical services. For example Harry, having spent some considerable time in long stay hospitals, finds it almost impossible to organise appointments with his doctor using the telephone. The people with whom we will have to deal are likely to have limited confidence in their own judgement or competence. They are likely to have little self-esteem. They are often people who experience a high degree of isolation, exclusion and dependency. Other people, including some of us who are paid to offer help, may regard these people as odd, awkward, unresponsive, feckless, frightening, worthless, sick, undeserving, or generally different.

Drawing upon these issues we can begin to identify our task. We are asked to provide social, emotional and psychological support to people who, to varying degrees, are disconnected or excluded from ordinary means of gaining such support. Harry turns to us for help with making appointments with his doctor because he is unable to gain the support of his family. Whilst we need to help him, if he can, to rebuild his relationship with his family, we will still need to phone his doctor. Special needs do not necessarily reflect peculiar wants, although the difficulties people have had with how they think or feel may give rise to peculiar or eccentric choices. What special needs do reflect is how difficult someone finds it to meet his or her needs in ordinary ways. The difficulties a person experiences will determine the extent to which help must be provided. For some people whose thinking and preferences remain eccentric and non-conforming, and/or whose disability remains marked and enduring, it will be necessary to fabricate their social support. Where this is necessary, these special facilities should operate in ways which afford the maximum expression of value to all those involved, including those paid to organise them.

An effective system for social support must be flexible. It should be built around the wants and needs of each person and should be capable of adapting to those needs as they change in character and intensity over time. Whilst being flexible and responsive, it must avoid becoming over intrusive. We should ensure that we offer no more help than is necessary to maintain positive community membership. The system must concentrate its resources around those who experience enduring disability, as well as responding to those who will

improve and recover. We must build our support
around the skills and abilities of each person,
providing a social process which acknowledges his or
her 'citizenship', and offers people opportunities
to develop power and control over their own lives.
To achieve this we will need to express positive
values and expectation towards those who need
support as well as those who provide it.
    Our work will need to provide structure and
support for three major areas of living:

* Work or purposeful valued activity, which
  engages our skills and interests

* Leisure and social contact

* Housing

    Importantly, this means ensuring that
sufficient time and energy goes to providing
practical assistance, as well as offering
experiences which assist people to overcome social,
emotional and psychological problems. Our efforts
should be directed to strengthen, where possible,
the natural support available to each person. All
too often we seem to ignore family and friends or
view their roles in wholly negative terms. Where
practicable, we should use the ordinary and usual
organisations and facilities of the communities in
which a person lives, or with which they identify.
    These are our core principles. We can expand
and clarify them.

USING EXISTING OPPORTUNITIES

    Community networks can often be harnessed as
elements of a community support system for people
with a range of mental health difficulties. Social
networks exist for most of us in a variety of
sectors: nuclear family, extended family, education,
religion, politics, ethnic group, work/profession,
social welfare, health, recreation, friendship
groups and neighbourhoods. It is clear that
community mental health work must, in part, be about
locating natural sources of support for the
individual in his/her environment, building on these
contacts, mending damaged networks, and linking
individuals to sources of support not previously
known or sought after.
    Given the present jobless climate and the
growing numbers seeking support, this requires us to

be knowledgeable about access to local facilities.
We are constantly seeking and compiling information
about facilities in the local community. Having our
own print workshop helps with the dissemination of
such information. Also, we often find ourselves
engaged in consultation and negotiation with family
members and neighbours when this is required. We
must seek to continually expand the network of
resources available to all members of our
communities. The project has played an active role
in the development of a Council for Voluntary
Service and Action in Chesterfield. The purposes
served are: to keep project workers in contact with
developments and resources in the voluntary sector;
to act as a link between the 35 community groups
using Tontine Road and the CVSA; to find out about
avenues of voluntary sector experience for people
who want only gradually to be invested with
responsibility; to discover practical sources of
assistance for those who are lonely and isolated.
    Having a 'base' allows natural friendship
systems to develop which serve as support groups for
people to become involved in community activities
together. Such friendship groups can be given
financial and personal support so that such
activities can flourish through the experiences they
have together. Small groups of CONTACT members go
together to cafes, cinemas, pubs etc. The shared
experience is hopefully a confidence-building
exercise although there is a danger of reproducing
segregation since the people involved usually have
in common a history of involvement with statutory
services. Our experience suggests that such natural
friendships are generally very fruitful and act to
promote, rather than inhibit, community
involvement. The 'invisibility' of many mental
health problems, coupled with the transient or
episodic nature of such difficulties, means that
project users can often easily cope together with
the hurdles of ordinary participation in local
facilities..

Principles in practice:

* Six members of the group began to use adult
  education facilities locally. They were given
  financial support to buy books, materials,
  briefcases, etc. We also set up a 'college
  support group' to enable these people to share
  anxieties, discuss problems and solutions to
  difficulties in their new situation.

240

* Every Monday evening a group from our Project go to a local nightclub. The manager of the club came to see us at the Centre. He expressed a lot of interest and gave us twenty tickets guaranteeing free entrance for a year. As well as this, he offered us a reduction of bar food prices. When he found out about our cheap printing facilities, he came to us to place orders for tickets, literature, etc, he wanted producing.

* In line with a general policy of wishing to promote general good health and to use ordinary community facilities, negotiations have secured us the weekly use of a multi-gym in a local community school. This provides opportunity for exercise locally and cheaply, in contrast to the expensive private clubs our group members could not afford.

For people whose income is low and whose ability to organise their own lives is impaired, the provision of holidays is part of a pattern of seasonal activity which makes up a 'normal' lifestyle. The Project has tried to provide opportunities for such people in the following ways:

* Use of a five-berth caravan at a local coastal holiday resort. The caravan was hired over several weekends to enable a succession of holidays for a number of CONTACT members.

* Use of a twenty-place outdoor pursuits centre in Yorkshire. Project staff and CONTACT members have organised a series of three-day holidays in a rural location financed by funds provided through the Project.

* Use of a twenty-five place holiday centre in North Wales, again financed and supported by Project staff.

FABRICATING OPPORTUNITIES

Quite frequently we find that when we assess an individual's needs thoroughly we end up searching for some facility or structure in the locality that does not appear to exist. Clearly the interests of individuals and the resources available in the

community are not always going to match up. Indeed,
quite regularly the people we support have been
rejected by, or alienated from, a range of social
and occupational situations. It is not that they
have never had access to them.

There is a need to 'bridge the gap' between
settings which people have rejected or been excluded
from, and settings which are segregated, devalue
people and offer them no future. The aim of
'bridging' provision must always be to offer
opportunities which will enhance skills and
stimulate motivation and interest in further
activities or experiences which enhance a sense of
community membership.

Part of our work must be about providing a
network of opportunities for people in the 'social'
sector - a web of possibilities for people to meet
other people, opportunities to practise their skills
and exercise their talents, to have good experiences
and to bring good experiences to others.

Principles in practice:

* Social events are organised at Tontine Road.
  CONTACT members are involved in arranging these
  events. Tickets are distributed through the
  community groups network and attract several
  hundred members of the wider community.

* For the Financial Year 1986/87, CONTACT
  received a £2,500 grant from the Project to
  organise its own activities. £600 was
  allocated by the CONTACT Committee to an
  established photography group. The group has
  14 members, none of whom are project staff. Of
  these, six have attended adult education
  classes in photography regularly for the last
  year. The 14 members make decisions
  collectively about how money is to be spent,
  supplement their grants by writing to local
  firms, and organise their own outings to places
  of interest.

* Each year there is a 'Medieval Market' in
  Chesterfield. The Market Square is given over
  to a variety of groups who set up stalls and
  sell a whole range of goods in order to raise
  funds for their particular causes. Some of
  these causes are political, many are
  charitable. For the last three years, CONTACT has
  organised a stall. This has meant weeks of

preparation beforehand to gather goods to sell, preparing, pricing and storing them. On the day itself up to 20 people are involved with the organisation and selling of items. The money raised in this way goes towards CONTACT Funds.

BUILDING AROUND INDIVIDUALS

People who experience mental health problems are not a homogeneous group. Indeed, by the very nature of their eccentric preferences, odd thoughts and behaviour, their needs are likely to be divergent rather than convergent. Traditional services seem to require that everyone conforms to a single prescribed method of giving and receiving help. Very often the method appears to be organised more to meet the needs of those providing the service rather than those seeking to use it. Failure to conform is met with sanctions or exclusion on the grounds that the person is incapable of responding to the help he or she needs.

The very nature of the people we seek to help, the manifestation of their needs, and the character of their experiences, demands that we develop a service of immense flexibility. The form and degree of support they need will vary over time and in response to the changing individuals who are involved with the system. The way our own need for help and support varies over time reflects not just our own abilities to manage, but the changing social and economic pressures we experience. We are usually able to gain assistance informally and unobtrusively through our intimate relationships and family connections. An effective 'fabricated' support system should aim at similar spontaneity and flexibility. The boundaries marking inclusion - eligibility to receive assistance - must be permeable. We must be willing to adjust the kind of help and our method of delivery. We must also ensure that access to support is easily achieved with the minimum of formality. People leaving the system must be allowed to gain increased support easily, should they need it again. Traditionally services have been organised around rigid boundaries. People are either in or out. Sometimes we make it very hard for people to get in, often because of our fears about being overwhelmed by demands for help. Many relatives have explained the serious problems they faced in getting help and support. "Things had to get very bad before anyone

243

would take any notice." This is a comment we
frequently hear.
This produces two problems. First it seems to
generate a reluctance to give up the help which was
hard fought for. People who have felt unable to
cope with their own lives will be reluctant to
relinquish their access to assistance, just in case
things don't work out. Consequently, they maintain
a minimal level of problems to ensure that help
continues to be forthcoming. The second problem is
that rigid boundaries seem to convey a distorted
sense of what is involved in being a 'well person'.
(This also links with the way traditional
professional relationships act to distance the gap
between coping and not coping.) The image conveys
an idea that 'well people' do not need any help,
will always feel happy and will never experience
anxieties. Such an image inhibits people from
returning to seek support for fear this will be seen
as a mark of 'failure'. Rigid boundaries to the
'support system' will tend to ensure that things
have got to go very wrong again before support can
be asked for, or gained.

FLEXIBLE CARE

In order to support people leaving institutions
or to prevent others from entering them, 'flexible
care' is sometimes used. Usually one person,
although sometimes more, is employed to provide
practical advice and support to an individual
identified as being 'at risk'. It is usually
organised and supervised by a combination of Area
Social Services staff or Community Mental Health
Team Social Workers and Mental Health Services
Project staff. The support provided is in
'ordinary' locations and is time-limited (usually
tapers off over a two year period).

Principles in practice:

Charlie spent two years in hospital while
protracted negotiations took place with the Housing
Department, who were unwilling to offer a new home
to him because of his previous difficulties in
managing to pay rent and maintaining himself with
only minimal support from statutory agencies. The
proposed package of support from the new Community
Mental Health Team and 37 hours per week 'flexible
care' support eventually won their confidence and
Charlie was given a home. Six months further on, he

244

is making substantial steps towards independent living.

There are setbacks. Sheila spent time in prison for fire-raising. She was given 37 hours a week 'flexible care' support upon discharge. However, she continued to experience problems at home. After a move into lodgings and a dispute with the landlord, she set fire to her room. She was subsequently sentenced to a further term of imprisonment.

Sharon spent time in adolescent units and hospital. She barely communicates and spends quite a lot of time pacing up and down. Her mother finds it difficult to cope with her as well as their other children. Flexible care support has concentrated on enabling Sharon to spend time away from a stressful home environment at Tontine Road. The support worker has also offered support to Sharon's mother by introducing her to the local National Schizophrenia Fellowship branch and by providing social outings which both Sharon and her mother enjoy.

Unfortunately flexible care has its limitations. For the people employed, it offers no long-term job security and the goal of independent living conflicts with the interests of the workers in maintaining secure employment. The pressure to reduce support provided is sometimes unrealistic. Furthermore, there are skill problems with securing independent housing in 'ordinary' locations - having opted for this kind of living situation, some people find that they are very lonely. We are promoting the idea of permanently employed 'flexible care' workers and looking for varied housing facilities which promote independence and lessen loneliness.

ABILITY, DISABILITY AND INDIVIDUALS

Individuals come to us from a variety of sources with a wide range of ability and disability. Our referral system is an open one. People are referred to us by community psychiatric nurses, general practitioners, psychiatrists, D.R.O.s, social workers, psychologists, voluntary groups, etc. Word of mouth sometimes leads to someone seeking help. Those who call meet a small group of CONTACT members and sometimes Project staff for an informal chat. If they express interest in joining us, a democratic vote is taken at the community meeting to indicate acceptance. Very few people are turned down by the group and few who are accepted find after entry that they do not want the forms of support we are able to provide.

No distinctions such as 'acute versus chronic' or 'requiring short-term intervention versus long-term support' are made. People themselves decide how long they stay and how often they come. No structure is laid down which individuals have to adhere to. Members of CONTACT may join groups which meet regularly for a while, (Social Skills, Life Experience, Swimming, Football, etc.) and/or get involved in spontaneously organised activities (going shopping, helping with a labour-intensive printing job, going to a cafe, etc.). The nature of activities available varies with the commitment of members and the cycle of changes in interest. Tasks available around the centre range from the minimally demanding, eg. stapling papers together, tearing up paper for brick making, to the very demanding, eg. organisation of a major social event, chairing community meetings. The range of activities available daily allow for the extremely wide range of interest, motivation, concentration span and level of responsibility that CONTACT members display. In this way, a series of informal filters operate to allow individuals access to routines which they find satisfying and suited to their abilities.

Having a flexible support system allows us to respond in a variety of ways to a variety of needs. Individuals with low motivation or people who have problems which would usually be described as 'agoraphobic' may find it difficult to engage in a network whose core is at the Centre. Some such individuals have expressed a wish to become involved with us via the Centre and other CONTACT members themselves have organised home visiting to make travelling easier for them. In other cases, paid Centre organisers have been available to provide transport for individuals who wish to use the Centre, over a period of months. In other circumstances still, workers from our Support Register, which lists people who offer temporary help on an individual basis, have supported individuals whose needs appear to revolve more around the home setting. In all these circumstances, our ability to respond to preferences and choices is the crucial element.

One of our strengths lies in supplying a framework which enables and encourages spontaneous support formations to appear. When members of CONTACT have some of their own needs met, they often begin to model on the practices around them and, in their turn, provide structured help to other members of CONTACT. Paul came to CONTACT with serious problems in managing to look after himself. His difficulty with self-care began to reflect itself in complaints from other members of CONTACT about his hygiene. After sensitive and open discussion, Tim offered to cut his hair and John offered to trim his fingernails. Larry is acting as an advocate on his behalf to procure a clothing grant from the DHSS.

VALUE

Ensuring that the service can adjust its response to each person ensures that we acknowledge each person's value. This becomes part of the process of restoring a sense of personal value to each man or woman who seeks support.

Ensuring that the service conveys a strong sense of value to each individual is not, in our experience, an optional extra. Giving people the feeling that they matter is an essential part of the process of building enduring personal support. In our own lives the relationships and experiences from which we draw most support are those within which our importance is confirmed. Many of the problems people face seem to be rooted in a crippling sense of insignificance. If we have no importance for others our own sense of integrity will begin to decline and with it our ability to manage the problems and demands of living. To convey a sense of value the service must:

Demonstrate respect for the opinions and view of each person.

Offer support and assistance in ways which are seen to be relevant and are preferred by the person concerned.

Provide the same opportunities for people using services as would be expected and preferred by those who provide the service.

POWER AND PARTICIPATION

Exercising power and control over our own lives is crucial to our sense of well-being. Powerlessness is a cause and consequence of mental health problems. People who experience mental distress are likely to perceive themselves as helpless, incompetent and not responsible for themselves. Their despair may be derived from a range of life problems which appear unresolvable events, over which they have no influence. They may actively seek to off-load responsibility for themselves onto others. At times of stress we are all rather inclined to do this. Unfortunately, the well-intended concern of doctors, social workers, and nurses provides a willing repository for the responsibilities people wish to dispose of. The maintenance of 'professional distance' widens the gulf of experience between the all-coping, over-competent 'professional' and the incompetent 'patient'. At times, unwittingly, we induce dependency.

If we are to break the cycle of dependency, which is traditionally seen as the responsibility of the 'incompetent patient', we must establish a radical change in the relationship between those who provide services and those who use them. This must be expressed by:-

Building the relationship around personal skills and abilities, not ascribed status.

Developing incremental stages towards power and control over the service.

Establishing expectations of competence and participation in ways which are not threatening.

Giving people access to and control over practical and financial resources.

Traditionally, paid workers within any service exercise the greatest power and control over the resources, physical and financial. This seems to be unhelpful. The exercise of power and control by paid workers can easily 'disable' people. It can impede the growth of people's ability to accept and manage their affairs. Inevitably, paid workers carry considerable influence within any group of people. However, we have found it valuable to try and limit the traditional scope of the power paid workers exercise, in order to reduce the harmful effects that the exercise of such power brings with it.

POWER AND RESPONSIBILITY

To be 'effective', the system has to provide

incremental levels of responsibility for decision making. These can range from managing a single area of personal activity, through to responsibility for the routine operation of a group or range of groups. We must recognise that taking responsibility, exercising power, must reflect the skills and confidence of each person. Small acts of responsibility, exercised in a 'culture' where people are expected to take responsibility for themselves, is a small step towards self-renewal.

If it is to have any real effect, we must really mean it. We have to convey sincere commitment to give people responsibility for themselves. Any sign of disingenuity will erode the value of the exercise. This means we must look at every aspect of our system. Within Local Authority Services it can be difficult to allow people to take responsibility for spending money. We still have much work to do to extend the involvement over the finance which people need to recreate real purpose in their lives. However, there are ways we can pass responsibility on, even within Local Authority bureaucracy, if we are willing. For instance:

Principles in practice:

* Applying for Local Authority grants for properly constituted self-help groups. We have a number of social support clubs/groups located in different population centres throughout North Derbyshire which are funded in this way.

* Allocating specific budgets for activities, in response to demand. Decisions about and arrangements for expenditure are made by the groups concerned and automatically approved by paid workers. Our two allotments, print shop, photography group, art group, athletics club, are all organised in this way.

* Independent fund raising. We have an Amenity Fund and Benevolent Fund. Decision-making for these is vested in formally constituted committees. These funds finance individual and group activities. They increase CONTACT members' real social and recreational choices.

THE SERVICE IN PRACTICE

"After making the decision that recovery

depends quite a lot on helping yourself, I
think it is then necessary to begin to explore
society external to the Centre, in order to
grow in confidence and ability to cope
effectively with everyday problems, until
hopefully one finds oneself spending enough
time with new friends and activities, that when
the time comes to leave the centre, there is no
sudden, painful release from the centre and its
'safety', but instead a natural drift into
normal living, pausing only to recognise the
point at which the decision to leave becomes a
conscious and hopefully permanent one. "

Project user

From the principles behind our model, let us
turn to practical details of staffing, premises, and
the component services which constitute the North
Derbyshire Mental Health Services Project.

The staffing of the Project has changed since
we were first established. Joint Funding provided
additional staff in 1983. The workers employed
directly by the Project are: one senior social
worker, three social workers, two part-time group
workers, two part-time clerical workers, four
ancillary staff and various staff employed on
short-term fixed contracts. The work of the Project
also relies on the formal and informal contributions
made by workers from statutory agencies and
voluntary/community organisations. In turn the work
of the Project includes the contribution we make to
their work. These organisations include:

- Social Services Departmental Planning and
  Monitoring Group
- Joint Planning Group for Mental Health Services
- Four Community Mental Health Teams based in the
  four sectors making up North Derbyshire
- Mental Health Local Planning Groups covering
  the same areas
- Four area Social Work Offices
- Two In-Patient Wards and one Day Hospital
- Community Rehabilitation Team
- Probation Department
- Library Service
- National Schizophrenia Fellowship
- Samaritans
- Chesterfield 'Concern Network'
- Chesterfield and North East Derbyshire Council
  for Voluntary Service and Action

- West Derbyshire Council for Voluntary Service
- Health Centres

Linking our efforts into the host of groups and agencies is an important principle and reflects our view that inevitably we can form only one part of the range of resources that people will need to organise their support. Establishing effective working relationships with the variety of people with whom we must be involved entails long term strategy. It requires patience and continuity.

At this point a brief description of our physical base would be helpful. The Tontine Road Centre was built in 1967 by the Chesterfield Borough Council Welfare Committee. It provided facilities for occupational and leisure activities for physically disabled people, as well as space for a small number of community organisations, such as the local Physically Handicapped and Able Bodied Club. The use of the Centre remained unchanged until 1980, when the then 'day centre' for physically disabled people moved to new premises. After being used for various ad-hoc purposes the building was recommissioned and opened in its present role in February 1982. It is situated just below the now redeveloped market square in the middle of Chesterfield. It is a rather inauspicious building, characteristic of its period, with flat roof and grey concrete. The site is next door to the regional bus station and surrounded by main roads.

Over the past three years we have developed the Centre as a multi-purpose facility. It now provides accommodation for 35 independent self-regulated community groups. They range from Scouts and Brownies to CONTACT, our principal mental health support group. This was not our original intention and it was never identified as our original brief. Almost accidentally, it has become a cornerstone of the way our physical base is organised. This provides us with the opportunity to explore new approaches to the management and operation of services.

GROUPS USING THE TONTINE ROAD CENTRE

Blind Social Club
Chesterfield Care Group
Chesterfield Deaf Society
Chesterfield and District Childminders
Chesterfield Epilepsy Club
Chesterfield and District Club for the Hard of

Hearing
Chesterfield Disabled League
Multiple Sclerosis Society
Physically Handicapped and Able Bodied Club
National Deaf Childrens Society
North Derbyshire Council on Alcoholism
Interact Club of Chesterfield
Chesterfield Branch of the National Association
of Widows
National Schizophrenia Fellowship
Chesterfield Branch of the Parkinsons Disease
Society
The Open Door
2nd Chesterfield Brownies
Alcoholics Anonymous (Two Groups)
Al-Anon Family Groups (Two Groups)
Samaritans
Gamblers Anonymous
Take Heart
North Derbyshire Womens Action Group
CONTACT
Tranquillisers Self-Help Group
In Touch (women's support group)
Spire Lodge Youth Group
Deaf Persons Church
Care for Carers
Agoraphobia Support Group
Asthma Society
Chesterfield Womens Support Group
Friends of the Samaritans

The use of the Centre is regulated through a management committee. This brings together all the organisations which use the building. This arrangement offers maximum control and influence over the service to the groups involved. It also encourages the development of a diverse network of relationships. It has taken time for the various groups to develop a sense of ownership over the building, an idea they are unused to. But now we see signs of a new partnership emerging. The old identities of the Centre still endure, but gradually they are being displaced in favour of a new, more positive, diverse image. It is an image which is not built around deviance, disability or welfare, but one which reflects collective effort, social value and self determination.

You would certainly never design a building like the Tontine Road Centre to be used in the way we have come to use it. But somehow it doesn't seem to matter. At times it even seems that the

inadequacy of the building provides new chances for
us to break the traditional divisions we impose on
ourselves. Every other Friday the toy library run
by the local association of childminders must run
from a large room which they share with members of
CONTACT. The latter use it for recreation or need
to pass through it to reach other rooms to which
it acts as a corridor. During the last two years
this arrangement has worked perfectly well, although
you would never plan it so.

The main office is small and cramped. It gives
only enough room for two clerks to work, cupboards,
filing cabinets and phones. Rooms have to be booked
and space is allocated according to need and prior
arrangement.

The building is used extensively. We estimate
that at its busiest the Centre will be used by about
1,250 people in a week. It is open seven days and
six evenings every week. It provides space for a
day care service for elderly people living in
Chesterfield and its surrounding areas, a meeting
place for women's groups, the Multiple Sclerosis
Society, the PHAB club, and many others. Facilities
include video equipment, a community printing
workshop, a minibus and van, equipment for
recreation and the provision of refreshment. People
organise social events, keep fit classes, education
classes and courses. There are over eight mental
health groups using the building, including CONTACT,
which provides the focus for social and occupational
activity for people living in Chesterfield who
experience mental health problems.

It is a real asset to have the building we
operate from re-organised in this way. It helps us
to break many traditional problems facing day
centres and community mental health centres. Now it
has multiple uses, the building is no longer insular
nor isolated. Although some of the old identities
still cling, it is losing them now. For many
newcomers, of course, it has never had a
stigmatising image. The message on the front door
is not 'Welcome - if you are sick'. Its multiple
use provides many roles and jobs for people. The
organisation of the Centre relies increasingly on
the efforts of the people using the facility, who
must take on key tasks. The opportunities to share
experiences based on a community of interest provide
people with access to new relationships and valued
activities.

SELF-REGULATED SOCIAL AND ACTIVITY GROUPS

The principles of our service and the character
of our base have a substantial influence over the
way our service has developed. Our system of
support has been built around self-regulated social
and activity groups. These groups and the social
'networks' which emerge from them give people
opportunities for friendships, inclusion in a full
range of social experiences, occupation, leisure,
and a small degree of financial assistance.
Continuity of care and support is mostly provided
through spontaneous relationships between group
members, cultivated by a 'culture' of positive
expectation and tolerance towards people who
experience difficulties in how they think, feel and
behave. The activities of these independent
community organisations vary, reflecting the skills
and abilities of members. Over time we have been
able to establish a number of these groups,
dispersed across North Derbyshire. Although they
are fabricated groups, specifically aimed to assist
people who have had mental health problems, every
effort is made to integrate them into the ordinary
social process of the communities within which they
work. The group in Matlock, ten miles from
Chesterfield, has traditionally met in an adult
education centre and a room in a public house.
Group activities seek to use the ordinary facilities
in the town and, beyond their formal meetings,
members get together in their own homes.
    The detail and character of these groups
varies, influenced by many different factors.
However, they are all modelled around our experience
with two groups, the Open Door Club and CONTACT.
The Open Door Club is referred to in some detail
later and is important since its history and
development made us aware that formal constitutions
are an essential requirement for any 'self help' or
self regulated group. Details of other important
groups and our 'outreach' work are also given
later. Before this we want to describe CONTACT.

CONTACT

    CONTACT has an interesting history and for us
has always played a central part in the development
of our work. The original general aims of the North
Derbyshire Mental Health Project indicated that the
bulk of the services would revolve around the
development of sessional group work. The Centre
would be used by voluntary groups and 'self help'

groups and there would be special therapy sessions
such as social skills training or art therapy.
People would attend only for specific sessions, then
leave the building. There would not be any general
Monday to Friday day centre service. Activities and
groups would be run by volunteers and professional
workers drawn from existing agencies. Such a
concept was not new and the model can be found in
many places, such as Eastgate House in Lewes. We
encountered just the same difficulties which others
have experienced in operating such a model.

     With few exceptions it proved difficult to
attract any 'sub-contractors'. Most professionals
from existing agencies were reticent about offering
any formal contribution. People looking for help
were largely unimpressed by this regulated,
professionally controlled approach to support. As
people began to hear about the availability of the
Centre as a place they could go to, we began to
accumulate people who were happy to use the space
the Centre provided, even if it was just somewhere
to come and make tea. Somewhere warm to sit, some
company and an absence of regulation seemed to
attract people. The demand at the front door began
to force a change in our original concept.
Necessity demanded that we respond to the actual
choices and preferences of the people who were
seeking help rather than stick to our abstract,
professionally determined policies. For us this was
an historic choice. Coupled with some limited
independent 'consumer' research - and later an
evaluation of our developing organisation - our
policies began to move in an entirely new direction.

     The number of people using the Centre as a base
for their social activity continued to increase
throughout 1983. Our direct involvement with them
grew. At that stage the group operated around some
loose principles of a 'therapeutic community'.
Efforts were made to emphasise personal
responsibility and the autonomy of the Group.
However, the absence of a clear identity for the
group led to an uncomfortable relationship between
the 'users' of the Centre and the Staff. Somehow
this collection of people did not fit into the other
work we were involved with. Our declarations of the
power and authority of members was continually
eroded by a lack of rules. There was no way for
people to assume responsibility for what was
happening. People continued to defer to the paid
workers, who ultimately had to assume responsibility
in the absence of any other mechanisms.

In March 1985, the group was formally
constituted as CONTACT. Modelled on our experience
with a host of other groups, the constitution
described the group as seeking to "... provide help
advice and support for people who experience
difficulties with their thinking and feelings; for
people who are lonely, isolated and unhappy, for
people who experience difficulties in coping with
their lives". Membership is open to "anyone who
feels the group may help them or who feels they can
contribute to the group." The Mental Health
Services Projects has "... a responsibility to
provide advice, support and material assistance
to the organisation." Project workers are
identified as 'advisors' with clearly defined powers
and duties.

The move to a formally constituted,
independent, self-regulated community organisation,
was a response to growing demands from people using
the Centre. The change was preceded by lengthy
discussions concerning the constitution, the wording
of a less formal leaflet describing the group, and
the selection of a name. The whole process took
over three months and was the culmination of a
steady trend towards the people who were using the
service becoming more involved in running it. It
has been the logical conclusion to a process set in
motion when we first chose to respond to the wishes
of the people who turned up on our doorstep in those
early days of the Project in 1982.

There have been many important advantages to
the change we have achieved. The constitution
clearly sets down rights and obligations between
group members and the paid workers who have a
responsibility to support the group. Such an
arrangement is in effect a service 'charter' and
defines the roles and responsibilities of everyone
involved. There now exist clearly defined ways and
means by which people can exercise power and control
over their lives. The whole group and the Committee
have control over funds, control over which has been
formally relinquished by the County Council.
However, the group is not abandoned to this
responsibility. Project workers have a duty to
provide 'advice' and 'material support'. Clearly
routine and sensitive assistance will be needed by
any self-regulated group which offers therapeutic
social experiences to people who have had a history
of difficulties in coping with their own lives. The
constitution provides a framework for this
assistance to be provided. Open membership for

anyone wishing to gain 'help' or 'contribute' to
CONTACT eliminates unhelpful distinctions between
people. There are no longer volunteers who are
separate from group members. CONTACT has in excess
of 120 volunteers since every member contributes to
the group in some way, no matter how small. We find
that as people grow in confidence so their capacity
and desire to contribute grows. This rising
capacity to give support is an expression of
someone's sense of well-being and regained
'citizenship'. But in the past we found this could
be inhibited by ascribing an artificial status, like
that of 'volunteer'. Many of the people who came as
volunteers revealed themselves to have serious
problems. Although we found it possible to help
people without removing their status as volunteer,
it is now much easier to help group members
regardless of the original motivation which brings
them into the group.

CONTACT reflects all the principles which
underpin the values and philosophy of the Project.
The group and its work is rooted in a firm belief in
the creative potential of each person. Such a
belief is balanced by a careful appreciation of the
limitations which exist for all of us. Working with
CONTACT requires Project staff to continually assist
the group to face its weaknesses. The actions of
individual members need to be sensitively monitored
so that someone can be helped to avoid taking too
much on.

David needed some practical financial help so
that he could offer his friend Peter a weekend away
from home when things were getting difficult at home
for Peter. In the past Peter has ended up in
hospital under such conditions. However, David also
needs help not to offer more help to Peter than he
can reasonably cope with.

As a social organisation CONTACT addresses the
most central social issue for people who experience
mental health problems - the loss, forfeiture or
disposal of power and control over their own lives.
If any organisation aims to provide helpful,
supportive experiences to assist people to overcome
major personal difficulties, it must tackle the
extent to which that person has access to valued
social opportunities which are under his or her
control.

CONTACT'S membership is now in excess of 120
people. Not everyone uses the organisation every
day. On average 55 people will use the facilities
available to CONTACT at the Centre during the day.

Many more people will use the informal opportunities
like visiting each other, the regular Thursday
evening in a local pub or shared recreation at local
leisure centres. The photographic club thrives with
members organising regular weekend and evening trips
to places of interest. Most club members are signed
up for classes in photography at a local adult
education centre. The running club has a hard core
of members who continue to plug away at occasional
half marathons. The allotments rented by the
Project are used by members of CONTACT and give
people a chance for weekend and evening activity at
their own initiative. The practical and financial
resources of the group give people access to a full
range of ordinary social activities from which they
might otherwise find themselves excluded. The way
CONTACT is organised enhances a sense of ownership
and belonging.

This radically different model of organisation
seems to challenge traditional assumptions. When
describing the group we are often asked whether we
deal with people who have experienced 'serious
mental illness'. Such questions suggest disbelief
that a social group can draw so strongly upon the
efforts of its members, if people who have
experienced serious mental health problems are
involved. A survey of CONTACT members in March 1985
revealed that out of the members at that time a
substantial number of people had had the term
'schizophrenia' or 'psychotic' used to describe
their experiences. At that time many people had
been described as suffering from depression. A
number of group members had seriously abused
alcohol. Members of the group displayed the full
range of difficulties you would expect to find
amongst people who predominantly have been involved
with formal psychiatric services, either currently
or in the past. Not everyone is capable of taking
on the responsibility of running the group. Not
everyone wants to try and nobody is likely to make
them. What CONTACT achieves is a culture of choice
and opportunity for everyone. For some members
exercising power and control might involve deciding
to go with a friend to a pub or cinema and having
the means to implement that choice. For other
members it might mean carrying the responsibilities
of managing the funds for the group or occupying the
position of Chairperson or Secretary. There are
those members who need considerable care and support
and there are those who gain so much by being
involved in giving that support. Someone may be

unable to manage much more than the basic personal
responsibility of getting up in the morning. But
this should not exclude him or her from being
involved with a social group where there are
substantial personal opportunities, providing that
the small choices and responsibilities such a person
will take are respected and acknowledged.
    The development of CONTACT involves many
important issues. It has demanded a transformation
of the relationships between those who traditionally
provide a service and those who use it. Roles and
relationships become the subject of continual daily
negotiation which reflect the skills and abilities
of each person concerning the task in hand. In such
circumstances ascribed status, the conventional
method of defining who will do what and when, is no
longer appropriate. It may even be a serious
impediment. In such circumstances the people
involved must work out a new framework of principles
which can be used to help them define the boundaries
between actions which reflect friendship and those
which reflect a concern which is 'paid for'. The
evolution of CONTACT has demanded a constant
appraisal of our actions set against our
intentions. It is one thing to find practical ways
to implement that commitment. CONTACT represents a
fundamental challenge to our traditional use of
professional power. For everyone involved, its
establishment has involved - and continues to
involve - a struggle to meet that challenge.

CONTACT PHOTOGRAPHY GROUP

    The CONTACT Photography Group is described by
Jim, one of its members:

    "Photography was introduced to the Centre by
    Tommy, about two years ago. Over the first few
    months that Tom came to the Centre he went
    round the members telling them that he was
    interested in photography and then asking if
    they were interested too. A small group of
    four people emerged. I think they all had a basic
    camera to start off with. To start off
    with they only went out perhaps once a week or
    once a fortnight, but as time went on they
    started going out taking photographs more
    frequently which cost more money. Up till now,
    they had all been paying for their own film,
    developing and printing, and as they were all
    out of work, they just couldn't afford to go

259

on.

Tom decided that he would ask Andrew Milroy (as there was no CONTACT or Executive Committee then) for a grant to support a Photography Group. I think they were allowed in the region of £130 to last them twelve months. What to spend the money on was decided by themselves. I think at this time, people were starting to notice that the Photogaphy Group existed, as the original four were bringing endless photos into the Centre and this started a lot of people thinking about photographs. Up till this time th 'original four' were having meetings only to discuss when and where to meet for the next load of photographs to be taken.

Next they decided to go to photography night clas once a week for three or four months. The fees or subscriptions were paid out of the allowance for their Group. The following morning they would talk about what had gone off at the night class and this would arouse interest in photography.

As the months went on Andrew Milroy was giving them as much moral and financial support as possible, and at the same time one or two other people joined the Photography Group. At this time the Centre or CONTACT hadn't got a mini-bus of their own, so travel was very limited. The photo group tended to go to places which had easy access by public transport. Their bus fares were paid for by either the Amenity Fund or came out of a Central Fund to cover fares, entrance fees etc.

At this time myself and Gary decided to join the Photography Group. We both had a little interest in photography and both had basic 35mm cameras. At first we went to a couple of meetings and were dismayed to see the lack of organisation within the group. Both Gary and I had a lot of ideas on how to help the group. All the time I am trying to urge them on to higher standards than they thought possible.

At this time now we have about 16 members. I have been elected Chairman, Kevin, Deputy Chairman; Gary, Secretary and Tom, Treasurer. We like to think that we are the most democratic group in the Centre. By that I mean

one or two of our members are very quiet and
have no confidence in their own beliefs but
before we make any decisions about anything, we
make sure these 'quiet people' have their say
and that their views and opinions are taken
very seriously.

Up to about September 1985, most of us had
limited knowledge about photography except
Tom. After a long discussion at one of our
Tuesday afternoon meetings it was decided that
those who wanted to, could go to Adult
Education Courses on Photography at the Hunloke
Road Centre. I think initially about ten of us
signed on but one or two stopped going, so six
of us finished the course in the end.

On a personal basis and I know one or two feel
exactly the same, the course was the most
satisfying thing I had ever done. When I first
started I never thought I would ever fully
understand how a modern 50mm camera works, so
to achieve something when you thought you never
would does a lot of good for your confidence.
I have never seen a photograph anywhere that is
out of my capability. I have that much
confidence in my own capacity. I have spent
about £350 to £400 on camera equipment and my
camera alone is worth over £200 so you see all
that I have got material wise and in confidence
comes from joining the Photography Group.

From the time I joined the Photography Group
the users of the Day Centre had formed into the
group CONTACT. Under the constitution of
CONTACT an Executive Committee has to be
elected. This year 1986 to 1987, the Executive
Committee was allocated £2,500 from the
Derbyshire County Council and it was left up to
individual groups to apply for a sum of money
from the Executive Committee, to use on their
group.

At one of our weekly Photography Club Meetings
we had to decide how much to apply for. I
recommended to the group that we should put in
for £1,000. We got £600. We knew we had
been given a lot of money and we wanted to make
sure it was spent wisely and not only on us
(the present members) but future members would
benefit from the large amount of money we had

been lucky to get.

At the night classes we had attended, we did a bit of studio photography with flash studio lighting. We all enjoyed this so we thought it would be a good idea to buy a studio flash system out of the money we had been allocated, as not only would we benefit from it, mainly in the winter evenings when most of us find very little to do, but future members would also benefit from the purchase. The group had already purchased a decent camera from the previous years, so we decided to buy a good lens for close up work like bird watching, etc. The reason behind a big expensive lens was that most of us had dreamed of taking photos through such a lens yet realised that the chances of being able to buy one, personally, was nil. So we now had the chance to buy such a lens and, once again, future members would benefit from it.

We now have good equipment but also now have our mini-bus for the Centre and the chance to go further afield. Also there are quite a few people who have passed the test to drive the mini-bus, some of whom are members of 'CONTACT' and some are paid workers. Obviously we try to go places where there are good photographs to be taken but sometimes we also go to places that are interesting to talk about afterwards. The kind of places we have been to recently are the Nuclear Plant at Sellafield in Cumbria, Whitby, Monsdale, Sherwood Forest, Hardwick Hall (several times), the Photography Museum at Retford. We have also had a few days of camping combined with photography in the Peak District and endless small runs in my car to the local countryside, within ten miles of the town centre. Any CONTACT member is eligible to join the Photography Group, just as long as they have some interest in photography.

As for the paid workers, we have very little to do with them in connection with the Photography Group, as we feel we have a good thing going for us and at present there is no need for advice from anyone. At the same time though it's good to know morally that we have the full support of paid workers and it's good to know that we are acknowledged as one of the strongest groups within the Centre. (I can't stress enough how important it is to us to have moral support from paid workers because it encourages us to stride forward for greater achievements).

At this moment in time, I cannot see the Photography Club collapsing or folding up. We see that by buying the equipment, this serves as a foundation stone for future members to build on. Most members are quite happy to stay with their present achievements and use what they have learnt as a hobby.

As for myself and Gary, we intend to go on by going back to night school to study and hope to pass the GCSE in Photography. We both have visions of trying to make some kind of living out of it. As I have said earlier on, I haven't seen a photograph anywhere that I couldn't take, if given the opportunities. CONTACT is the place that is most likely to give us these opportunities."

T.O.D. - THE OPEN DOOR CLUB

The Open Door Club evolved from a group originally sponsored by the Chesterfield and District Association for Mental Health. The group existed before the establishment of the North Derbyshire Mental Health Services Project and was originally called MASH, standing for Mental Aid Self Help. The Chesterfield and District Association for Mental Health later on ceased to exist.

MASH was the first formally organised "self help" social support group in Chesterfield. Most of the support for the group was provided by staff working in the local psychiatric hospital. Prior to the re-opening of the Tontine Road Centre the group had met in a church hall, some two miles from the centre of town. The group and their parent body, the Chesterfield and District Association for Mental Health, had been given a commitment that they could have the use of the Tontine Road Centre. In March 1982, the group moved to the Centre and was meeting there two evenings and three afternoons each week. The move exposed problems in the group. Initially these difficulties were expressed as dissatisfaction with the building. Within a few weeks people began to complain that "the club was much better when we

were at St Thomas's". The relationship between the
group and the staff based at the Centre had not been
properly defined. There was considerable suspicion
on the part of key group members. It became clear
that there were basic problems in the organisation
and support of the group.

The group had no constitution. Membership
seemed to be defined by how often you turned up and
'once a member, always a member'. It seemed that
no-one could leave. There were a couple of powerful
personalities in the group who had obviously gained
considerable benefit, in particular from the power
and status given by the roles they had established
in the group. However, the absence of a
constitution meant no-one else shared in such power
and status. Indeed, sometimes it seemed that the
positive experiences enjoyed by some members were at
the cost of other members. Some members could act
in rather patronising, even punishing, ways towards
others. People might find their competence or
reliability continually challenged at group meetings
by the dominant few. A critical problem was the
lack of legitimate means to intervene. This was
caused by the absence of a constitution. MASH was
after all a "self help" group, run for and by its
members. So although there were obvious serious
problems, nobody could tackle them.

There were other senses, too, in which a lack
of rules trapped the group with its problems. A
couple of key members seemed burdened by the
responsibilities they had accrued and half-inclined
to share some of their power. But they needed a
social formula to explain such a step as something
other than failure to cope. Time-limited elected
roles, for instance, would have supplied such a
formula, had there been rules and a constitution.
As it was the lack of rules left them with no way
out. They had to hang on to the group.

Steadily we struggled with these difficulties.
Slowly we worked to establish an effective
relationship with the group and its members, while
discussing the problem with the Chesterfield and
District Association of Mental Health. Eventually
it was possible to persuade the 'parent' group to
insist upon a re-organisation. We had been working
to get a constitution adopted by the group. This
was eventually achieved and after careful
negotiations the group was re-launched with a new
name and a proper framework for its organisation.

The Open Door Club provides leisure and
recreational activities for members. It now meets

three time a week at the Centre, providing a warm,
low key atmosphere where people can meet, chat, play
darts, snooker, etc. The group organises trips and
seasonal social events at Christmas, Easter, etc, as
well as organising joint activities with members
from other groups.

T.O.D. receives a grant from the County Council
annually. This mainly covers travelling expenses
for members, plus a small amount towards subsidising
activities. The group has an average membership of
around 50 people.

The relationship between the group and the
Mental Health Services Project is now clearly
defined by the Constitution. Project workers act as
advisors to the group and have certain closely
defined duties which might loosely be described as
similar to those of "trustees". One of the Project
Social Workers carries an overall responsibility to
maintain our support for the group and meets
regularly with the Committee.

While it uses the same building as our main
social support group, CONTACT, T.O.D. maintains its
independence and identity. CONTACT is generally
regarded as the one which will offer a more
demanding and more intensive range of social
experience. CONTACT meets formally five days each
week and every second week on a Sunday. It has a
larger number of members and receives more intensive
support from Project Staff. Although they are
separate, a number of members of CONTACT will also
be members of T.O.D. A number of these people will
have joined CONTACT through T.O.D, referring
themselves for membership as they became aware of
and wished to gain access to a wider and more
demanding range of opportunities. Membership of
CONTACT, for instance, brings opportunities like
Drama and Assertiveness groups, as well as social
and work activities. T.O.D therefore seems to
provide a kind of collecting point for potential new
members of CONTACT. People are able to get to know
CONTACT informally as a result of them being based
in the same building. It is interesting to note that
while some people do join one group from the other,
both groups retain a majority of people who are
members of only the one group.

T.O.D. plays an important part in the
development of the 'system of support'. It adds
flexibility and variety, operating so close to
CONTACT. It is more informal than CONTACT, offering
lower and therefore less challenging or threatening
membership than CONTACT. The ease of crossing from

one group to the other enables people to become gradually involved in a more demanding social process.

INCOME SUPPORT I - AMENITY AND BENEVOLENT FUNDS

If we acknowledge that the loss or forfeiture of power is a central social experience for people who experience difficulties in thinking, feeling and behaviour, then we must also acknowledge the extent to which a restricted income will inhibit recovering the power and control lost, or gaining that not yet experienced.

Having money in our pockets is a key means of establishing choices in our lives. The extent of our income will influence the choices we can make about where we live, with whom we associate, what we eat, how we dress and what we do for leisure and recreation.

A good income is usually only available through a good job, except if you are fortunate enough to have inherited substantial wealth. In this age of rising mass unemployment, a good job is difficult if not impossible to get, if you have experienced serious mental health problems.

Whilst we are largely impotent to create good jobs with good incomes for people, we can pay some attention to the importance of financial support to people who have spent many years struggling with their mental health. In the Project this has led us to use the traditional County Council Amenity Fund as a means of generating and distributing funds for group activities, without the restriction of local government financial regulations. It also prompted us to use the established mechanism of the Amenity Fund to set up a Benevolent Fund.

The Benevolent Fund provides a source of financial assistance for individuals. It is no replacement for the increasing inadequacies of our social security system and we should not allow it to be used as a justification for the steady erosion of a properly funded state income maintenance system. Managed by staff and users of the service, the Benevolent Fund provides at least some limited means to resolve financial problems. It can offer help with fuel bills, clothing and even food, as well as making holidays, recreation and social activities feasible. The fund is used as a last resort, reflecting the modesty of its financing and our concern that people should find more usual means of maintaining their income. Coupled with the Amenity

Fund it provides some means for people to gain
control over their own lives. It is a direct and
relevant response to the realisation that for people
confined to a potential lifetime supported by an
income from some kind of social security, a few
pounds can represent a 100% increase on their
disposable income! The money in these funds is
raised through various fund raising events. The
Benevolent Fund managed by CONTACT is for group
members only. To remove the sense of charity,
members of CONTACT pay a weekly levy into the
Benevolent Fund.

BENEVOLENT FUND - ADVISORY COMMITTEE TERMS OF
REFERENCE

1.   GENERAL

1.1 The Mental Health Services Project
Benevolent Fund exists to provide financial or
material assistance to people who experience or
have experienced mental health problems. The
Fund aims to provide relief to people using the
services of the Mental Health Services Project,
whose mental health is at risk or whose
continued rehabilitation is likely to be
impeded, by reason of financial or material
difficulties.

1.2 The administration of the Fund is subject
to all existing financial regulations of the
Derbyshire County Council, or any regulations
as may be determined in the future. Nothing
stated in these Terms of Reference shall be
construed as overriding such financial
regulations.

2.   ADVISORY COMMITTEE MEMBERSHIP

The Fund shall be administered by the Amenity
Fund No.1 Committee and all the terms of
reference which apply to Amenity Fund No.1
Committee shall be applied to the Fund.

3.   POLICY OF THE FUND AND CRITERIA FOR ELIGIBILITY

3.1 The Fund is available for people who have
been using the services of the Mental Health
Services Project for more than three months.

3.2 Payments from the Fund can be made at the

discretion of the Advisory Committee when the Committee is satisfied, having regard to all the relevant circumstances, that payment is necessary to relieve psychological stress which might otherwise lead to a deterioration in the health and welfare of the person concerned; or where financial or material help is likely to assist in the rehabilitation or continued support of the person seeking assistance from the Fund.

3.3 The Advisory Committee shall have regard to all other statutory or charitable means of financial or material help. Payment from the Fund shall only be made if the Committee is satisfied that attempts have been made to seek financial help from other sources and that no other help is available or that to seek other sources of help would result in unreasonable delay to the serious detriment of the person seeking assistance from the Fund.

3.4 No payment may be made from the Fund which will result in a regular supplement to the income of any person seeking assistance.

3.5 Payments from the Fund can be made as grants or repayable loans. At the discretion of the Advisory Committee payments may meet all or part of the financial help sought.

4.   SPECIAL PROVISION

In the event that one of the User members of the Advisory Committee needs to seek assistance from the fund, the request will be passed for decision to the Principal Assistant responsible for the Project.

NORTH DERBYSHIRE MENTAL HEALTH SERVICES PROJECT - AMENITY FUND NO.1

ADVISORY COMMITTEE - TERMS OF REFERENCE

1.   GENERAL

Nothing in these notes shall override the policies of the County Council for the administration of Amenity Funds. These notes should, therefore, be operated with reference

to guidelines laid down in the Administrative
Handbook (pages 110-113).

2.   MEMBERSHIP

Membership of the Amenity Fund Advisory
Committee will be as follows:-

The Project Co-ordinator
One Project Social Worker
One member of the Project Administrative Staff
Three representatives invited to serve on the
Committee drawn from groups/organisations
supported by the Project

3.   CHAIRPERSON

3.1 A Chairperson for the Committee shall be
elected by the Committee and where possible
will be a person using services which are a
part of, or are supported by the Mental Health
Services Project.

3.2 Money needed from the Amenity Fund will
need to be referred to the Chairperson of the
Amenity Fund Advisory Committee. In most
circumstances this should be a request which
has been considered by the Users' Group and the
request for Amenity Fund money will be made by
the Users' Co-ordinator.

4.   ROLE AND RESPONSIBILITIES OF CHAIRPERSON

4.1 The Chairperson will be responsible for
convening meetings and compiling an Agenda of
business to be discussed.

4.2 Any expenditure necessary, consistent with
the principles of the Amenity Fund, which
cannot reasonably await a meeting of the
Committee, can be made at the approval of the
Committee Chairperson, and Project Co-ordinator
up to a maximum of £30.00.

4.3 Such expenditure will be reported to the
next meeting of the Committee.

4.4 The Chairperson will ensure that minutes
are kept of each meeting.

5. POLICY

5.1 The Amenity Fund is available to finance things which are for the direct benefit of groups supported by the Mental Health Services Project where money is not available from any other source.

5.2 Money can be made available in the form of payments for specific activities; the purchase of equipment, or in the form of a grant to the organisation.

5.3 Where payment from the fund is made in the form of a grant, this must be endorsed by a full meeting of the Advisory Committee. No grants can be made under the Chairperson's discretion.

5.4 Money is not available for financial help to individuals, ie. paying fuel bills, rent or personal loans and no request for financial help of this kind can be considered.

5.5 All decisions of the Advisory Committee shall be made by a simple majority vote of all those present, provided that more than 50% of current members are at the meeting.

INCOME SUPPORT II: WELFARE RIGHTS

People with disability are the last to be employed. Their incomes are low and their opportunities few. Promoting an active policy of encouraging a full take-up of benefits is the least that statutory workers can do.

A computer is regularly used which allows individuals in contact with the Project to assess their right to benefit. If they are failing to claim the maximum entitlement, or are being wrongly paid, they can identify the shortfall and representation can be made to the DHSS.

Weekly advice sessions are held with workers on hand to explain the benefits system and to help individuals use the computer facility.

Discussion is encouraged within the networks supported by project workers. Thus take-up is promoted and consciousness is raised about the role of the DHSS and the nature of welfare.

INCOME SUPPORT III

TURC - TONTINE USERS REPAIR COLLECTIVE

This was initiated during 1983 in response to the interest of several members in establishing some opportunities for work. The constitution indicates the framework within which the group organises its activities.

From the beginning, one important principle has been that members themselves define their own interests. Thus several different schemes were proposed and followed through. Peter had some skills at repairing cane rush chairing and so advertised his services to the community. Work came in regularly for which Peter set a price himself. Gordon went in for the manufacture of paper bricks using waste paper. The work was undemanding but was steady and allowed for opportunities to talk to others whilst the paper was being shredded and pulped. A number of regular customers took the bricks, including shops. Mike helped both Peter and Gordon with their respective tasks. The working day began at their leisure and they were free to involve themselves with the other social/recreational/ educational activities organised by the groups of which they were members. Two other members, Steve and John, decided to operate a bicycle repair service.

The enterprise, although independently constituted, had workshops in the Tontine Road Community Centre and was in this sense sheltered. Rent, and heating and lighting costs did not have to be paid for. Any paperwork was administered by the clerical staff attached to the building. TURC never set out to be a workscheme which would make its members financially independent in the way that a work co-operative might set out to be. Its constituent members were not that keen to take on vast amounts of work and public demand for their products was insufficient. A substantial income would have been required to lift them out of the social security system. So the result was, for them, a small supplement to their weekly state benefit. For those on Invalidity Benefit this could make a marked difference to income. However, for those on Supplementary or Unemployment Benefit, the extra income was but small due to the particular 'earnings disregard' rulings for different benefits.

The scheme has gone through turbulent phases. Peter, a key individual in the original line up, was prone to being absent unexpectedly. Sometimes this would be for substantial periods of time. Although he did not require support at these times, he did not make adequate arrangements for administration of TURC's affairs while he was away. A pattern of reluctance to relinquish control, combined with frequent absences, had a demoralising effect on Mike and Gordon. The other two members of the collective, Steve and John, successfully moved on to take up full-time work opportunities, one in London and one abroad. The bicycle repair function of TURC thus folded.

A new Secretary, Brian, joined TURC with the intention of helping organise around a new scheme to find and rent a shop somewhere in the town to sell products produced by TURC and to broaden out its activities. However, Brian left the group. At a later stage, Brian returned but TURC was again left without proper administrative support. Peter began to lose interest in the workscheme and Gordon spent more time in other activities at Tontine Road. The workshop was due to undergo refurbishing around this time and TURC's activities virtually ceased, apart from the new member, Clive, who managed to ply a good trade in birdboxes for a while.

A new group of members organised around the scheme for a base in a shop. However, when a suitable location had been identified the application for funding was ignored by the County Council. Enthusiasm waned and a gradual dispersal again took place. Although a new Secretary was installed at this time, he did not follow up the funding application, nor try to maintain the group which had formed. The manufacturer of woodcrafts, Clive, needed to move house and work ceased. For periods TURC has existed on paper only despite the involvement of a fair number of people over the space of three years. Several lessons may be drawn from this experience:

-   Although independently constituted, the group may well have benefited from the permanent involvement of a paid worker to recognise when TURC was foundering and to provide support at such times.

-   Key individuals involved in TURC faced substantial personal difficulties on a number of occasions. Dealing with these hindered the smooth operation of the scheme.

- At no point did the scheme ever look like providing a genuine wage to its participants. Thus the work opportunities provided could not be seen as providing genuine alternatives to the open labour market.

- Some of the individuals involved moved on to take up positions in the open labour market and · so the scheme may have served them well as a temporary measure. However, their departure also created problems for TURC since they provided much of its stability.

- For those members who could only take on limited work roles due to enduring disability, such schemes offered an opportunity for the individual to decide on his type and level of contribution and could combine with a range of other leisure/educational/social experiences. They may thus offer a genuinely non-alienating alternative to labour in a competitive industrial market.

OUTREACH

Our outreach programme was strongly influenced by our principles and the experience of other organisations, such as the Erconwald Street Mental Health Project in Hammersmith. We were initially established to operate from one base located in the centre of Chesterfield, but faced with the customary expectation that, as the only specialised support service in North Derbyshire, we should offer assistance to anyone who could be got to us. Such an expectation was clearly inconsistent with our principles. Trying to meet it would make our practice ineffective. If social support is organised through a fabricated social process away from the area in which someone lives, it will offer largely un-transferable experiences. Outside the hours when the organisation is available, the people involved are likely to remain isolated and excluded to the same extent as before. At the same time as our model was developing, the North Derbyshire Health Authority and the County Council were planning Community Mental Health Teams in each of the four districts which make up North Derbyshire. This 'sectorisation' of mental health services clearly required an adjustment at our end. Our outreach programme was aimed to provide a social worker from the Project to work within each sector

to develop services in conjunction with the
Community Mental Health Teams, amongst others. We
contribute both through the time each worker invests
in their sector and through a limited annual
development budget. This money is used in a variety
of ways. It may be used to fund established groups
who provide services which are mental health related
and organised by individuals with whom we have
regular contact, but to whom we do not directly
provide a service. For example, Operation Neighbour
is a scheme to provide visitors for elderly,
isolated people. One of the organisers works
closely with us in providing a service to carers of
elderly people via another group, Care for Carers.
Listening Ear received a starting grant from us
although they have been explicit about not wanting
any input from people employed by the Social
Services Department. They want as much autonomy as
possible. Groups may be established by members of
the Community Mental Health Teams and then may
receive a grant from us. For example, a Community
Psychiatric Nurse in Bolsover helped establish a
group to teach anxiety reduction methods.

The major area of development concerns the
groups which we directly help to establish and
maintain. The aim is to establish facilities on a
local level which are, in so far as is possible,
comprehensive in scope and modelled on the
principles underlying the groups at the Tontine Road
Centre. In the rural West Derbyshire sector, for
example, a group called SPECTRUM meets at Matlock
twice a week 'formally'. Besides this, it is a
principle of all outreach work that we help people
find out about resources which can be used as
sources of support at times of the week not
designated as formal meeting times. SPECTRUM meets
at an adult education centre and at a pub. Again,
meeting places are sought out which are 'ordinary'
and, if possible, provide opportunities for contact
with non-stigmatised community agencies and
facilities.

In North East Derbyshire sector, a group called
TASC meets twice a week at Clay Cross, with support
from project workers and the Community Mental Health
Team.

COMMUNITY DEVELOPMENT: CRESWELL OPEN DOOR

This group was initiated by a woman who had
already been in contact with the Chesterfield Open

Door Group for some time. She used public transport
to travel to and fro three times a week. The
journey was a 24 mile round trip and she wanted to
establish a similar facility in her own village so
that she would not have to make this journey. She
contacted a paid worker at Tontine Road Mental
Health Services Project with a development role in
the Creswell area. She identified a planned
'community house' in the village and gave the names
and telephone numbers of people who she thought may
be interested and some of whom she had already
spoken to. They included the local vicar, a local
social worker and a member of the Parish Council who
was involved in establishing the community house.

These people were interested and more was
discovered about the local community, its resources
and the degree of support for a mental health
self-help group. The village has a population of
6,000 and is a mining community in an economically
deprived area. The worker was asked by the Parish
Councillor to write in with general proposals and
told to expect contact when the house was ready.
Some months later we were contacted by the newly
appointed workers at the Community House. Under the
Community Programme three clerical/administrative
workers had been appointed at the house and two
others were using it as a base for Youth and
Community Outreach work. These five people visited
Tontine Road and we discussed the implications of
setting up a group. They were able to see similar
projects in action at the Mental Health Services
Project.

A meeting was convened at the Creswell
Community House with the help of the woman who had
initiated developments (we can call her Joan to
maintain confidentiality). Joan contacted other
people in the village who she thought would use a
self-help facility and the worker phoned his
previous contacts. An inaugural meeting was held,
attended by about twelve people and a committee of
four was established: Joan as chairperson, a project
worker as an advisory member, one of the community
house workers as treasurer, and a secretary.

We had further meetings to establish a name for
the group, times and days when the group would
convene and worked out a constitution and set of
rules. Three of the members of the new group had
already participated in the Chesterfield Open Door
group and so had some idea of the philosophy and
nature of organisation of self-help groups. Joan
had been involved on the organisational side for

275

some time and brought those skills to the benefit of the new group. A starter grant of £100 was negotiated from the Development Budget of the Mental Health Services Project. Later in the year another grant of £350 was given. The constitution and rules were closely modelled on those used by the Chesterfield Open Door group. They allow for the election of committee members, Annual General Meetings, rules on repayment of bus fares and club fees, etc. The 3 objectives laid out in the constitution are:

1. To provide fellowship and mutual support for people who experience or who are recovering from mental health problems.

2. To provide social and recreational activities for members.

3. To assist members to develop and sustain ordinary social contacts, so that members can join other social groups in the areas where members live.

One year on, the group has grown to a membership of 25. The group meets formally twice a week (Monday evenings and Wednesday afternoons) and informal support is given outside these hours.
Many activities have been arranged, including outings to a brewery, to see the illuminations at Matlock, to spend a day in York, theatre trips to Chesterfield, to parties organised by other self-help networks, etc. Many links have been established in the village, and a new committee was elected at the recent Annual General Meeting. Planned and current activities include raffles, jumble sales, coffee mornings and more outings. One of the most encouraging changes was the appointment of one of the original members of the group to a position of Community Programme Worker at the Community House. The original five workers have gone and there are now only two employees. Good relations have been maintained with the house management committee and the local community. Joint activities have been arranged with a group of people in a neighbouring village who also have emotional difficulties.
Another encouraging feature has been the involvement of friends, neighbours and relatives in events organised by the group. Although they do not define themselves as members, their involvement

helps to create a broad net of support and understanding for the concept of community mental health support services.

Another principle of development is that individuals who have had some experience of responsibility for mutual help groups, like those at Tontine Road, are encouraged to use their skills to help foster the newer developments. This would be, of course, for individuals who identify with the communities where the new groups are being developed.

When the groups initially come together, they may decide on a variety of activities. Frequently these are recreational and social. Through discussion, a process of education takes place. People come to find services that are available in the district and discover how to gain access to local resources. Sessions may become problem-solving and problem-sharing. Exchange of information and ideas between different groups is encouraged. The next step may be to link the groups by means of some executive body which could act as a consumer pressure group within Health and Social Services.

The members of these groups meet outside formal meeting times and networks of informal, spontaneous support begin to grow. Representatives of the MHSP encourage such informal links and try to ensure that the needs of the most disadvantaged members living in these localities are met. Such people may have great difficulty in organising their own lives so as to take advantage of opportunities for participation and being valued. Thus visiting them, giving them very basic practical help, supporting them through crises and changes in their lives, as well as acting as advocates on their behalf, are all important activities which help their needs to be met. MHSP workers fill some of these roles. Members of the groups often meet many of these needs. Again, the emphasis is on empowering individuals within the groups. That is, giving them opportunities to participate and take on positions of responsibility in order that their sense of self-worth and confidence is heightened.

The groups mentioned tend to be formally constituted. That is they usually have Executive Committees, Officers, provision for Annual General Meetings, etc. These constitutions are flexible but this form of organisation serves several purposes. It allows for self-determination. It defines people as 'members' not 'clients'. It offers positions of

responsibility for those who wish to take on
leadership roles. It builds in to the groups a
means of ensuring financial accountability. It
identifies the duties and responsibilities of
professional workers in ways which permit
appropriate intervention but without undermining the
principle of self-regulation.

An issue arises as to the type of need being
met by these groups. It is true that the groups
could serve as models for realising the skills of
any group of unemployed people. But there is very
good reason to believe that they are in fact serving
a very disadvantaged population. Overwhelmingly,
the members of these groups are poor, unemployed and
have been in contact with mental health services for
substantial periods of time. The way the groups are
publicised (tending to focus on isolation, boredom,
depression as problems which such groups can help
overcome) and the 'filters' through which people
pass before they become involved (via community
mental health teams, social workers and GPs, other
self-help groups, word of mouth, etc.) result in
particular types of needs being met.

To take the evidence a little further, one of
the groups mentioned above, SPECTRUM, has been cited
as an important component in the West Derbyshire
sector's response to mental health needs. Some
interesting trends have emerged from an evaluation
of the joint effects of a new community mental
health team with SPECTRUM alongside it as an
integral part of the service. Referral rates have
gone up dramatically. Admissions to hospital have
gone down. Use of neuroleptics and ECT has been
dramatically reduced and a survey of GPs and people
who have used the service reported overwhelming
confidence and satisfaction with the new service.

It is hoped that such evaluations will become a
regular feature of the new service. The initial
survey is encouraging evidence that the types of
groups mentioned above may have qualities which
allow us to claim that they are essential elements
of the new structure of community mental health
services.

HOUSING RESPONSES

The Mental Health Services Project provides
housing both directly and indirectly. It became
involved with housing because it widened our range
of responses to individual needs. Too often people
in need are told: "You've got your name on the

278

Housing Department waiting list. We've written to
them supporting your application. We can't do
anything else." Following up housing department
applications is important. But there are other
things which can be done also.

HOUSING SUPPORT I

A two-bedroomed terraced property is leased to
the Mental Health Services Project from the
Derbyshire County Council Estates Department. It
has been used over the last three years in a variety of
ways. Originally it was seen as a 'transitional'
facility for individuals moving from a situation of
dependence to one of independence. Length of stay
has been variable (up to 18 months) and in some
cases the use of the house was part of a 'contract'
made with the individuals concerned.

Towards the end of 1984, we used the house as a
'crisis' resource when John's (false name) home
situation collapsed. Conflict with his brother and
mother led to his virtual 'expulsion' from the
house. John has profound difficulties in
concentrating, in looking after himself and in his
self-image. To receive support during the day he
normally had to be accompanied to the group he was
involved with. With these problems and a history of
hospitalisation, the institutional response seemed
likely. However, a number of friends and
acquaintances from the CONTACT group meeting at
Tontine Road, who valued John, agreed to establish a
rota to stay with him at the house for a few
days. They received expenses until we were able to
obtain agreement for a 'flexible care' package for
John. Since that time, two or three people have been
employed to support John 24 hours a day at the house.

HOUSING SUPPORT II

This is another two-bedroomed terraced property
but this house belongs to a local housing
association, Northern Counties. They manage the
property and any damage to property or rent arrears
are covered by a guarantee that the Mental Health
Services Project will underwrite such costs should
they be incurred.

Harry had spent much of the last 20 years in
secure institutions when he was referrd to us 18
months ago. Previous attempts to get him out had
failed as he actively rejected hostels, half-way

homes and traditionally organised day centres.
Two people were appointed as full-time residential
social workers and one part-time 'back-up'. In
conjunction with the Home Care Aide Service they
provided support to Harry 24 hours a day. Over a
period of three months, the frequency of their
residence reduced until Harry felt able to manage
alone. One of the workers continued to work part-
time with Harry to provide help with coping and
working through difficult periods. Three months
ago, Harry moved into ordinary council accommodation
to be nearer his mother's home. She is very elderly
and he now spends a large part of the day caring for
her. He seeks support from the Mental Health
Services Project (usually in the form of very
practical help) as and when he needs it.

Another project member, Bill, lived with his
wheelchair-bound mother and had been on a Housing
Department waiting list for some time. When this
house became vacant he moved in. His mother receives
substantial help from the local Social Services Area
Office. Bill is in his thirties and is a very
anxious individual who has some difficulties in
communicating clearly with others. A friend of his
from CONTACT, George, offered to help him redecorate
the house. Materials were provided by the Mental
Health Services Project and Bill, with George's
help, redecorated the house. George himself used
the CONTACT group, meeting at Tontine Road, to spend
time away from an emotionally charged and
overcrowded home environment. George's own home
situation eventually became intolerable. Depression
and overdoses were the previous patterns of response
to difficulties. On this occasion he asked Bill
could he stay with him for a while. Bill agreed and
the two are temporarily sharing the house,
providing valuable campanionship to one another.

HOUSING SUPPORT III

NORTHERN COUNTIES HOUSING ASSOCIATION

Good links are maintained with this local
housing association. In addition to the house
referred to above, they have a number of other
properties available which can be accessed
preferentially. Two CONTACT members live in flats
which are part of multi-occupancy housing near
Tontine Road.

The housing association also has available a
large site with a number of two, four and six

person flats. They house young people(under 35 years)
in these. Many young people wish to achieve
independence quite naturally or have problems
associated with living in difficult family
circumstances. We try to help assess such needs
with young people who become CONTACT members and,
where required, we will support their application
for housing with a written statement and sometimes a
personal contact. Such applications are usually
favourably received and preferentially responded
to. Young people are then housed in flats with
other people who have not had contact with the
mental health services. Over the last two years, a
number of people, dispersed throughout the site,
have been housed in this way. Spontaneous support
networks have grown up in these circumstances.
Where it is required, we will build on these in turn
and enhance the level of care provided by employing
coping CONTACT members to provide highly localised
support to less coping members. We have found this
to be a highly effective means of delivering mental
health care in conjunction with ongoing involvement
from Mental Health Services Project workers.

PRINCIPLES FOR HOUSING SUPPORT

Good practice in housing, and discussions of
the principles underlying it, cannot be divorced
from the concept of 'flexible care'. Having access
to a flexible care budget, ie. being able to employ
people at short notice to support others, round the
clock if necessary, is an indispensable part of the
strategy. Bricks and mortar are nothing without
sensitive and flexible aid as a complementary
element.
We have given some examples of our involvement
in housing issues. Our practice has taught us
important principles and lessons about such
involvement:

- Provision of practical help is essential. This
  may involve help with furniture removal,
  identifying sources of obtaining furniture,
  providing materials for redecoration,
  identifying sources of help with redecoration
  etc.

- The concept of 'core and cluster' is a useful
  one. Ordinary housing to be provided, with
  perceived lines of support and a recognised
  point of access to spontaneous, flexible and

responsive assistance.

- Establishing and supporting mental help networks such as CONTACT has benefits from the housing angle. We have witnessed the formation of natural networks of support developing 'out of hours' among members who live relatively close to one another, and could cite several instances where members of the group have provided shelter of their own volition to other members who have needed somewhere to stay temporarily other than their usual accommodation or who have lost their usual accommodation.

- Individual choice, about where people wish to be and the level of support which should be provided, is a priority and should be responded to.

- The need to be sensitive to neighbours and the need to negotiate with them on occasions when they become aware of eccentric, noisy or intrusive behaviour which unsettles them.

- The contribution of inter-agency co-operation to the successful provision of residential support. Links need to be formed with specific representatives from housing associations, local authority housing departments, Home Care Aide/Home Services, Community Nursing Services, and with other relevant individuals or interested bodies eg. voluntary organisations.

CONCLUSION

The 'system' which has evolved offers a multiplicity of opportunities. These reflect the wide range of needs and skills of the people using and, of course, contributing to the service. Engaging people in the development and operation of their own service enhances the value of the service to that person and increases its range and scope. People can receive help and at the same time offer help to others. Indeed, the experience of taking some responsibility for the needs of another person is a valuable experience for us all. Eric Fromm in his book, 'The Art of Loving' comments: "Giving is the highest expression of potency. In the very act of giving, I experience my strength, my wealth, my power". We must strive to offer the 'potency' we experience through our own giving, to all those we seek to help. So often we have developed ways of denying people the opportunity to give.

Problems of 'throughput', characteristic of traditional systems, are reconceived. 'Throughput', the processing of people on to something else, is the concern of those who 'own' or 'control' the service. For us, those who use the service 'own it' and will determine for themselves when and how to move. The responsibility of the paid workers is to continually seek to expand the range and levels of opportunity available. We also need to recognise that some people will remain 'in' the system without changing. We must acknowledge that this is appropriate. People can also remain in the system and yet change. As people grow in confidence, so they look to move on into situations where they can be valued and acknowledged as 'well' people. Current levels of unemployment are hitting people with any disability particularly severely and represent a serious impediment to personal growth. Our own experience suggests that this problem requires a redefined concept of 'day-care' service.

As people 'grow' so the system should adjust to provide space for that personal growth to be acknowledged. We have seen many people, over time, transform themselves from the 'shattered', highly dependent and vulnerable individuals they were when we first met them into the confident, independent, self-sustaining people they are now. Some of them have left for work (paid and voluntary), education or other reasons. Some have remained, gaining paid employment within the system or working as 'volunteers'.

Working in the way we do creates a network of personal relationships. These individual contacts provide for the 'inclusion' of people in ordinary social experiences beyond the time limits set by the opening hours of a building. The system evolves a capacity to support members twenty four hours a day, seven days a week. This support comes in routine ways, helping someone with their shopping, decorating or gardening, through shared leisure and social experiences, to help at times of crisis. Someone may suddenly need somewhere else to live or for someone to be with them in the middle of the night. We have found that this kind of spontaneous support develops. With care and proper back up, it can be directed towards someone who needs help but who is not yet actually part of the spontaneous network.

Our response to the problems we have faced has been to transform our work from a traditional model of day care to a wide-ranging 'community support system'. The process has drawn not only upon our own efforts, but also substantially on the contributions of many others. This work cannot exist in isolation and we have been supported morally, politically and practically by many individuals and agencies. Very plainly it depends on the contributions of other services - hospitals and community mental health teams, for instance, area social work teams, and general community services like adult education. Our Project is very much part of the wider process whereby a community mental health service, which involves many agencies, is now growing in North Derbyshire. Our objective, after all, has always been to facilitate the work of the many people in our area who have committed themselves to the care and support of people who have experienced mental health problems.

Chapter Sixteen

MENTAL HEALTH BEGINS AT HOME

Gillian Lomas

Editorial Introduction

Whatever its particular brief, every mental
health project must take into account the home
situation of each user. It needs the ability
sometimes to help an individual to change their
housing as the crucial first step to making
other changes in his or her life. Transient or
insecure housing, for instance, can put even the
most basic personal goals on ice. Another reason
why a mental health project needs some housing
knowledge and contacts is that for some people a
rewarding home situation can meet a whole range
of other needs besides shelter. Gillian Lomas
was Co-Director of the Community Psychiatry
Research Unit (CPRU) based at the psychiatric
unit at Hackney General Hospital, East London
from 1979 to 1985. During that time CPRU set up
a range of housing schemes, serviced by a
detached support team whose members variously
had teaching, social work, occupational therapy
and handyman skills.

Our experience has shown us that mentally ill people
on the road to recovery have to start with their
most basic needs and build on those to achieve more.
Successful training and employment are consequent
upon having somewhere safe and comfortable to live.
An idea we have found useful in helping people
resettle after mental illness is Abraham Maslow's
concept that there is a universal hierarchy of
different physical and psychological needs and a set
order whereby people experience and satisfy these
needs. This principle has some very practical
implications for the housing and occupation needs of
people who have been psychiatric patients.
    In his book 'Motivation and Personality' Maslow
describes a hierarchy of six universal levels of
needs, ranging from the most basic survival needs
for food, water and shelter, through the needs for
safety, the need to belong socially and the need for
esteem from other people, up to the quest for self-

ABRAHAM MASLOW'S HIERARCHY OF NEEDS

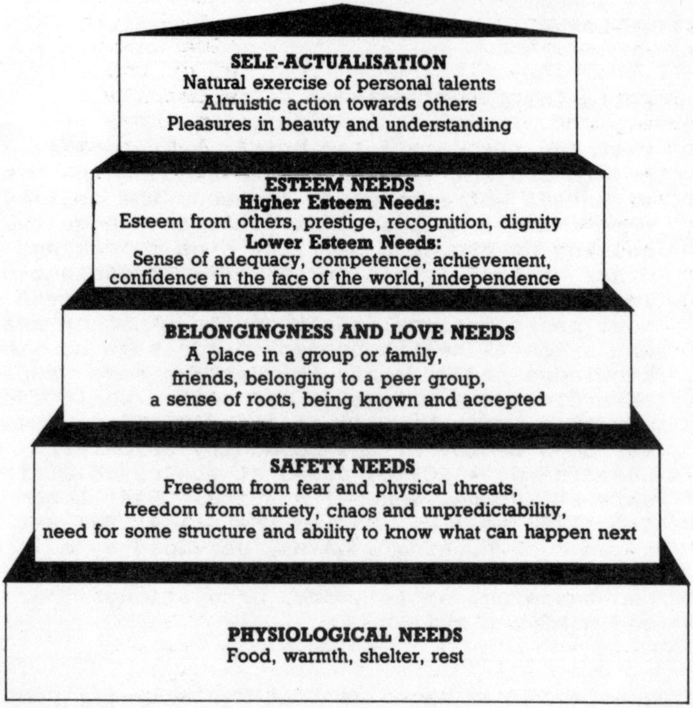

SELF-ACTUALISATION
Natural exercise of personal talents
Altruistic action towards others
Pleasures in beauty and understanding

ESTEEM NEEDS
Higher Esteem Needs:
Esteem from others, prestige, recognition, dignity
Lower Esteem Needs:
Sense of adequacy, competence, achievement,
confidence in the face of the world, independence

BELONGINGNESS AND LOVE NEEDS
A place in a group or family,
friends, belonging to a peer group,
a sense of roots, being known and accepted

SAFETY NEEDS
Freedom from fear and physical threats,
freedom from anxiety, chaos and unpredictability,
need for some structure and ability to know what can happen next

PHYSIOLOGICAL NEEDS
Food, warmth, shelter, rest

Figure 16.1

fulfillment (1). His idea is that a person is
dominated by one level of need at a time. This need
will occupy all their energies until they satisfy it.
Then the next need level up becomes their new
major concern and all their energies become
redirected towards satisfying this higher set of
needs. So for people to wish to meet 'higher needs'
like self-esteem or eventually self-fulfillment, or
'self-actualisation' as Maslow called it, their
lower needs must be satisfied first.

When working with people who are recovering from
mental illness, it is essential to meet basic
survival, shelter and safety needs before trying to
help them meet any 'higher needs'. There is no

286

point at all in working with someone to try to get
them interested in getting a job, for instance, if
they do not have an adequate roof over their head.
Sometimes people do not know where they are going to
be living next week, or when the next meal or the
next Supplementary Benefit cheque will be coming or
how they are going to fill the daytime hours when
their hostel requires them to be out of the
building. In such situations these immediate
pressing concerns will dominate their lives and
crowd other needs out of awareness. A frequent
source of failure in rehabilitation is that people
who don't have these needs satisfied - who don't
have anywhere suitable to live, who don't feel safe,
who lack even enough food and warmth - are offered
places in re-training centres or day centres which
focus on meeting needs which are at a much higher
level. It is hardly surprising that few people can
benefit from this.

A first step in mental health work then is to
check on a person's housing needs and, if necessary,
give this priority. Nor is it enough just to put a
roof over someone's head. We found that people
rarely settled, much less developed, in housing
circumstances which were either short-term or not
the sort of thing which the person really wanted.
Housing is strongly linked to what Maslow called
safety needs or security needs. One issue is the
sense of insecurity which comes from transient
housing. One of the most unsatisfactory aspects of
arranging housing is the indefinite waiting, of not
knowing when an offer might come through. In terms
of Maslow's hierarchy of needs, this uncertainty
impinges on the basic need for safety and security.
In the history of the CPRU Support Network there
have been several instances of people finding the
stress so unbearable as to necessitate re-admission
to hospital. In other cases the strain of not
knowing when they would be rehoused made quite
severe inroads into their confidence and their
capacity to cope with things like getting furniture
or arranging benefits.

Maslow's theory has another practical
implication for housing. It is that you can look at
housing arangements with a view to opening
opportunities for meeting higher needs, like social
needs, as well as basic needs for shelter. Maslow's
theory predicts that after someone has met their
basic needs for shelter, safety, security and
autonomy, then they will hunger for company, for
belonging with people and, after that, for the

esteem of others. As one set of needs is met, his
theory says, you should expect the next set to
emerge. So mental health workers arranging
someone's housing should consider the next needs
likely to arise once the person is settled. They
could consider whether there are any housing
options which might anticipate these subsequent
needs and open up opportunities for meeting them.
Sometimes, for instance, it is appropriate to seek
housing which might satisfy a variety of needs all
at once, in the way that some shared households give
company and a routine of shared tasks and activities
which can give structure to day and week.

This is particularly pertinent now that the
great rise in unemployment has robbed many people
of the opportunities a job can offer for satisfying
a considerable range of needs. Through wages a job
can contribute to survival and security needs. It
can contribute to needs for autonomy through the
choices which money makes possible. Through
providing a daily and weekly routine it meets the
need for some framework whereby one can predict
one's own future. Through the sense of being a
team or making friends within a workplace,
employment can satisfy 'belonging' needs. It can
meet 'esteem' needs through the approval and regard
of workmates or superiors or through being
successful in some task, making a good product or
having a good idea. A job can meet a combination of
needs on different levels. Thus, in particular, it
represents an asset of special importance to
someone who may be short on opportunities for
meeting their needs. Now that people with
long-term mental illness, by and large, have so
much less chance of getting a decently paid,
permanent job, we need to consider how the benefits
which accrue though employment might be acquired
through other areas of life - through housing in
particular. We have to think of other resources
which might represent the same sort of major,
positive asset for the person who is low on every
sort of opportunity for meeting their needs.

Certain types of housing can offer people a
sense of belonging and company through communal
or shared household arrangements. Housing can
also offer a great deal of work or occupation
through cleaning, shopping, cooking, decorating
or repairs. This can be a source of self-esteem -
or esteem in the eyes of others if the work is a
contribution towards a shared household.

288

At one of our communal households, for
instance, there are evident opportunities to feel
wanted and valued. Producing a good meal for the
whole household takes skill, hard work and
organisation. Accomplishing it understandably
gives residents satisfaction. Some shared
households can also give a sort of daily or
weekly routine, through mealtimes or regular
outings. Whether living alone or with others,
some people can make their home a creation of
which they are very proud. So housing can
sometimes meet some of Maslow's higher 'aesthetic
needs' as well.

Of course, while shared households have their
strengths, we must remember that many people who
have suffered mental illness prefer to live alone,
though with ready access to other people's company.
For them this autonomy is a key need. We have been
planning a series of single-person Council flats
near to our other housing with these people
specially in mind. Thus their housing can provide
autonomy but also ready opportunity for satisfying
social needs through contacts with people living in
other flats nearby.

Individuals vary enormously in their needs.
Quite different sorts of housing suit different
people. Different individuals are satisfied with
different amounts of social company, for instance.
Some people are quite happy to spend a lot of time
on their own; others feel bereft if there is
no-one to chat to almost all the time. Some
people need very close relationships; others are
better suited with a larger number of more distant
friends and acquaintances. All these things are
more important than is generally realised when a
social worker is trying to find somewhere for
someone to live. But they are not complicated
ideas. Everyone can give some indication, even
when fairly ill, as to at which end of the range
they feel most comfortable. In discussions over
what housing would suit a person one often
encounters much emphasis on the level of 'support'
required. Rather less attention is given to the
type of support. It is assumed that a 'warden' or
'supervisor' multiplied by one, two, three, will
intrinsically alter the nature of some
accommodation. But those involved in the
practical business of caring for long-term
sufferers from mental illness now realise that it
is the variety and flexibility of support which
provides the crucial ingredient.

If seeking to match housing to someone's needs:

1. Identify their main needs, their
    resources, their interests,
    likes and dislikes. Make sure
    you get to know them as a
    person, not as a list of
    symptoms and skills.

2. Consider your client's main unmet
    needs against their positive resources
    in all areas of life - any jobs or
    daytime activities, their family
    links, their friends, acquaintances,
    skills, hobbies. Can you see ways
    these existing resources might
    possibly open opportunities to meet
    their main unmet needs? Identify
    which needs seem least likely to be
    met through their present resources.
    These, then, are the needs where a
    solution through housing might be
    especially helpful, if it were
    possible.

3. Having ascertained the needs you are
    hoping to meet, consider as wide a
    variety of relevant housing solutions
    as possible. Bear in mind that a
    person's needs can usually be met by
    several different housing arrangements
    besides that which first springs to
    mind. Remember how needs alter for
    many reasons. One housing
    arrangement, though, will be more
    likely than the others to match your
    client's preferences and style of
    life. Discuss with the person all the
    time about how they see things and
    what they want. Many people can
    readily fill you in about how
    different aspects of housing would
    affect them.

Of course there are others who can't, if the
question is asked them in an abstract way, or who
seem to make unrealistic choices. But in Hackney
we consistently found that if people were taken to
see an actual house, bedroom or flat, they
could decide clearly if they'd like to live there.

Furthermore, if they had moved in as a result
of a choice based on such a visit, they were more
prone to settle and stay. We found it necessary
to accept that people recovering from mental
illness often have neither the imagination,
experience nor patience to decide in an abstract
sense what living arrangements they would like.
We found it necessary to first discuss with a
person a range of actual flats or houses, then
make informal, no-obligation visits to see for
themselves and understand the ethos and daily
life-style. No piece of paper describing a
housing option can substitute for direct
observation.

In fact we have found it all-important to
respect the desires of an individual. Trying to
meet someone's 'dream' of how they want to live
can be the best guide to success. Even when the
arrangements a person chooses may seem beyond
their abilities to manage, we have found that
motivation and determination to make it work can
make up for quite considerable lack of skills.
Some unlikely candidates for single-person flats
in terms of their competence, illness and skills,
have managed to settle to an independent way of
life because that was their 'dream'. One
middle-aged lady had been living in our commune
and doing well there, she had a poor history of
settling on her own. Nevertheless she pestered
the CPRU team to get her a flat. We imposed
conditions - she had to attend a day centre, show
responsibility in paying her rent etc. But she
has now moved into a flat in our Independent
Living Scheme, has decorated it, bought furniture
and lives pretty happily. Her personal competence
has improved to the extent that not only did she
agree to a friend moving in with her but she was
also able to negotiate a civilised move-out when
she found that the arrangement was not working.

Conversely we have found that people rarely
settled, much less developed, in housing which was
not the sort of thing they wanted, even when it
was well within their coping abilities. One man
returned from a large psychiatric hospital to live
in Hackney. He was pretty competent, articulate,
well-organised and motivated to live away from
hospital. He agreed to move into one of our
communal homes but relapsed fairly quickly and
returned to hospital.

When we compared that first home with a subsequent one where he established himself very successfully, we felt that it had been a social situation which he just could not accept as his home. He had had to live a complete communal life, share household duties and accept just the same status as everyone else in a housing arrangement which did not permit a hierarchy among residents. The second house, where he has flourished, is also communal but gave him opportunity to take charge of things. He quickly and extremely competently organised a washing-up rota and a whole range of other activities. He is happy with having some responsibility, being able to make some rules and see that others carry them out. He is proud of the house and likes to have visitors. Perhaps his Navy background has something to do with his need to be in charge of something! He is an extremely useful household member and has a talent for giving orders to his fellow residents without antagonising them. Thus although he could cope with a more independent life-style, even a flat of his own, he feels happier in a setting which is actually at the more supportive end of our spectrum housing. The house has features like everyone eating their meals together in the dining room at set times, for instance. But it allows him some power, responsibility and reason for being orderly. And that really is his element.

It is so important that we aim for our clients to get housing which matches each person's own vision of the way of life they want, however much that differs from our own view. We should seek housing which makes a person really feel at home. Most of us take for granted our right to choose our companions and our way of life with no other limitation than our budget. What is rarely acknowledged though is that it is not only desirable, but, in most cases, perfectly feasible that people in special housing or supported accommodation schemes have the same rights. Often it can actually be done. People can be helped to a home situation which sufficiently fits their needs and inclinations to be a real foundation for the next phase of their life. It requires that staff always confer with clients, think flexibly, and put respect for an individual's wishes before staff preconceptions.

It is a salutary thought that the ultimate
criterion of any scheme should be whether each
resident is able to have a social life of his or
her choice and follow a life-style which suits him
or her. We are often side-tracked by thinking that
people with mental illness are somehow different
from the rest of us. They're not. We all have our
weaknesses. Mental illness exacerbates these and
means that people cope with them less competently.
But it doesn't make them different in nature.
      We all share the same broad needs as
described by Maslow's hierarchy. How far our
needs are met often depends simply on whether good
fortune has brought us those opportunities which
match our particular needs at the time and thus
enable us to move on to the next stage. So we
should strive to increase the variety of
opportunities coming the way of former psychiatric
patients. Surely we can widen the range of
housing situations which a person gets a chance to
try. This way they will have a greater chance of
finding something which really suits them, really
is right for them, makes them at home and able to
grow and develop further.

NOTES

1.   Abraham Maslow 'Motivation and
     Personality' 1954 Harper and Row,
     New York

293

Balloch S., Hume C., Jones B., Westland P. (1985) 'Caring for Unemployed People', Bedford Square Press, London

Birch A. (1983) 'What Chance Have We Got? Occupation and employment after mental illness - patients' views', Manchester MIND

Edwards C. and Carter J. (1979) 'Day services and the mentally ill', chapter in 'Community Care for the Mentally Disabled' Ed. Wing & Olsen, OUP

Falloon I., Talbot R. (1982) 'Achieving the goals of day treatment', Journal of Nervous and Mental Disease, Volume 170, pp. 279-285

Floyd M., Gregory E., Murray H., Welchman R. (1983) 'Schizophrenia and Employment, Occasional Paper No.5, Tavistock Institute of Human Relations

Lehman A., Ward N., Linn L. (1982) 'Chronic mental patients: the quality of life issue', American Journal of Psychiatry, Volume 139, pp. 1271-1275

Lipton F., Cohen C., Fischer E., Katz S. (1981) 'Schizophrenia: a network crisis', Schizophrenia Bulletin, Volume 7, Issue No. 1

MIND Publications (1985) 'Life after mental illness? Major papers from MIND's 1984 Annual Conference'

Warner R. (1985) 'Recovery from Schizophrenia', Routledge & Kegan Paul, London